D0923414

Fieldbook of
Native Illinois Shrubs

PRAIRIE ROSE *Rosa setigera* Michaux

STATE OF ILLINOIS
DWIGHT H. GREEN, *Governor*

DEPARTMENT OF REGISTRATION AND EDUCATION
FRANK G. THOMPSON, *Director*

Fieldbook of
Native Illinois Shrubs

By

LEO R. TEHON

MANUAL 3

Printed by Authority of the State of Illinois

NATURAL HISTORY SURVEY DIVISION
THEODORE H. FRISON, *Chief*

Urbana December 1942

This manual is a contribution from the Section of Applied Botany and Plant Pathology

(A49741—6-41) 2

FOREWORD

THIRD in a series of fieldbooks, the present publication is, like the first on wild flowers and the second on land snails, intended primarily for amateur naturalists and nature lovers who wish to become acquainted with the flora and fauna of Illinois. Dr. Leo R. Tehon, the author, has since 1921 held the title of Botanist with the Illinois Natural History Survey and is well acquainted with the flora of the state.

The introductory section includes a discussion of the various shrub habitats of Illinois, directions for the use of botanical keys, and keys to the families and genera of shrubs found growing wild within the state borders. The descriptive section mentions 210 species and 27 varieties, representing 77 genera and 43 families. This section contains, also, keys to the species and illustrations of most of the shrubs described. A glossary is appended to aid the beginning botanist in an understanding of technical terms.

For a number of years, the Natural History Survey has systematically made collections of the Illinois flora and of records related to it. The present manual reflects some phases of this activity. In preparation is a complete report of the flora of the state.

Miss Kathryn M. Sommerman, Artist and Entomological Assistant for the Natural History Survey since 1939, made the accurately detailed drawings for the 72 line figures that illustrate the fieldbook. Adapting the material to the general format of the Survey's manual series was the work of James S. Ayars, Technical Editor.

Of the colored photographs reproduced in this fieldbook, those of the Prairie Rose, Silky Dogwood and American Bittersweet are by Ray R. Hamm, University of Illinois photographer; that of the Indigobush is by Dr. Tehon; those of the Smooth Sumac and Trumpetcreeper are by Mr. Ayars.

This fieldbook is published in the hope that it will prove as useful to the people of the state as have the two similar publications that preceded it.

THEODORE H. FRISON
Chief

Urbana, Illinois
June 15, 1942

CONTENTS

COLOR ILLUSTRATIONS

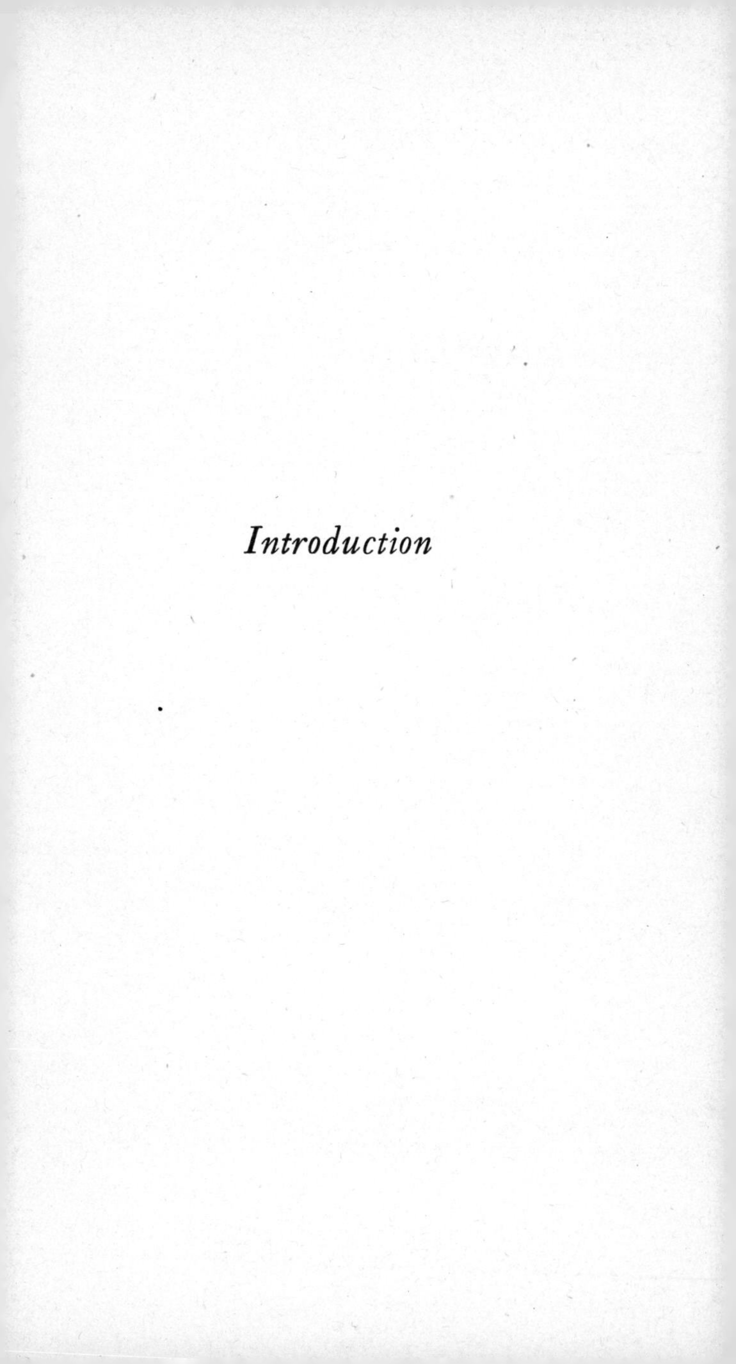

Introduction

INTRODUCTION

THE number of kinds of shrubs and woody vines that grow in Illinois as natives and as naturalized introductions is surprisingly large. Definite mention is made in the following pages of 210 species and 27 varieties. These represent 77 genera and are distributed among 43 botanical families. In Indiana, the only nearby state in which the shrubs have been cataloged separately, there are about 150 species, and in Minnesota, among about 275 native and cultivated woody species, approximately 160 are native shrubs.

This large variety in Illinois is, however, to be expected. Geographically, the state is so located as to include sections of the eastern deciduous forest, extensive prairies, remnants of the northern forest, and a remarkable representation of the Gulf Coast forest. Illinois extends some 380 miles north and south and more than 200 miles east and west. In the northeast it borders on Lake Michigan, and on much of its periphery it is bordered by large rivers, some of them the greatest on this continent. In altitude, it ranges from about 280 feet above sea level at the Ohio River to about 1,250 feet at Charles Mound, in Jo Daviess County; and the average elevation is about 700 feet. Most of the state has been subject to glacial action, but the extreme northwest corner, essentially Jo Daviess County, and the Ohio valley in the south, have not been influenced by glaciers. Both the extension of the Ozark Mountains in the south and the hills of the northwest present a great variety of physical conformations and favor a great and varied display of plant species.

Shrub Habitats.—All of the above factors and many others besides have given rise to great diversity of habitats. Some habitats are extensive and cover very large areas of land. In them the shrub population is relatively uniform. Others are smaller and specialized; and in them the shrubs usually are different from those occurring nearby. Not infrequently small, specialized habitats support shrubs found nowhere else in the state.

The predominant shrub habitats of the state, both as to areas covered and number of kinds of shrubs, were formerly the prairie and deciduous forest regions. Most of the prairies and forests have been destroyed, but forest remnants that have escaped destruction harbor a large number of shrub species, and non-arable and abandoned portions of the prairie support a smaller number. The completeness with which prairies and forests have been sacrificed to the interests of agriculture and industry has affected as markedly the abundance and distribution of shrubs as of trees, grasses and herbs. But, fortunately for the plant lover, many kinds of shrubs survive in out-of-the-way, neglected corners, in woodlots, along streams, roadsides and fence rows, and in young forest growth that has been permitted to spring up following destruction of the original forest.

The Prairie.—In the great expanse of land once grass covered but now given over to plowed fields, small differences in soil, elevation and exposure provide opportunity for the existence of a wide variety of shrubs such as the Prairie Willow, Dwarf Pussy Willow, Meadow Spirea, Prairie Rose, Leadplant and Wolfberry. Stream margins support numerous willows, and prairie groves and timber along larger streams encourage thickets of varied composition. Plow-broken land, when abandoned, is often covered with sumac and brambles.

The Forest Margin.—In general, the richest growth of shrubs takes place at the forest edge. Here the transition from forest to prairie is accompanied by changes in soil, moisture, sunlight, shade, protection and other factors that furnish conditions ideal for many types of shrubs.

The Forest.—Within the forest itself the number of kinds of shrubs is large, also. Here shrubs, especially adapted to life in deep shade, still air and a humid atmosphere, form a dense, low understory beneath such lesser trees as Ironwood, Blue Beech and Redbud. Here, also, climbing woody vines are numerous.

Lake Michigan Moorlands.—This region, which extends some distance inland along the shore of Lake Michigan, is characterized especially by its sandy soil, which ages ago was arranged by the action of the lake and later by wind into great, flat reaches, shallow swales and swelling dunes. Low-lying portions have remained until recently as marshes. In this region Common Juniper, Speckled Alder, Alder-Leaved Buckthorn, Jersey-Tea, Buffaloberry, Bearberry and American Cranberry-bush are characteristic shrubs.

Cold Bogs.—An exceedingly interesting habitat is the bog area in Lake and McHenry counties. Many small lakes and bogs are spread over a considerable territory and present a remarkable and for Illinois a unique type of shrub association, which includes Purple Chokeberry, Vacciniums, Poison Sumac and Sweetfern.

Sands.—Remarkable also are the small and large sand regions. There are six of real importance, and together they cover many hundreds of square miles. The Havana sand area covers some 20 per cent of Mason County and extends northward into Tazewell and across the Illinois River into Fulton and Peoria counties. In Jo Daviess and Carroll counties, there is the region along the Mississippi River known as the Sand Prairies, and in Lee, Bureau and Henry counties, along the lower course of the Green River, are the Green River sands. Along the Mississippi River in Henderson and Mercer counties, the Oquawka sand lands are extensive, and in southeastern Kankakee and northern Iroquois counties the St. Anne sands stretch for miles. The somewhat lesser region of Wilmington sands lies in Will and Grundy counties. There are smaller areas in Whiteside County, in northern Winnebago, in eastern Ogle, in Cass and in Lawrence counties. Sands such as the Green River, Havana, Wilmington and St. Anne are the outwash from glaciers; some others are the result of disintegration by wind, rain and sun of St. Peter sandstone, now represented at Castle Rock, Starved Rock and elsewhere.

The Ozarks.—Across the southern part of the state runs an extension of the Ozark Mountains, with numerous summits approaching 1,000 feet above sea level. Here diverse formations of sandstone, limestone and shale are exposed, and great irregularities in topography provide a wide variety of habitats favorable to many kinds of plants. The shrub flora in this region has not been investigated as carefully as might be wished, but it is among the richest in the state in diversity of kinds and in abundance.

The Ohio Valley.—South of the Ozarks lies a flat region, including essentially Alexander, Pulaski and Massac counties, which in Tertiary times formed the northern tip of the Gulf of Mexico. Many of the herbs, trees and shrubs that grow in this region are so typically southern that they are known best as Gulf Coast inhabitants. Here are to be found woody Clematis and Wisteria, Crossvine, Virginia Willow, the Bumelias and numbers of other interesting species. Northward along the

Wabash and Mississippi rivers, a gradual transformation of this southern flora occurs, but deciduous Holly, Swamp Privet, Silverbell and other species remain to mark its earlier existence as far north as Wabash and Pike counties.

Usefulness of Shrubs.—Were one to classify wild plants according to man's interest in them, trees probably would rank first, herbs second and shrubs third. For this there is a very practical set of reasons. Trees have been exceedingly important to man, first in providing weapons and shelter, later as material for household equipment, machinery, transportation and beauty. Wild herbs are important because many of them have medicinal values and are serviceable in maintaining or restoring health and because the brilliance of their blossoms adds cheer and beauty to even the dullest of habitations; and cultivated herbs are the sources of man's most important foods.

The usefulness of shrubs, although less apparent, is in reality great. They do not yield lumber in quantity, but such of them as produce useful wood furnish it as a rule for very special purposes. Certain of them have become important in commerce as plants furnishing food; in the main, as is true of grapes, raspberries, blackberries, dewberries and hazelnuts, such foods are luxuries rather than necessities. The use of shrubs in beautification is very extensive, also. Although only a few of them produce the flower splendor exhibited by herbs, their desirability in adornment of habitations has been enhanced by their adaptability for artistic effects in hedges and massed plantings and as specimen plantings.

In their native habitat, shrubs furnish shelter, food and cover to woods-loving birds and animals. The beauty of wild shrubs, their usefulness as occasional sources of food and the protection they give to wildlife have long been appreciated and justify more than the usual general interest in their habits, occurrence and distribution. For beauty alone, few things surpass the dogwoods, shadbush and hawthorns in the early spring landscape.

Purpose of the Manual.—This manual is not a technical contribution to the science of botany but a series of descriptions and illustrations, based on good scientific procedure, intended to be understandable and useful to the nature lover. To this end, descriptions of species cover all the botanical features that a person ordinarily will have need or occasion to notice. They depart from the usual botanical method, however, in two respects. Full sentences are used throughout, and commonplace words are employed wherever they can be made to fit accurately. This, it is hoped, will make the text more easily read and will give the botanically untrained user more vivid pictures of the shrubs that are described. Measurements, given as inches or fractions of an inch for small plant parts, are not so accurately stated as would have been possible with the less-used metric system, but the more familiar standard will be interpreted more easily.

It has not been possible to avoid technical words entirely. In botany, as in every branch of knowledge, meaningful words replace circuitous expressions. Many of the technical words of botany are adaptations of words in common use that express the resemblance of plant parts to familiar objects. The number of technical words with which one must be familiar is not large, but there is a considerable number of terms that have special meanings in the descriptions of particular shrubs. For the interpretation of all these terms, a glossary is appended.

Common and Scientific Names.—To the uninitiated, imposing scientific names may be confusing, as also may be the fact that a single shrub is given two or three common names.

Common names differ from locality to locality. A shrub known in one place under one name may be known in another place under a different name. It is true also, now more than formerly, that in one locality a shrub may be known by a number of common names. It is therefore impossible to determine what common name is proper. In this text, common names known to be in use in Illinois are preferred to those used elsewhere.

To some extent scientific names prevent the confusion that arises from common names. In principle, at least, there should be only one scientific name for each kind of plant. This principle does not work out perfectly in practice, but its convenience and serviceability cannot be doubted.

In general, the scientific nomenclature used here is that of the Second Edition, published in June, 1940, of Alfred Rehder's *Manual of Cultivated Trees and Shrubs*. But some deviation has been necessary, since, at the time of the publication of Rehder's Second Edition, this text had been completed for two years, the illustrations for one year, in the form in which they were to be presented. Genera are more freely segregated into families; and certain genera and species have been retained, although they are not recognized as distinct in Rehder's *Manual.* In cases such as these, also in instances where Rehder's usage departs widely from that to be found in the familiar Seventh Edition of *Gray's New Manual of Botany* or in Britton and Brown's *Illustrated Flora of the Northern United States, Canada and the British Possessions,* it has been possible to add explanations which will enable the user of this fieldbook to reconcile the differences.

Excluded Species.—There are records of occurrence in Illinois for a considerable number of shrub species not listed in the text. In part they are printed reports of species that, according to present understanding of range limits, ought not to occur within the state. In many instances it has not been possible to test such reports by examining specimens, and inability to verify the reports has been considered adequate cause for omitting the species. In other instances, in which specimens could be seen, it was clear that records were based either on misdeterminations or on determinations according with older species concepts. The occurrence of dubious species has been recorded in part, also, by specimens deposited in herbariums. It is true particularly of the older collections that the specimens, properly named in accordance with botanical concepts extant at the time they were collected, fit into newer species. Redetermination of such material has unified it with the species treatment embodied in this text.

Naturalized Shrubs.—This manual is intended particularly to cover the native shrubs, but a few naturalized shrubs have been included. When white men began to settle in Illinois, they brought with them from their eastern homes shrubs which they had grown there, some of which had been brought earlier from Europe. Other shrubs were purchased from nurseries, to decorate the bare prairie home sites. Some of these shrubs made themselves so much at home that they reseeded in wild habitats and have become naturalized members of our native plant communities. A number of these shrubs have been given, in this manual, the same full descriptions as have native species. If, however, there is evidence that certain introduced shrubs persisting in the wild state do not multiply sufficiently to insure their permanent existence here, attention has been called to them and to the fact that they may be encountered from time

SILKY DOGWOOD *Cornus Amomum* Miller

AMERICAN BITTERSWEET *Celastrus scandens* Linnaeus

to time; but the lengthy descriptions accorded other species have not been given.

How to Name Shrubs.—The first purpose of a manual is to assist persons in finding names for plants in which they are interested. With the keys in this manual, a person without botanical training can, with a little time and effort, find the names of shrubs utterly strange to him.

It always has been difficult to explain how to use a botanical key. This is true, perhaps, because a key provides directions both for coming to a conclusion and for obtaining a set of facts upon which to base the conclusion. It is puzzling to the inexperienced user at first. However, it has this advantage: it predetermines for its user the items that must be observed and, when they have been observed and properly followed through, provides immediately the required conclusion. The things to be observed are the distinguishing characteristics every kind of shrub possesses, and the conclusions drawn from them are names of shrubs.

To illustrate the manner in which a key works, we might imagine that a stranger has asked what house is occupied by a person living on a street with which we are very familiar, although we cannot quite remember the house number. When we give directions to the stranger for finding the house, we may not say all of the following things, but our process of thought may be imagined as this: "The house is not in the first four or five blocks, but somewhere in the sixth, seventh or eighth block. It is on the south side, not on the north side, of the street, and it is a brick, not a frame, house. It has a wide porch across the front, so that the door does not open immediately to the sidewalk, and it is moreover the only house of this general description where three small evergreens stand on each side of the steps leading to the porch."

With such a set of directions our stranger will know about how far to go, which side of the street to look on, and the kind of house to look for. And he will know one definite fact that will enable him to recognize the house, when he comes to it, as certainly as though he knew its number.

The key for naming shrubs works on exactly the same basis, except that it must include, so to speak, every house on the street or, in our case, every shrub in the state; it is based similarly on important characteristics. These characteristics are set down in outline form and generally are arranged in pairs, so that a choice can be made between important characters first, less important characters second and still less important characters third. By continued choosing as the outline proceeds, a point is reached where no further choice is possible, and the final distinguishing characteristic tells exactly the name of the shrub.

As a further example, let us "run down" in the key to genera, page 17, two wild shrubs with which we already are familiar. One of them, let us say, is a wild juniper, the other a dogwood. The key begins with two contrasting lines labeled I and II, the first of which says "Leaves very narrow; linear, or scalelike, and small," the second, "Leaves broader, with proper blades; not pinelike." Obviously line I describes the leaves of the juniper and line II the leaves of the dogwood. Hence we must search for the name of our juniper under I and the name of our dogwood under II. Taking the juniper first, since it comes in the first part of the key, we find set in under I two lines labeled A. The first says, "Leaves evergreen, glabrous; more than 1/8 inch long." The second says, "Leaves persistent but not evergreen, pubescent; less than 1/8 inch long." The leaves on our juniper fit the description given by the first A, and under it we find two lines labeled with uncapitalized a's, in which the descriptions contrasted are "Leaves apparently in 2 ranks; green above," and "Leaves in whorls of 3; with a white line above." Examining our juniper carefully, we find that the leaves are set three in a ring around the stem and that each leaf does have a fine white line on the upper side, which is exactly what the key requires. So we know that the juniper is to be looked for under the botanical genus *Juniperus*, on page 27 in the body of this manual.

Now, let us see what we can do about the dogwood. Since we know it is included under II in the key, we start there. We find first a line labeled A, which reads, "Leaves simple, though often toothed or lobed," and further down in the key we find, on page 21, another line labeled A, which reads "Leaves definitely compound, composed of 2 or more leaflets." Our dogwood's leaves are simple, that is, each one is a single piece and is not made up of two or more small, leaflike pieces. Hence, we know we will find it somewhere in the part of the outline included under the first A, on page 17. The following line, labeled B, says, "Leaves opposite or whorled; 2 or 3 at a node." Farther along in the key another line labeled B reads, "Leaves alternate; 1 at a node." On the small dogwood branch that we have at hand, leaves arranged as pairs are set opposite each other on the stem. Again it is clear that our dogwood is included somewhere under the first B. Under this first B, we find a C line reading, "Leaf margins entire." Contrasted with this, a little farther down, is the other C, "Leaf margins toothed." As nearly as we can see without a hand lens, there are no teeth of any kind on the dogwood leaf margins; so we follow through under the first C and come to the D lines, "Leaves and twigs densely coated with silvery or rusty scales," and "No silvery or rusty scales present." Finding no such scales on our dogwood, we proceed under the second D to the lines labeled E, "Leaf blades with translucent dots," and "Leaf blades without translucent dots." Holding our dogwood leaves up to the light, we try to see any special places in the blade, however minute, where the light shines through clearly. We find none, and so we know that we must continue under the second E. Beneath this are two lines labeled G. The first one says, "Leaves often 3 at a node," the second, "Leaves definitely 2 at a node." If we happen to be near this shrub while we are trying to name it we may examine several stems; otherwise, the single stem that we have at hand will have to do, and we find that there are only two and never more than two leaves at a node. This carries us on under the second G. The distinction between the lines labeled H is quite apparent, since the first H line, which reads, "Leaves thick; parasites growing on tree branches," does not at all describe our dogwood, whereas "Leaves normally thin; not parasites" does at least include it. So we come to the next pair of lines, labeled I, "Secondary veins running together near the margins and meeting at the leaf tip; leaves often mealy beneath," and, contrasted with this, "Leaves without such veins; often glaucous beneath." Now, if we examine the dogwood leaves carefully, we shall find that secondary veins run out at intervals from the main vein of the leaf and that, very near the margins, they run together into fine marginal veins, which follow the margin of the leaf on each side from the bottom secondary vein up to the tip of the leaf, where they unite. This apparently is what is meant by the first of the letter I lines in the key, and so we learn that our dogwood belongs in the genus *Cornus,* which is described and pictured beginning on page 212 in the manual. Turning to page 213, we find a similar but short key, which enables us to "run down" the shrub to its species without having to read all the species descriptions.

These two examples have been fairly simple. At least they have "run down" in the early part of the key. But almost any of the wild shrubs of the state can be named in the same way, even though the names appear near the end of the key. Although the key looks complicated, the process of naming is simple, because as a rule only a relatively small number of the many items listed in the key have to be considered in the naming of any given shrub. In making choices at the beginning of the key, we may eliminate from consideration large sections of the key that do not apply, just as in giving directions to our stranger we eliminated quickly the first few blocks and all of the frame houses.

Verification of Identifications.—The user of this manual should be able, by using the key and the descriptions in this volume, to identify most of the native shrubs with which he comes in contact. But from time to time even persons well practiced in identification are certain to encounter specimens too difficult to name with certainty. In such cases the assistance of a professional botanist may be sought.

The Section of Applied Botany of the Illinois Natural History Survey is always ready to assist in the identification of shrubs, and of other plants of all kinds. Samples may be sent in fresh condition or as prepared botanical specimens, and verification of the collector's determinations or accurate determinations of the specimens will be given in return. Fresh specimens may be sent by mail if they are wrapped in waxed paper so as not to wither badly before arrival. Dried specimens, carefully packed, may be sent by parcel post or express. Persons who ask this service should remember, of course, that the botanist to whom they write sees only the sample that is sent to him. The samples should be typical and whenever possible they should contain stem, leaves, and flowers or fruit. For the accurate determination of certain kinds of shrubs, both flowers and fruit are necessary. Care in selecting samples not only makes the botanist's work easier but also helps him render good service.

Local Shrub Collections.—As has been intimated on another page, knowledge of the shrubs that grow in Illinois is by no means perfect. The catalog of species occurring in the state undoubtedly is very nearly complete, but too little is known of the exact distribution of individual species. To one interested in shrubs, a survey of the township or county in which he resides and the making of a local collection for the region in which he lives will yield results of real scientific value, especially if publication of a species list and habitat notes can be achieved.

ANALYTICAL KEYS

The shrubs described in the text belong, without exception, to the division of plants known as Spermatophyta. They bear true flowers which contain either pistils or stamens, or both, and produce seeds which contain embryos. By two genera, they represent the Gymnospermae; by one genus, they represent the Monocotyledones; and, by all other genera, the Dicotyledones of the Angiospermae.

Although they can be identified most easily by means of the artificial characters used in the genus key beginning on page 17, their botanical relationships are more accurately expressed by the natural key below, which leads to their families. The shorter keys given, where necessary, under the individual families, lead to genera; and, under genera, keys lead to the species.

Natural Key to the Shrub Families

I. Gymnospermae

Ovules and seeds borne in an open bract; stigma wanting.

A. Pistillate flowers borne singly or in pairs, each developing into a berry-like fruit........................**Taxaceae, p. 25**

A. Pistillate flowers in small, few-bracted catkins, each catkin maturing as a berry-like fruit. .*Juniperus*, in the **Pinaceae, p. 26**

II. Angiospermae

Ovules and seeds borne in closed ovaries; one or more stigmas present.

A. Monocotyledones: Flowers with 3 petals and 3 sepals, dioecious; staminate flowers with 6 stamens; pistillate flowers with 3 united carpels and 3 sessile stigmas........ ....*Smilax*, in the **Liliaceae, p. 28**

A. Dicotyledones: Flower parts commonly in 4's or 5's, at least not in regular whorls of 3.

- B. Corolla wanting; calyx present or absent.
  - C. Calyx wanting; both staminate and pistillate flowers in catkins.
    - D. Fruit a 1-celled, many-seeded pod; seeds hairy tufted................................**Salicaceae, p. 34**
    - D. Fruit nutlike, 1-seeded; seed not hairy tufted.............................**Myricaceae, p. 59**
  - C. Calyx present at least in either staminate or pistillate flowers.
    - E. At least the staminate flowers in catkins; fruit a nut or achene..............................**Betulaceae, p. 61**
    - E. None of the flowers in catkins.
      - F. Carpels 2, united; stigmas 2; ovary 1-celled and 1-ovuled..............................**Ulmaceae, p. 69**

F. Carpels 1 or several and distinct or united.
G. Ovary inferior, compound.
H. Ovary 1-celled, becoming a 1-seeded drupe.......................**Loranthaceae**, p. 71
H. Ovary 6-celled, becoming a 6-celled, many-seeded capsule...........**Aristolochiaceae, p.** 72
G. Ovary superior.
I. Carpels 3 to many, separate.
J. Fruit a 1-seeded achene with a persistent plumose style...*Clematis*, in the **Ranunculaceae**, p. 74
J. Fruit a thin-fleshed drupe...................*Calycocarpum*, in the **Menispermaceae**, p. 76
I. Carpel 1; fruit a 1-seeded berry or drupe.
K. Stamens 9, in 3 whorls.......**Lauraceae**, p. 82
K. Stamens 8, opposite and alternate with the corolla lobes.
L. Flowers perfect; alternate stamens longer; leaves alternate.......**Thymelaeaceae**, p. 206
L. Flowers dioecious; stamens equal; leaves opposite...............**Elaeagnaceae**, p. 208

B. Both calyx and corolla, or at least a corolla, present.
M. Petals separate, or only 1 petal present.
N. Carpels 1 or several and distinct.
O. Stamens inserted at the base of the receptacle.
P. Carpels 2 to 6, each maturing as a fleshy drupe ....**Menispermaceae**, p. 76
P. Carpel 1, maturing as a 1- to few-seeded berry ....**Berberidaceae**, p. 80
O. Stamens inserted on the margin of a disk which often more or less incloses the gynoecium.
R. Flowers regular; petals 5.
S. Carpels several or numerous, becoming follicles, achenes or drupelets.......**Rosaceae**, p. 98
S. Carpel 1, becoming a fleshy drupe.......... ....**Amygdalaceae**, p. 139
R. Flowers irregular; petal 1...................................*Amorpha*, in the **Leguminosae**, p. 144
N. Carpels 2 to several, united basally or by their styles.
T. Ovary superior.
U. Stamens inserted at the base of the receptacle.
V. Stamens more than 10 in number; leaves black dotted....................**Hypericaceae**, p. 200
V. Stamens usually (but not more than) twice as many as the petals.
W. Ovary 1-celled.............**Cistaceae**, p. 204
W. Ovary 2- to several-celled.
X. Stamens 5; carpels united by their styles ....*Zanthoxylum*, in the **Rutaceae**, p. 149
X. Stamens 2 to 4; carpels united basally ....**Oleaceae**, p. 244

U. Stamens inserted on the margin of a disk which more or less incloses the gynoecium.
  Y. Stamens opposite, and of the same number as, the petals.
    Z. Sepals evident; upright shrubs .... **Rhamnaceae**, p. 177
    Z. Sepals minute (or obsolete); vines .... **Vitaceae**, p. 184
  Y. Stamens alternate with, and of the same number as, the petals.
    a. Leaves compound, alternate .... **Anacardiaceae**, p. 153
    a. Leaves simple, or opposite if compound.
      b. Leaves simple, alternate or opposite.
        c. Ovule 1 in each cell of the ovary; fruit a drupe .... **Aquifoliaceae**, p. 161
        c. Ovules 2 or more in each cell of the ovary; fruit a capsule; seed arillate .... **Celastraceae**, p. 166
      b. Leaves compound, opposite.
        d. Flowers regular, leaves pinnate .... **Staphyleaceae**, p. 173
        d. Flowers irregular, leaves digitate .... **Hippocastanaceae**, p. 175

T. Ovary inferior or partially included.
  e. Stamens more than double the number of petals.
    f. Fruit a capsule .... *Philadelphus*, in the **Hydrangeaceae**, p. 85
    f. Fruit a pome .... **Malaceae**, p. 128
  e. Stamens double the number of petals, or fewer.
    g. Styles distinct or wanting.
      h. Ovules several in each cell of the ovary.
        i. Leaves opposite; fruit a capsule .... *Hydrangea*, in the **Hydrangeaceae**, p. 85
        i. Leaves alternate; fruit a berry .... **Grossulariaceae**, p. 91
      h. Ovule 1 in each cell of the ovary.
        j. Styles and carpels 5; ovary 5-celled; flowers 5-merous .... **Araliaceae**, p. 210
        j. Styles and carpels 2; ovary 2-celled; flowers 4-merous.
          k. Fruit a fleshy drupe containing a 2-seeded stone; leaves opposite .... **Cornaceae**, p. 212
          k. Fruit a woody capsule; leaves alternate .... **Hamamelidaceae**, p. 96
    g. Styles united.
      l. Stamens 8 or 10; anthers opening by pores; fruit a berry .... **Vacciniaceae**, p. 228
      l. Stamens 5; anthers opening lengthwise; fruit a dry capsule .... **Iteaceae**, p. 89

M. Petals more or less united.
  m. Ovary superior.
    n. Stamens free from the corolla.
      o. Carpel 1; corolla irregular.... **Leguminosae**, p. 144
      o. Carpels several, united; corolla regular........ .... **Ericaceae**, p. 220
    n. Stamens more or less adnate to the corolla.
      p. Stamens 5; petaloid staminodes 5............ .... **Sapotaceae**, p. 236
      p. Stamens 4; staminodes, when present, not petaloid........................ **Bignoniaceae**, p. 246
  m. Ovary inferior.
    q. Stamens twice, or more than twice, as many as the corolla lobes.
      r. Ovary 1-celled................. **Styracaceae**, p. 239
      r. Ovary 4- to 10-celled.......... **Vacciniaceae**, p. 228
    q. Stamens the same in number as the corolla lobes.
      s. Leaves joined by stipules......... **Rubiaceae**, p. 249
      s. Stipules wanting............ **Caprifoliaceae**, p. 252

Key to Genera

I. Leaves very narrow; linear, or scalelike, and small.
  A. Leaves evergreen, glabrous; more than 1/8 inch long.
    a. Leaves apparently in 2 ranks; green above... **Taxus**, p. 25
    a. Leaves in whorls of 3; with a white line above...... .... **Juniperus**, p. 27
  A. Leaves persistent but not evergreen, pubescent; less than 1/8 inch long........................... **Hudsonia**, p. 204
II. Leaves broader, with proper blades; not pinelike.
  A. Leaves simple, though often toothed or lobed.
    B. Leaves opposite or whorled; 2 or 3 at a node.
      C. Leaf margins entire.
        D. Leaves and twigs densely coated with silvery or rusty scales...................... **Shepherdia**, p. 208
        D. No silvery or rusty scales present.
          E. Leaf blades with translucent dots.
            F. Branchlets round; creeping shrubs........... .... **Ascyrum**, p. 200
            F. Branchlets 2-edged; upright shrubs......... .... **Hypericum**, p. 201
          E. Leaf blades without translucent dots.
            G. Leaves often 3 at a node.... **Cephalanthus**, p. 250
            G. Leaves definitely 2 at a node.
              H. Leaves thick; parasites growing on tree branches.................. **Phoradendron**, p. 71
              H. Leaves normally thin; not parasites.
                I. Secondary veins running together near the margins and meeting at the leaf tip; leaves often mealy beneath.... **Cornus**, p. 212

I. Leaves without such veins; often glaucous beneath.
J. Buds superposed .... **Lonicera**, p. 268
J. Buds not superposed .... **Symphoricarpos**, p. 265
C. Leaf margins toothed.
K. Decumbent shrub, rooting at the nodes .... **Euonymus**, p. 167
K. Upright shrubs.
L. Internodes with decurrent, pubescent lines .... **Diervilla**, p. 272
L. Pubescence, if present, not in decurrent lines.
M. Hollow petiole bases covering buds .... **Philadelphus**, p. 89
M. Petiole bases not hollow, buds axillary.
N. Stems squarish .... **Euonymus**, p. 167
N. Stems round.
O. Stipules or their minute scars present .... **Viburnum**, p. 255
O. Neither stipules nor their scars present.
P. Leaves acute to acuminate at both ends .... **Forestiera**, p. 244
P. Leaves rounded or cordate at the base .... **Hydrangea**, p. 86
B. Leaves alternate; 1 at a node.
Q. Leaf margins entire, neither toothed nor lobed.
R. A pair of tendrils at the base of the petiole; spiny or prickly, green vines with blue-black berries in axillary clusters .... **Smilax**, p. 29
R. No tendrils at the base of the petiole.
S. Armed with spines arising in the leaf axils .... **Bumelia**, p. 237
S. Unarmed shrubs or vines.
T. Low, creeping, or prostrate shrubs with persistent leaves.
U. Leaves obovate, green beneath .... **Arctostaphylos**, p. 227
U. Leaves oblong to ovate, glaucous beneath .... **Vaccinium**, p. 229
T. Erect shrubs, whether low or tall, or climbing vines.
V. Leaves linear, revolute, white-puberulent beneath, persistent .... **Andromeda**, p. 223
V. Leaves broad, deciduous.
W. Leaves and bark spicy and aromatic, fruit a red drupe .... **Lindera**, p. 83
W. Leaves and bark neither spicy nor aromatic.
X. Leaves broadly cordate, palmately 3- to 7-veined; twining vines .... **Aristolochia**, p. 73

X. Leaves not cordate, or if so each with only 1 main nerve.
 Y. Petioles concealing buds in their hollow bases .... **Dirca, p. 206**
 Y. Petiole bases solid and buds axillary.
  Z. Leaves with marginal veins ending in the tips .... **Cornus, p. 212**
  Z. Leaves without such lateral veins.
   a. Buds covered by 1 scale only ... . **Salix, p. 34**
   a. Buds with 2 to several scales.
    b. Leaves resinous-dotted beneath .... **Gaylussacia, p. 228**
    b. Leaves not resinously dotted.
     c. Leaf blades mucronate-tipped..... **Nemopanthus, p. 165**
     c. Blades not mucronate.
      d. Blades thick and revolute, leaves and branches scurfy with scales .... **Chamaedaphne, p. 224**
      d. Blades thin, not revolute, no scurfy scales present .... **Vaccinium, p. 229**

Q. Leaf margins either lobed or toothed, often both.
 e. Leaves definitely lobed, often toothed also.
  f. Leaves linear; margins cut to the midrib to form 20 or more half-wedge-shaped lobes .... **Comptonia, p. 59**
  f. Leaves not linear.
   g. Vines with palmately veined leaves.
    h. Tendrils opposite at least some of the leaves; margins serrate.
     i. Petioles uniformly glabrous or pubescent .... **Vitis, p. 185**
     i. Upper half of petiole pubescent, lower half glabrous............ **Ampelopsis, p. 194**
    h. No tendrils present; margins without teeth.
     j. Leaves densely pubescent beneath, fruit red........................ **Cocculus, p. 77**
     j. Leaves glabrous except on the veins beneath.
      k. Leaves peltate, fruit blue............ .... **Menispermum, p. 78**
      k. Leaves deeply cordate, fruit black .... **Calycocarpum, p. 80**
   g. Erect shrubs.
    l. Leaves palmately lobed and veined.
     m. Armed with spines or prickles.......... .... **Grossularia, p. 94**
     m. Unarmed.

n. Petioles and branchlets glandular-pubescent .... **Rubus**, p. 10
n. Without glandular pubescence.
o. Leaves resinous-dotted beneath .... **Ribes**, p. 9
o. Leaves without resinous dots .... **Physocarpus**, p. 9
l. Leaves pinnately veined .... **Crataegus**, p. 134
e. Leaf margins toothed but the blades not lobed.
p. Armed with spines or thorns.
q. Glands present on the petiole near the blade .... **Prunus**, p. 139
q. Petiole not bearing glands.
r. Large, straight thorns on twigs and branches .... **Crataegus**, p. 134
r. Small branched spines on twigs and branches .... **Berberis**, p. 81
p. Not armed with spines or thorns.
s. Twining vines .... **Celastrus**, p. 170
s. Spreading or upright shrubs.
t. Leaves clustered or in groups of 3 to 7 at ends of branches.
u. Upright shrub; leaves oblong to ovate .... **Azalea**, p. 221
u. Prostrate, creeping shrub; leaves ovate to nearly round .... **Gaultheria**, p. 226
t. Leaves distributed along the twigs; upright shrubs.
v. Leaves with 3 to 5 main veins.
w. Low shrubs with glandular-serrate leaves .... **Ceanothus**, p. 181
w. Tall shrubs with plainly serrate leaves .... **Celtis**, p. 69
v. Leaves with 1 main vein.
x. Buds inclosed by 1 scale .... **Salix**, p. 34
x. Buds inclosed by 2 or more scales.
y. Lower leaf surface stellate-pubescent .... **Halesia**, p. 240
y. Leaves without stellate pubescence.
z. Small, dark glands on the midrib, above .... **Aronia**, p. 130
z. Midrib glandless.
1. Petiole gland-bearing near the blade .... **Prunus**, p. 139
1. Petiole glandless.
2. Leaf base cordate or notched.
3. Teeth rounded and large, resembling scallops .... **Hamamelis**, p. 96
3. Teeth sharp and fine.
4. Leaves acute, entire margin serrate ..... **Corylus**, p. 62

4. Leaves obtuse, only the distal half or third of the margin serrate.................... **Amelanchier**, p. 133

2. Leaf base rounded or tapered to the petiole.

5. Teeth distant and low...................... **Styrax**, p. 242

5. Teeth close and usually prominent.

6. Teeth rounded..... **Ilex**, p. 162

6. Teeth sharp pointed.

7. Low shrub with wrinkled bark.. **Vaccinium**, p. 229

7. Tall shrubs with smooth or rough bark.

8. Veins conspicuously straight and extending to teeth.

9. Usually 4 or 5 pairs of veins per leaf .... **Betula**, p. 64

9. Usually 8 or 9 pairs of veins per leaf .... **Alnus**, p. 66

8. Veins either not conspicuously straight or not ending in teeth.

10. Buds superposed, pith chambered .... **Itea**, p. 90

10. Buds solitary, pith solid.

11. Veins parallel and distinct nearly to the margin........... **Rhamnus**, p. 177

11. Veins not conspicuously parallel, branching toward the margin ...... **Spiraea**, p. 101

A. Leaves definitely compound, composed of 2 or more leaflets.

12. Leaves opposite, 2 at a node.

13. Leaf margins entire.

14. Leaflets 2 per leaf.................. **Bignonia**, p. 246

14. Leaflets 3 per leaf.................. **Clematis**, p. 75

13. Leaf margins toothed.

15. Leaflets few, palmately arranged.

16. Leaflets 5 or 7 per leaf............**Aesculus**, p. 17
16. Leaflets 3 per leaf...............**Staphylea**, p. 17
15. Leaflets many, pinnately arranged.
17. Climbing vines with aerial roots...**Campsis**, p. 24
17. Erect shrubs...................**Sambucus**, p. 25
12. Leaves alternate, 1 at a node.
18. Leaf margins entire.
19. Leaflets 3 per leaf....................**Ptelea**, p. 15
19. Leaflets usually 5 or more.
20. Twining vines....................**Wisteria**, p. 14
20. Erect shrubs.
21. Stems armed with spines....**Zanthoxylum**, p. 14
21. Stems unarmed.
22. Leaflets mostly 5 (3 to 7) per leaf.............................**Potentilla**, p. 10
22. Leaflets 7 or more per leaf.
23. Leaflets obtuse and mucronate at the tip.......................**Amorpha**, p. 14
23. Leaflets taper pointed to acuminate..............................**Rhus**, p. 15
18. Leaf margins toothed.
24. Leaflets 3 per leaf.
25. Both leaf surfaces black dotted......**Ptelea**, p. 151
25. Leaves not black dotted.............**Rhus**, p. 153
24. Leaflets 5 or more per leaf.
26. Stems armed with spines or prickles.
27. Leaves twice compound...........**Aralia**, p. 210
27. Leaves once compound.
28. Stipules attached to the petioles...**Rosa**, p. 117
28. Stipules free and deciduous......**Rubus**, p. 105
26. Stems unarmed.
29. Vines.
30. Leaves palmately compound.......................**Parthenocissus**, p. 196
30. Leaves pinnately compound.**Ampelopsis**, p. 194
29. Tall shrubs; leaves pinnately compound.
31. A cluster of glands in the rachis channel at the base of each leaflet.......**Sorbus**, p. 129
31. No glands on the rachis..........**Rhus**, p. 153

Description of Species

TAXACEAE

The Yew Family

The yews are trees and shrubs, evergreen in America and similar in aspect to the pines, having linear leaves and usually bearing pistils and stamens in separate floral structures. The male flowers are globular, with a few stamens, the anthers of which are arranged beneath a shieldlike, usually more or less lobed connecting plate, and the pistillate flowers bear one ovule each, which develops into a bony-coated seed with a large, fleshy scale for cover.

The family is represented in North America and in Illinois only by the following native species.

TAXUS CANADENSIS Marshall

American Yew Canada Yew Ground Hemlock

The American Yew, fig. 1, is a low and sprawling evergreen usually less than 3 feet high, though occasionally it grows upright to a height of nearly 5 feet. Its branches, which spread 3 to 5 feet from the center of the plant, generally turn upward

FIG. 1
Taxus canadensis

toward the ends and are clothed with linear, sharply pointed green leaves one-third to 1 inch long by usually less than 1/8 inch wide. These leaves, which are keeled on both faces, appear to be disposed in two rows, or ranks, along the twigs but in reality they are in spirals, and the twisting of their petioles arranges them in rows to face the light.

Flowers, which appear in April, are borne in leaf axils on year old branches. The pistillate flowers develop first into shallow, scaly cups, which by September are transformed into oval red, berry-like structures one-third inch long, each with a bony seed, or nutlet, buried in its coral-red, jelly-like pulp.

Distribution.—Distinctly North American, the American Yew ranges from Newfoundland south to Virginia and westward into Ohio and Manitoba, occupying in this territory the same habitat as the Hemlock, for the seedling of which it readily is mistaken. In Illinois, it is known to occur in the bogs of Lake County, where it is associated with other unusual plants in a type of habitat rare in the state, in the Apple River region in Jo Daviess County, at Starved Rock, and in the White Pine preserve in Ogle County. Many years ago it occurred elsewhere in the state, as in Kankakee County along Rock Creek and in Winnebago County, but it is no longer to be found in those localities. The last collection in Kankakee County was made by E. J. Hill in 1847. Certain recent records, for example in Cook and Carroll counties, are apparently based on specimens taken from cultivated plants.

PINACEAE

The Pine Family

This is a family of trees and shrubs that are generally evergreen and that bear short, awl-shaped or long, needle-like leaves and produce seeds in the familiar dry cones or in fleshy, berry-like structures. It is world wide in distribution and of great economic importance, both for lumber and other products taken from the coniferous forests of the mountainous regions and coastal plains and for the decorative value of its many ornamental tree and shrub species.

Although it is represented in North America, in both tree and shrub form, by more than a dozen native genera, only one shrubby species is native in Illinois.

JUNIPERUS (Tournefort) Linnaeus

The Junipers Red Cedars

The junipers are evergreen trees and shrubs having small, awllike or scalelike evergreen leaves arranged on the twigs in whorls of three, and berry-like, bloom-covered fruits, which contain 1 to 3 oval, bony seeds. They are best known in Illinois by the Red Cedar, a tree species that grows throughout the state as a weed in desolated soil and is in evil repute in orchard regions because of its relation to important rust diseases of apples. The single shrubby species native in the state is the following.

JUNIPERUS COMMUNIS Linnaeus

Common Juniper

The Common Juniper, fig. 2, is generally low and spreading, with branches clothed in short, awllike leaves, but occasionally it attains a height of 6 or more feet. Its spreading, sharply pointed leaves, set in close or distant whorls and lacking petioles,

FIG. 2
Juniperus communis

are straight or somewhat incurved, green, convex beneath and concave above, striped lengthwise by a white line about one-third as wide as the leaves; they measure hardly more than one-twentieth inch in width and are one-third to ½ inch long. The flowers, of which the polleniferous and ovuliferous are separate, are borne in leaf axils on younger shoots. After a period of 3 years the fruits, developed from the ovulate flowers, mature as very short, globular, dark blue berries conspicuously covered by white bloom and generally contain in the dry, resinous pulp 3 horny, warty, somewhat 3-sided seeds less than ¼ inch long.

DISTRIBUTION.—A common shrub in both northern Europe and North America, the Common Juniper ranges westward across the Boreal part of our continent, from Greenland to Alaska and southward by way of mountain ranges into Georgia in the east and into Texas, New Mexico and California in the west. In Illinois, it occurs in extreme northern and southern parts of the state but not in intermediate regions. In the north, in Cook and Lake counties, it is characteristically shrubby, but in a few southern Illinois counties it assumes an upright habit.

Juniperus horizontalis Moench, the Creeping Juniper or Creeping Savin, though not native in Illinois, was seeded on the Waukegan moorland nearly three-quarters of a century ago and now occurs there as an established, naturalized species. It differs from the Common Juniper in that its leaves, on mature branches, are scalelike and set in pairs. Also, its fruit matures in the second, instead of the third, year. On the Waukegan moorland it has developed from the original seeding as a low, trailing shrub with bright steel-blue foliage which, in autumn, turns pale purple and becomes glaucous. These distinctive characteristics, valuable when this shrub is used as an ornamental, have given rise to a common name, Waukegan Juniper, and to technical recognition as forma *Douglasii* Rehder.

LILIACEAE

The Lily Family

Plants of the lily family are, in the main, herbs, but a few members are woody. The colored flowers are regular, consisting of symmetrical parts including 3 sepals, 3 petals, usually 6 stamens bearing 2-celled anthers, and a single pistil made up, as a rule, of a 3-celled ovary and 3 distinct, or more or less united, styles. The petals and sepals usually are colored alike and are similar in size and shape. The ovary ripens into a pod, as in the lily, or into a berry, as in asparagus, containing many or few seeds.

This is an exceedingly large family of varied aspect and wide distribution, well known in our gardens, both for its decorative members and for those useful as vegetables. It is represented in Illinois by a great many native herbs and the woody greenbriers.

SMILAX Linnaeus

Greenbriers Sawbriers

The greenbriers are woody or, less often, herbaceous vines, which climb and cling by means of tendrils arising in pairs from leaf petioles. Their stems frequently are armed with prickles. The greenish or yellowish, dioecious flowers, which occur in small, axillary umbels, are small, and each has 3 regular, separate sepals, 3 similar petals, and 6 stamens or a 3-celled, very shortly 3-styled ovary, which develops into a small, 2- to 6-seeded, pulpy berry. The petioled, broad-bladed leaves are alternate on the stems and are characterized by the 2 to 4 prominent veins that run parallel with the midvein through the length of the blade.

Key to the Greenbrier Species

Leaves green on both sides.
  Leaves of young plants contracted on the sides and appearing hastate . . . . **S. Bona-nox**, p. 32
  Leaves of young and old plants not contracted or hastate.
    Three nerves of the leaf reaching the apex; fruit more or less glaucous . . . . **S. rotundifolia**, p. 29
    Five nerves reaching the apex; fruit not glaucous . . . . **S. hispida**, p. 33
Leaves green above, glaucous beneath . . . . **S. glauca**, p. 30

SMILAX ROTUNDIFOLIA Linnaeus

Common Greenbrier Horsebrier Round-Leaved Brier

The Common Greenbrier, fig. 3, is a large, climbing vine with dull green, ovate leaves and with stems and often branchlets rather sparsely beset with long, sharp spines. The vines arise from long underground stems and become, with age, rather angular at the base. They branch abundantly, and the branch-lets are definitely 4-sided and zigzag. The spines are flattene at their bases and extend their sharp, black tips outward to a distance of about one-third inch. As a rule there are no spine on the nodes, but on the internodes, particularly of the mai stem, from 3 to a dozen may occur. The leaves generally ar ovate but vary from nearly round or rotund to lanceolate, an occasionally some leaves are constricted below the middle. The measure 1½ to 6 inches in length by ½ to nearly 6 inches wide The blade is acute and often cuspidate at the tip, narrowed rounded or cordate at the base, and more or less denticulat along the edges. The denticulations are rarely colored. Gener-ally the leaf is a little paler beneath than above and usually dul green on both faces but sometimes glossy green. The mai nerves are most apparent beneath and number 5 or 7. Usuall 3 of them, less frequently 5, unite at the leaf tip. The petiole are round and short, measuring one-fifth to four-fifths inch i length.

The flowers, standing in umbels in leaf axils, are borne o pedicels generally shorter than the leaf petioles, and the pistil-late and staminate flowers are produced in separate umbels, th pistillate numbering about 20 per umbel, the staminate generall fewer. From 3 to 8 of the pistillate flowers of each group ma-ture into globose, blue to blackish, bloom-covered berries, ¼ inch or a little more in diameter. Each berry contains 1 to : mahogany-red seeds.

DISTRIBUTION.—The North American range of the Commo Greenbrier extends from Nova Scotia southwestward int Iowa and southward from this northern limit into most of th territory included between Georgia and Texas. In Illinois, i has been reported from all parts of the state, but in the extrem northern counties it is rare.

SMILAX GLAUCA Walter

Sawbrier

The Sawbrier, fig. 3, is a spiny, slender-stemmed vine wit abundant, longish, rather straight, leafy branchlets. Its stem are green and smooth, ⅛ to ¼ inch in diameter, and beset wit numerous short, straight or recurved spines up to one-third inc long. The slender branchlets are round or, less often, somewha

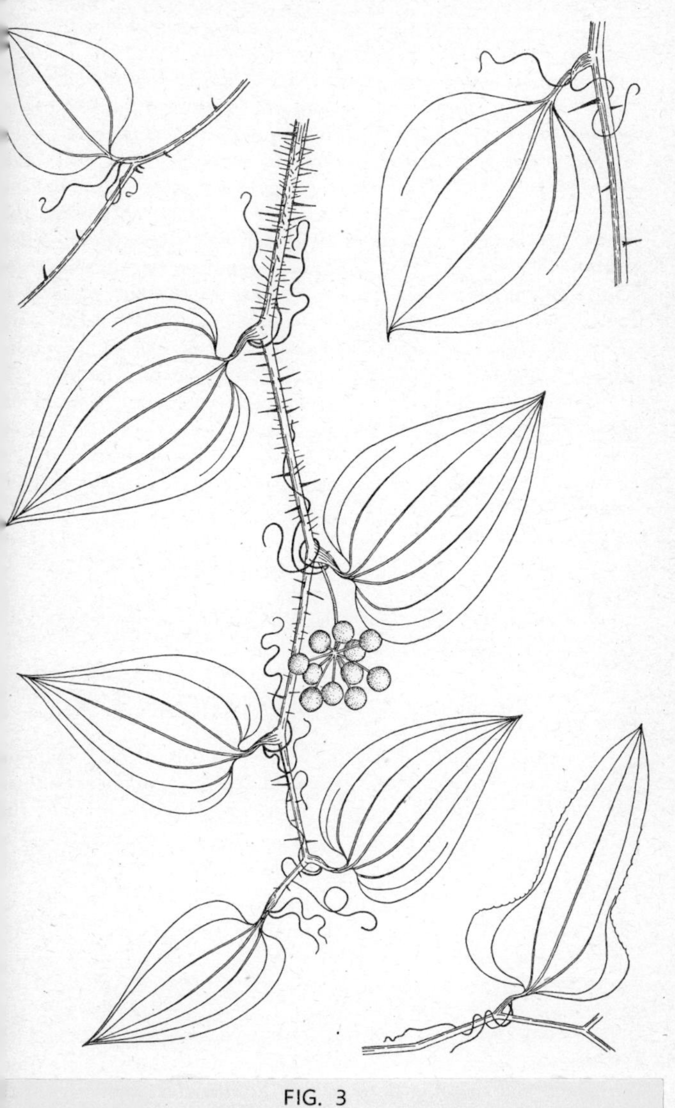

FIG. 3

ɩmilax glauca Smilax rotundifolia
Smilax hispida
Smilax Bona-nox

4-angled, occasionally glaucous, and bear as a rule a varying number of scattered, short spines. The leaves, 1½ to 5 inches long by ½ to 4 inches wide, are mostly ovate or broadly lanceolate, though they vary from broadly ovate to nearly linear and are sometimes a little constricted near the middle. They are acute and often cuspidate at the tip, wedge shaped to broadly cordate at the base, and smooth and toothless at the edges, which turn under. The blade is smooth and either glaucous or green above, but glaucous and densely papillose beneath, and has 3 or 5 strong nerves, 3 of which unite at the leaf tip. The petioles are ¼ to ½ inch long.

Flowers appear in May or June in umbeled groups of 5 to 10 in leaf axils. Three to 5 flowers of each pistillate umbel mature into bluish-black, bloom-covered berries ¼ to one-third inch in diameter, each of which contains 1 to 3 mahogany-red seeds. In this species the peduncles, ⅜ to 1⅛ inches long, are characteristically longer than the petioles.

Distribution.—The Sawbrier is southern in its range, which extends from Virginia westward into southern Illinois and southward to Florida in the east and Texas in the west. In Illinois, it occurs north to Lawrence County in the east and Union County in the west, but intermediately does not come north of the Ozarks.

SMILAX BONA-NOX Linnaeus

Fringed Greenbrier

The Fringed Greenbrier, fig. 3, is a large, high-climbing vine with crooked stems, zigzag branches and deeply constricted leaves. Toward the base the stems are ¼ to ½ inch in diameter, rounded but usually with 1 prominent edge or angle, usually covered by a thick, white pubescence of stellate hairs, and beset with scattered (3 to 8 per node) pubescent spines, 1 of which in each internode is flat at the base and colored at the tip, the others being straight or a little recurved and one-third to ½ inch long. The branches are noticeably zigzag, angular and spineless. Leaves on vigorous vines are ovate-hastate, dark yellow green on both faces, 1 to 6 inches long by ½ to 5 inches wide and have rather thick blades with acute or cuspidate tips, narrowed, truncate or cordate bases, and smooth or more or less denticulate margins, which are colorless and thickened, though the denticulations are more or less colored. There are 5 to 9 nerves per leaf, 3 of which unite at the apex. The petioles are round, 1/4 to 1 inch long, and shorter than the peduncles.

Flowers occur in umbels arising from leaf axils. The pistillate flowers are distinctly smaller than, and about twice as numerous as, the staminate, and 3 to 10 in each umbel mature in October or November into black, faintly bloomy berries about 1/4 inch in diameter, each with light mahogany-red seeds.

DISTRIBUTION.—The Fringed Greenbrier ranges from New Jersey, Virginia and Florida westward to Illinois, Missouri, Kansas and Texas. In Illinois, it is found only in the extreme southern part of the state, along the Ohio River.

SMILAX HISPIDA Muhlenberg

Greenbrier — Hispid Greenbrier

The Greenbrier, fig. 3, is a long, climbing vine, with stems coarser than the other Smilax species and with straightish, leafy branches. Near the base the stem is nearly 1/2 inch in diameter, smooth and somewhat striate. Above it is round or nearly so and is rather densely set both on the nodes and in the internodes with bristle-like, very thick spines up to 1/2 inch long. The branches are generally round, less often a little angled or 4-sided, and rarely spiny. The leaves are generally ovate but vary from orbicular to lanceolate. They may be 6 or 7 inches long by 5 or 6 inches wide but usually are 3 by 2 1/2 inches. The blades are thin, dark green above and below, acute or cuspidate at the apex, narrowed to broadly cordate at the base, with erose or denticulate margins and 5, 7 or 9 nerves, 5 of which unite at the apex. The petioles are about one-third inch long and only one-third to one-half as long as the peduncles.

The flowers occur in axillary umbels, the pistillate having 20 to 40 flowers each, the staminate 10 to 25 flowers. In the pistillate umbels, 10 to 12 flowers mature in October or November into globose, black, bloomless berries about 1/4 inch in diameter, each containing 1 or, less often, 2 mahogany-red seeds.

DISTRIBUTION.—The Greenbrier ranges from Connecticut westward into Ontario and Minnesota and southward into Virginia, Tennessee, Kansas and Texas. It occurs throughout Illinois, preferring the rich moist soils of woods and stream banks but growing also in the poorest soils.

SALICACEAE

The Willow Family

This family is made up of trees, shrubs and herbs, which bear simple, alternate leaves and produce pistillate and staminate flowers in deciduous catkins, the two kinds of flowers being borne on separate plants. The fruit is a small, lanceolate capsule, which splits lengthwise into 2 recurving valves to liberate numerous oblong, tiny seeds, each of which has a small tuft of down at its base. There are no sepals or petals in the flowers The bark of all members of the family is bitter.

Of wide distribution and great usefulness, the willow family is represented in Illinois as trees by both willows and poplars 17 species of willow shrubs are native in the state.

SALIX (Tournefort) Linnaeus

Willows Osiers

The willows may be trees, shrubs or herbs, the shrubby forms having clustered stems, round, slender branchlets, variously shaped leaves, and catkins that appear before, with or after the leaves.

Salix is a very large and complex genus, of wide distribution in the world. In Illinois, only trees and shrubs are present, and these are useful for many purposes, including basket withes charcoal, ornamental plantings and hedges. The members of the genus are very difficult to identify with certainty by vegetative characters alone. For accurate identification, it is desirable to have both flowers and fruit.

Key to the Willow Species

Because of the confusion that might arise in mistaking for shrub species the young specimens of native or naturalized tree-size species, the key given below includes both shrubby and tree species

I. Leaves green on both sides.
  A. Margins remotely denticulate, teeth spinulose.
    B. Blades long and very narrow, acute at both base and apex (2–4¾ by ¼–½ inches) .... **S. longifolia**, p. 4
    B. Blades oblong (2–4 by ¼–¾ inches) .... **S. longifolia** var. **Wheeleri**, p. 4
  A. Margins closely serrate.
    C. Blades linear-lanceolate (tree) .... **S. nigra**

C. Blades broad, lanceolate to oblong-lanceolate, and usually paler beneath .... **S. cordata**, p. 42
C. Blades broadly lanceolate to ovate.
D. Upper surface shiny, apex acute, petioles glandular.
E. Both surfaces glabrous.
F. Leaves ovate and short acuminate (tree) .... **S. pentandra**
F. Leaves ovate-lanceolate, long acuminate .... **S. lucida**, p. 38
E. Thinly covered beneath with soft hairs .... **S. lucida** var. **intonsa**, p. 39
D. Upper surface dull, apex acute, petioles not glandular .... **S. adenophylla**, p. 46

II. Leaves green above, whitened with bloom beneath (glaucous).
H. Margins distinctly, if only finely, serrate.
I. Petioles glandular.
J. Blades lanceolate, acuminate.
K. Blades linear-lanceolate; branchlets pendulous, slender and tough (introduced tree) ... . **S. babylonica**
K. Blades broader, lanceolate; branchlets spreading, stouter and fragile.
L. Blades somewhat sericeous; teeth very close together (introduced tree) .... **S. alba**
L. Blades glabrous; teeth farther apart .... **S. fragilis**, p. 40
J. Blades elliptical, acute .... **S. serissima**, p. 39
I. Petioles not glandular.
M. Blades narrowly lanceolate, acuminate .. **S. longipes**, p. 36
M. Blades broadly lanceolate to ovate.
N. Leaves ovate-lanceolate; acuminate; petioles long and slender (tree) .... **S. amygdaloides**
N. Leaves ovate, short acute; petioles short .... **S. glaucophylla**, p. 44
M. Blades lanceolate, acute.
O. Leaves glabrous or only slightly hairy.
P. Pale green or subglaucous beneath, coarsely reticulated above .... **S. cordata**, p. 42
P. Glaucous and finely reticulated above and below .... **S. petiolaris**, p. 49
O. Blades pubescent beneath, glabrous or only finely hairy above.
Q. Leaves gray pubescent and reticulated beneath .... **S. capraea**, p. 58
Q. Leaves silvery-silky, not reticulated beneath.
R. Pubescence silvery-silky only .... **S. sericea**, p. 54
R. Pubescence with tawny hairs intermixed .... **S. subsericea**, p. 56
H. Margins entire or at most remotely dentate or serrulate, mostly revolute.

S. Blades glabrous or nearly so above and below.
  T. Leaves small (1–2 inches long), oblong, closely reticulated . . . . **S. pedicellaris**, p. 47
  T. Leaves large (2–4 inches long), coarsely reticulated beneath.
    U. Obovate, thin and entire . . . . **S. discolor**, p. 48
    U. Elliptic-oval, thick, coarsely repand-dentate . . . . **S. discolor** var. **eriocephala**, p. 49
S. Blades tomentose and more or less rugose, at least beneath.
  V. Linear-oblanceolate; white-woolly beneath . . . . **S. candida**, p. 57
  V. Oblanceolate; gray-tomentose beneath.
    W. Leaves 2–4 inches long . . . . **S. humilis**, p. 51
    W. Leaves 1–2 inches long . . . . **S. tristis**, p. 53
  V. Elliptic-oval or rhomboidal . . . . **S. Bebbiana**, p. 52

SALIX LONGIPES Shuttleworth

Ward's Willow

Through most of its range Ward's Willow, fig. 4, is a low, gray-barked shrub 3 to 10 feet high, but it may become tall and treelike. Its narrowly to broadly lanceolate leaves, 2½ to 6 inches long by ⅜ to 1¼ inches wide, taper from the rounded base to a long, acuminate point. The margin is finely and closely serrate, and the blade is dark green above but densely and whitely glaucous beneath, at first more or less pubescent but later glabrous above and usually also below, though often remaining somewhat pubescent beneath, especially on the midrib. The petioles are ¼ to ½ inch long, moderately stout, thinly to densely pubescent, and yellowish to dark brown. The conspicuous stipules, often ¾ inch long, are ovate to reniform, acute or rounded, sharply serrate like the leaves, eventually glabrous, and densely white-glaucous beneath. Branchlets are rather slender, glabrous or finely pubescent, yellowish to dark red brown, and terete. The reddish-brown buds are about ⅛ inch long, blunt ovate, appressed, and thinly to heavily pubescent.

Catkins appear before the leaves. They are slender, lax, and 1½ to 4 inches long. At first nearly sessile, eventually they terminate leafy peduncles ½ to 2 inches long. The scales of the flowers are ovate to oblanceolate, yellowish, and villous. The staminate flowers have 5 to 8 stamens, the filaments of which are hairy toward the base. The pistillate flowers have very short styles terminated by 2 very short, entire stigmas. The

FIG. 4

Salix serissima
Salix lucida
Salix fragilis

Salix longifolia

Salix longipes

capsules when mature are narrowly ovate, often so contracted above the middle as to seem acuminate, glabrous, 1/8 to 1/4 inch long, and they stand on short but distinct pedicels.

DISTRIBUTION.—Ward's Willow is a southern species that ranges from the Potomac River and Cuba to Texas and Oklahoma and from the Gulf of Mexico northward to the Ohio River and up the Mississippi into Illinois in the region of East St. Louis.

The form occurring in the north, especially that in Illinois, is recognized by some botanists as the variety *Wardii* (Bebb) Schneider, for which the distinguishing characteristics are obtuse stipules and glabrous branchlets. It grows along with the Black Willow on the banks of rivers and swamps, but does not stray inland, as the Black Willow does.

SALIX LUCIDA Muhlenberg

Shining Willow

The Shining Willow, fig. 4, is a shrub of moderate height, usually 3 to 10 feet tall or occasionally treelike and up to 20 feet high, with moderately stout, shining branchlets and large, long-pointed, shiny green, leathery leaves. The leaves, though variable, are generally ovate to ovate-lanceolate, 2 to 6 inches long by 3/4 to 2 inches wide or even larger, with long acuminate tips and acute or rounded bases. The margins are flat, non-revolute, and closely serrate with sharp, gland-tipped teeth. The blades are glabrous and green, and shining above and below. They stand on moderately stout, chestnut to dark brown petioles furnished with glands above on their outer ends. The stipules are semilunate to reniform, glandular toothed, up to 1/4 inch long, and eventually deciduous. The twigs and branchlets are terete, moderately stout, shiny as if varnished, light to dark brown, and glabrous, and the large buds are glabrous, narrowly ovate, blunt to pointed, somewhat appressed, and 1/8 to 3/8 inch long.

The catkins emerge from lateral buds on the old wood before the leaves appear. They terminate leafy peduncles 1/4 to 3/4 inch long and are stout, oval or oblong, 3/4 to 2 inches long in flower, with oblong to obovate, obtuse, yellowish, thinly long-hairy scales, the apices of which are entire or irregularly notched with shallow indentations. Pistillate catkins become 2 to 3 inches long in fruit. The staminate flowers have each 3 to

5 or sometimes more stamens, the filaments of which are free and pubescent at the base. Each pistillate flower has a short, undivided style, capped by a short, thick, deeply cut stigma. The capsules, three-sixteenths to five-sixteenths inch long at maturity, are lanceolate-ampuliform, brownish, and glabrous, and are raised on the pedicels to a height half their length.

Distribution.—The Shining Willow inhabits wet situations and stream banks from Newfoundland westward to Manitoba and southward to Delaware, northern Indiana, northern Iowa, and North Dakota. In Illinois, it occurs only in the northern third of the state.

The variety *intonsa* Fernald is distinguished by having its first year branchlets and the under surface of its leaves permanently though thinly covered with reddish pubescence. It occurs in northern Indiana about as frequently as the typical form and may be encountered in Illinois.

SALIX SERISSIMA (Bailey) Fernald

Autumn Willow

The Autumn Willow, fig. 4, is a shrub 3 to 12 feet high with shining, olive-brown branches and shining, glabrous, yellowish-brown branchlets, which bear elliptic or oblong-lanceolate leaves that usually are rounded at the base and acute or short-acuminate at the apex. The leaf blades are 2 to 4 inches long by about ½ to 1¼ inches wide, closely and finely glandular-serrate on the margins, dark green, shining, and glabrous above, and pale to subglaucous beneath. The slender petioles are usually glandular at the outer ends, and stipules are wanting.

The short, stout catkins, which appear on the end of short, leafy, lateral branches after the leaves are out, are oblong to oval and ½ to 1 inch long. Pistillate catkins are about ¾ inch wide and lax at maturity. The catkin scales are obovate, pale yellow, and covered with long, white hair. Mature capsules are narrowly conical, about ¼ inch long, thick walled, brown, and glabrous, and stand on stout pedicels. Staminate flowers bear 3 to 5 or more stamens with free, finely long-hairy filaments, and pistillate flowers bear short styles capped by very short, 2-lobed stigmas. The flowering period ranges from late June to the middle of July, and capsules mature from early August into September.

Distribution.—The Autumn Willow inhabits swamps and bogs from Newfoundland west to Alberta and south to Massachusetts, northern Ohio, and Indiana. Its occurrence in Illinois is substantiated for a single locality near Beach, in Lake County.

SALIX FRAGILIS Linnaeus

Crack Willow Brittle Willow

The Crack Willow, fig. 4, is often shrubby, although at maturity it becomes a slender tree up to 80 feet tall with gray, roughish bark and reddish-green twigs that are very brittle at the base. Its leaves are lanceolate, long-acuminate at the tip, acute at the base, distinctly and rather sharply serrate with rather widely set, small teeth, glabrous both above and below and distinctly glaucous below, dark green above, 3 to 6 inches long, and ½ to 1 inch wide. The glabrous, gland-bearing petioles are ½ to two-thirds inch long. The semicordate stipules are early deciduous.

The catkins in flower are 1 to 3 inches long, the staminate bearing 2-stamened flowers, the filaments of which are separate and pubescent below. The pistillate catkins, which stand on the ends of lateral, leafy peduncles, are rather loosely flowered and at maturity become 3 to 5 inches long. The female flowers, bearing pistils with short styles and 2-notched stigmas, develop into conic, glabrous capsules up to ¼ inch long, which are set on short pedicels that scarcely exceed the glands. The species flowers in early May with the leaves, and the fruit matures in June.

Distribution.—The Crack Willow, a native of Europe, has been planted more or less widely throughout eastern North America. It is reported to have become an escape in northern Atlantic Coast states. In Illinois, it is somewhat doubtfully recorded from Kankakee County and in the Chicago region, where it is said to be a common escape along roads and fences.

SALIX LONGIFOLIA Muhlenberg

Sandbar Willow Longleaf Willow

The Sandbar Willow, fig. 4, is a fairly tall shrub with clustered, gray-barked stems that attain a height of 5 to 15 feet, sometimes more. The usually linear-lanceolate leaves, which may vary to linear-oblanceolate or very narrowly elliptical, are acute at the tip, narrowed to the petiole at the base, 2 to 5 inches long by 1/4 to 1/2 inch wide, green on both sides, thinly to silvery villous when young, and glabrate or entirely glabrous in age. The flat, non-revolute margins are interrupted by fine, divergent, widely spaced, spinulose teeth. The short petioles, only one-sixteenth to 1/4 inch long, are moderately slender and pubescent at first but later glabrous. There are no stipules. The twigs and branches are moderately stout, terete, reddish brown to brown, and generally pubescent at first. As a rule they become glabrous, although sometimes branchlets retain their pubescence for a year. The small buds are one-sixteenth to 1/8 inch long, pubescent at first, later glabrous, and a little redder than the twigs.

The catkins, which appear after the leaf buds unfold, develop singly or in groups of 2 or 3 on slender, leafy lateral or subterminal twigs 1/4 inch long. The staminate catkins are 3/4 to 1 3/4 inches long, the pistillate 1 to 3 inches long and rather loosely flowered. When in groups, the lower or lateral catkins appear later than the terminal ones. The deciduous catkin scales are yellow, lanceolate, and only thinly pubescent. Staminate flowers have 2 stamens, the filaments of which are free and pubescent, and each pistillate flower has a single gland and a very short, divided stigma capping an almost obsolete style. Capsules, when they are mature, measure 1/4 to 3/8 inch long and are ampuliform in shape. They are thinly to silvery villous when young but glabrous at maturity, reddish brown to light or dark brown, and raised on very distinct pedicels. This species flowers in southern Illinois in early or mid April and in northern Illinois in early or late May, and fruit matures in June or even to late July.

DISTRIBUTION.—The Sandbar Willow is one of the most common willows of northeastern North America. It ranges from Quebec to New Brunswick, southward to Delaware, across the continent to Alaska in the north, over most of the Great Plains, and south to southern Louisiana. In Illinois, it probably occurs throughout the entire state, growing, as its name implies, very commonly on sandy shores and abundantly on the moist alluvial soils of streams and marshy regions, particularly where land is subject to overflow from adjacent waters.

The variety *Wheeleri* (Rowlee) Schneider is distinguished chiefly by its leaves, which are shorter and broader, *i.e.,* 2 to 4 inches long by about 3/8 to 5/8 inch wide, and also densely covered by long and rather permanent hairs. It is in this last respect said to resemble the *S. argophylla* of the Pacific Coast. In Illinois, it appears to be rare and is definitely recorded only in St. Clair, Winnebago and Cook counties.

SALIX CORDATA Muhlenberg

Heartleaf Willow Cordate Willow

The Heartleaf Willow, fig. 5, is a shrub of rather large size, generally 5 to 25 feet high, with a bushy habit and moderate to rather slender twigs that bear long, narrow, dark green leaves. The leaves are narrowly to broadly oblanceolate or lanceolate, acuminate at the tip, generally cordate but often rounded to the petiole at the base, dark green above and glaucous-white or at least lighter green beneath. They are closely and finely serrate but not revolute on the margins, often puberulent upon emergence but later glabrous, and 3 to 5 inches long by 1/2 to 1 1/2 inches wide. In age they become rigid, with strong, conspicuous, white or yellowish to light brown petioles at first more or less pubescent but later glabrous and about 1/4 to 1/2 inch long. They are subtended by semicordate to rotund, sharply serrate, glabrous, persistent stipules up to 1/2 inch long. The yellowish to dark brown twigs are terete, often lined or ridged below the leaf-scars; they are pubescent at first and often, the floral twigs especially, remain so throughout their first year, otherwise becoming glabrous. The appressed buds are dark yellow to dark brown, conical, pointed and pubescent, and measure about 1/8 to 1/4 inch long.

The catkins, which appear simultaneously with the leaves, are nearly sessile. They are 1 to 2 3/4 inches long and quite slender, being only about 1/4 inch wide. Pistillate catkins become 2 to 3 inches long at maturity. Staminate flowers have 2 stamens, the filaments of which are glabrous. The styles of pistillate flowers are short and undivided and bear 2 entire or divided stigmas half as long as the style. Mature capsules are lanceolate, about 1/4 inch long, glabrous, greenish to tan brown, and provided with a short pedicel about equal in length to the scale, which is oblong, lanceolate, brown, and more or less hairy.

FIG. 5

Salix pedicellaris
Salix adenophylla
Salix discolor

Salix cordata
Salix glaucophylla

Distribution.—The Heartleaf Willow is distributed widely over northeastern North America, ranging from New Brunswick southward to Maryland and westward into Manitoba in the north and Kansas in the south. In Illinois, it is common in most of the northern section of the state, from Lake Michigan westward to the Mississippi in Jo Daviess County, and ranges southward into Lawrence County in the east and Menard County in the west. It is subject to attack by an insect which causes the deformation of terminal buds into large, conelike structures.

It is stated by authorities that this species hybridizes freely with *S. sericea*, less commonly with *S. nigra*, and resulting hybrids may be expected throughout its range in Illinois.

Collections made by E. J. Hill near Kankakee and two specimens taken by Dr. Frederick Brendel near Peoria have been referred to the variety *angustata* Andersson, but these specimens are so like the general run of the species that they hardly seem worth varietal segregation. It is the opinion of C. R. Ball that the species is common in Indiana but that the variety does not occur there. Very probably we have the same situation in Illinois. The variety *myricoides* (Muhlenberg) Carey, thought by one authority to be the hybrid of *S. cordata* and *S. sericea*, is distinguished by its cinereous or canescent twigs with permanent pubescence, elongate leaves with blades tapering and acute at the base, sparsely appressed, small, ovate, pointed stipules that are hairy beneath, and capsules at first silky but later glabrate. The range of this variety, from Massachusetts to Wisconsin and south to Kansas, includes Illinois, and specimens collected by V. H. Chase in Stark County, by E. J. Hill in Kankakee County, and by Elihu Hall in Menard County seem to be representative.

SALIX GLAUCOPHYLLA Bebb

Blueleaf Willow Glaucous-Leaved Willow

The Blueleaf Willow, fig. 5, is a low, spreading shrub up to 7 feet tall with clustered stems, stoutish branches, and leathery green leaves that are densely blue-glaucous beneath. The leaf blades, elliptical-lanceolate to ovate-lanceolate or even ovate, are 2 to 4 inches long by ¾ to 1½ inches wide, acute to shortly acuminate at the tip, acute, rounded or even somewhat cordate at the base, with serrate to crenate-serrate margins and inbent teeth that are gland tipped. The leaves are glabrous or somewhat tomentose beneath on the lower portion of the midrib, and the nerves are rather prominent on old leaves. The stout branchlets are terete, glabrous in age, and yellowish to dark brown. They bear rather large, plump buds, 1/8 to 1/4 inch long, ovate in shape and blunt, reddish yellow to yellowish brown to dark brown in color, glabrous or occasionally quite noticeably though thinly pubescent. The stipules are subcordate to broadly reniform, 1/8 to 3/8 inch long, and acute, with serrulate, glandular margins, glabrous, glaucous beneath like the leaves, and persistent or deciduous. The stout petioles are reddish yellow to dark brown, glabrous or pubescent on the upper side, and 1/4 to 1/2 inch long.

The catkins generally appear before the leaves, arising laterally from old wood above small, bractlike leaves. They are nearly sessile or peduncled and at first 1 1/2 to 2 3/4 inches long. The pistillate catkins become at maturity 2 to 4 inches long and 1/2 to 3/4 inch wide. The rachis and peduncle are pilose, and the brown scales, which blacken in drying, are also pilose. The staminate flowers bear 2 stamens, with glabrous filaments 1/4 to 3/8 inch long. The pistillate flowers have short, entire styles about twice as long as they are thick, and entire or divided stigmas. Mature capsules are ampuliform, 1/4 to 3/8 inch long, glabrous, and greenish to reddish yellow. They are raised on slender pedicels 1/8 inch or more long.

Distribution.—The Blueleaf Willow, a shrub of northern sandy and alluvial situations, ranges from eastern Quebec westward into eastern Wisconsin. In Illinois it is limited to the northern section of the state. It grows in Winnebago County, in Lake County on the sands with *S. adenophylla* north of Waukegan, and on sandy ground near Lake Michigan in Cook County. Flowering occurs in late April and early May, and the fruit is ripe in late May and early June. This species has been considered a variety of *S. glaucophylloides* Fernald, which ranges much farther north and northeast.

The variety *angustifolia* Bebb has narrower leaves, that is, not over one-fourth as wide as long, and they are acute at the base as well as at the tip. It is said to have the same general range as the species as a whole, but in Illinois it is reported only at Colehour and Englewood in Cook County.

SALIX ADENOPHYLLA Hooker

Gland-Leaved Willow Dune Willow

The Gland-Leaved Willow, fig. 5, is low and spreading, often straggling, 3 to 5½ or rarely 6 feet high, with short, stoutish branches, which bear crowded, short-stalked, ovate, thick and leathery, deep green leaves above conspicuous, subcordate stipules. Leaf blades, which vary from ovate to ovate-lanceolate, are at first silvery with long, silky tomentum but eventually become glabrous on both surfaces. They range from 1½ to 3 inches long by ¾ to 1¾ inches wide. Their bases are generally cordate, though sometimes only broadly rounded, and the apices are acute or abruptly acuminate. Their margins are closely, finely and regularly serrate, and the teeth are gland tipped. The petioles are short, being ⅛ to ¼ inch long and, like the leaves, hairy at first but eventually nearly or quite glabrous. The semicordate to nearly ovate stipules, ¼ to ½ inch long, also are silky at first but become glabrous, and their margins are serrate with gland-tipped teeth. Twigs when young are silvery with silky hairs and remain more or less puberulent through 2 or more seasons. The bark, at first light reddish brown, becomes dark red to brown and bears numerous orange lenticels which appear in the second season. The conical buds, ¼ to ⅜ inch long, are orange red, glabrous on the upper half, silky pubescent below, and stand closely appressed to the twigs.

Catkins appear with or before the leaves, both kinds standing erect on divergent, pubescent peduncles ¾ to 1½ inches long, and they often are subtended by 3 to 5 small leaves up to ¾ inch long. Scales of the catkins are generally villous, oblong, and pale brown. Both kinds of catkins are at first ¾ to 1½ inches long, but the pistillate catkins lengthen in maturity to 2½ to 3 inches and continue to be pubescent on the rachis. Staminate flowers contain 2 stamens, the filaments of which are glabrous; and pistillate flowers bear 2 entire or slightly divided stigmas at the top of the short styles. The glabrous capsules in maturity are reddish, conic and without distinct beaks. They stand ⅜ to ⅝ inch high on glabrous pedicels nearly twice as long as the floral glands.

Distribution.—The Gland-Leaved Willow is a shrub of northern sandy regions. It ranges from Labrador to James Bay and south to the Great Lakes region, reaching its most southern stations in northern Indiana and Illinois. It was at one time an abundant shrub on the sandy shores of Lake Michigan north of Chicago but is now much reduced in distribution and in abundance. It does not grow inland.

SALIX PEDICELLARIS Pursh

Bog Willow

The Bog Willow, fig. 5, is a low, spreading or trailing shrub with erect, leafy shoots 1 to 5 feet high, which arise from long, creeping, root-covered stems that penetrate deeply into the bog. The leaves are glabrous, narrowly to broadly elliptical, 3/4 to 1 1/2 inches long by 1/4 to 1/2 inch wide, thick and somewhat leathery, pale green above and often glossy, paler and usually white-glaucous beneath, obtuse or occasionally somewhat pointed at the apex and narrowed to the petiole at the base. The margins are entire and usually distinctly revolute, and fine glands often are present. The yellowish leaf veins are finely reticulated both above and below. Twigs and branchlets both are moderate in diameter to rather stout, brown to olive brown, glabrous, and generally terete, but often fine yet distinct ridges run down from the leaf-scars. The petioles are slender, glabrous, and only 1/8 to 1/4 inch long. The light brown buds are glabrous, rather plump and bluntly ovate, one- to three-sixteenths inch long, and stand appressed against the twigs. Stipules are entirely lacking.

Catkins, which appear with the leaves, are cylindrical to oval and 3/8 to 1 1/2 inches long. They arise from lateral buds on old wood and stand erect on leafy peduncles 3/4 to 2 inches long. The pistillate catkin becomes lax in fruit, though not pendulous, and its yellow scales are oval to obovate and either obtuse or somewhat pointed, glabrous, and a trifle pubescent. Staminate flowers have 2 stamens, the filaments of which are free, and pistillate flowers bear very short, entire styles capped by short, thick, entire or bifid stigmas. Mature capsules are lanceolate to narrowly conic, orange brown to brown, glabrous, spreading and loosely arranged, three-sixteenths to 1/4 inch long, and raised on a slender pedicel about 1/8 inch high.

Distribution.—The Bog Willow grows in bogs and wet meadows or marshy ground from eastern Quebec across the continent to British Columbia, southward into New Jersey and

Pennsylvania and, in the west, into Idaho and Washington. In Illinois, it is a rare plant, probably limited at the present time to the bogs of Lake County. Formerly it grew near Peoria, and Dr. Frederick Brendel collected specimens in Woodford County, "1 mile beyond the upper ferry," a locality said to be the farthest south in the Mississippi valley for this species.

SALIX DISCOLOR Muhlenberg

Pussy Willow

The Pussy Willow, fig. 5, usually is a shrub 6 to 12 feet high but occasionally is more or less treelike and up to 24 feet high, with unusually smooth stems, reddish-brown bark, and moderate to stout branchlets upon which the leaves appear after flowering. The leaves are lanceolate to rather strongly elliptical, with acute or shortly acuminate tips, acute or rounded bases, entire or coarsely toothed margins, and glabrous surfaces dark and shining above but densely glaucous and, in some varieties, also more or less pubescent beneath, especially on the midvein. They are 2 to 4 inches long by 1 to 1½ inches wide. The rather stout petioles upon which they stand are ¼ to ½ inch long and glabrous in the typical form. The stipules are roundish to lanceolate, entire or toothed, glaucous beneath, and up to ¼ inch long. Both branchlets and twigs are terete, reddish purple or dark brown, and glabrous in the typical form, with rather prominently raised leaf-scars. The typically glabrous buds are ovate to subconical, and their scales are bright orange brown to dark brown. Those that produce leaves are blunt, appressed, and about ⅛ inch long; those that produce flowers are rather divergent, with sharp, incurved points, plump, and ¼ to ⅜ inch long.

Catkins appear before the leaves, bursting from buds on old wood. Both sorts are sessile, stout, and dense, without basal leafy bracts. The staminate catkins, commonly known as "pussies," are ¾ to 2 inches long. The pistillate catkins, at first the same size, attain at maturity a length of 1 to 3½ inches. The catkin scales are elliptic to oblanceolate, dark brown, and clothed with long, shining hair. Staminate flowers bear 2 stamens, the filaments of which are pubescent and free from each other. Pistillate flowers have short, entire styles about as long as the usually entire stigmas. The capsules at maturity are conic, beaked, and densely pubescent with gray, woolly hairs. They are about ¼ inch long, and stand on distinct pedicels that much exceed the floral glands. Flowering time is late March in the southern part of the state and mid April in the north. Fruit ripens about a month later, almost simultaneously with the unfolding of the leaves.

DISTRIBUTION.—The Pussy Willow is a common shrub in wet and swampy situations throughout northeastern North America. It ranges from Newfoundland and Nova Scotia westward into Saskatchewan and southward into eastern Delaware, Kentucky and southern Missouri. It grows in all parts of Illinois.

The variety *eriocephala* (Michaux) Andersson differs from the typical form especially in having pubescent branches and bud scales, but also its leaves are thicker, more distinctly lanceolate, and pubescent beneath. It has the same range as the typical form, and numerous collections indicate that it is common in Illinois.

SALIX PETIOLARIS J. E. Smith

Slender Willow

This willow, known generally by no common name though sometimes called Slender Willow, fig. 6, is a few-stemmed shrub or small, gray-barked tree 3 to 6 or even 10 feet high. Its linear-lanceolate to lanceolate leaves, 2 to 4 inches long by ¼ to ⅝ inch wide, are green and often shiny above but more or less densely glaucous and reticulate-veiny beneath; thinly pubescent with silvery hairs when young but glabrate or glabrous when mature. The leaves are acuminate at the tip and acute at the base, and the margins are not revolute but are finely glandular toothed. The petioles are rather slender, brownish, and ¼ to ½ inch or more long. Stipules are not present. The slender twigs are terete, dark brown, and glabrous to somewhat puberulent, and the branches diverge from the stems at angles of about 45 degrees. The flat, blunt buds, set above conspicuously raised leaf-scars, are orange brown to brown, small, ovate, about one-sixteenth to ⅛ inch long, and appressed to the stems.

Catkins appear at the same time as the leaves. They are bracted and bear linear to spatulate, acute-tipped, light brown, thinly hairy scales. The nearly sessile staminate catkins are

FIG. 6

Salix tristis
Salix Bebbiana
Salix petiolaris
Salix humilis

obovoid and ⅜ to ¾ inch long. The pistillate catkins, about the same size when in flower, stand on leafy peduncles ⅜ inch long and at maturity reach a length of ¾ to 1½ inches. Staminate flowers bear 2 stamens, the filaments of which are free, slender, and glabrous or only finely pubescent at the base. Pistillate flowers have short, entire or divided stigmas joined to the ovary by an exceedingly short style. The mature capsules are lanceolate, thinly pubescent with silvery hair, ¼ to ⅜ inch long, and stand on slender pedicels one-sixteenth to ¼ inch high.

Distribution.—The Slender Willow is a northern shrub which inhabits moist alluvial soil and ranges westward from New Brunswick into Saskatchewan and southward to New Jersey in the east and South Dakota in the west. Northern Illinois lies just within the southern limits of its range, and it has been recorded in Cook, Winnebago, Kankakee and Peoria counties. In the Chicago region, it is a shrub of low ground and is generally overlooked, although nowhere is it common.

Almost without exception, specimens collected in Illinois belong to the variety *gracilis* Andersson, which is distinguished by its more slender and more graceful twigs, narrower and more sharply toothed leaves, and longer capsule pedicels.

SALIX HUMILIS Marshall

Prairie Willow Upland Willow

The Prairie Willow, fig. 6, is a low shrub, generally only 2 to 7 feet, less often 10 feet, tall, with clustered stems bearing moderate to stout branchlets and crowded, leathery leaves. The leaf blades vary from linear-oblanceolate to obovate but are chiefly long-oblanceolate and measure 2 to 5 inches long by ⅜ to ⅝ inch wide. They are acute or short acuminate at the tip and narrowed at the base, rich green above with whitish veins and glaucous below, puberulent to glabrous above and more or less tomentose beneath. The veins, beneath, are rather strongly reticulated, and the leaf margins are distinctly revolute, entire to undulate or, more commonly, undulate-serrate. The yellowish brown petioles are moderately stout, pubescent to glabrate, and ⅛ to ⅜ inch long. The twigs and branchlets are terete, yellowish, purplish or brown, and pubescent to glabrate. The linear to broadly lanceolate stipules are serrate, acute at the tip, asymmetrically acute at the base, distinctly stalked, pubescent, and glaucescent. The broadly ovate, appressed buds are yellowish, orange brown or even darker, heavily pubescent to glabrate, blunt to rather pointed, one-sixteenth to 1/4 inch long, and stand above prominent, closely spaced leaf-scars.

The catkins appear before the leaves, in the latter part of April in the southern counties and in the early part of May in the northern. They are borne on old wood and arise from lateral and subterminal buds. They are sessile, naked, obovoid to cylindrical, and 1/2 to 1 1/4 inches long. Pistillate catkins become 3/4 to 1 1/2 inches long in fruit and are then divergent or often recurved. Staminate flowers have 2 stamens, the filaments of which are free and glabrous, and pistillate flowers have short, entire styles capped by short, divided stigmas. The capsules at maturity are slender, ampuliform, long beaked, gray-pubescent and brown. They are 1/4 to 3/8 inch long and stand on pedicels about one-sixteenth inch high.

DISTRIBUTION.—The Prairie Willow is a shrub of very wide range extending from Newfoundland westward into North Dakota, and southward in the east to Florida and in the west to Texas. Throughout this region it is a frequent, even common, shrub of uplands and prairies. In size and texture of leaves, pubescence and other characteristics it is exceedingly variable, forms of it having been assigned no less than five distinct, mostly specific names. Practically all Illinois material is assignable to the variety *rigidiuscula* Andersson, which differs from the forms found in the north and east in having narrowly oblanceolate leaves that in age become both glabrate and strongly veined beneath.

SALIX BEBBIANA Sargent

Beak Willow Bebb's Willow

The Beak Willow, fig. 6, is a tall shrub, or sometimes a small tree up to 25 feet high, with 1 to a few stems that bear numerous slender, widely spreading branchlets, which are glabrous to pubescent, yellowish to brown, and abundantly marked with bud scars. The thick, firm leaves are obovate to narrowly oblanceolate, acute to abruptly acuminate at the apex, acute at the base, and 1 1/2 to 3 or 4 inches long by 3/4 to 1 1/4 inches wide. The margins are entire to wavy-crenate and a little revolute, and the surface is dull green and finely pubescent above but paler to glaucous and densely pubescent and rugose beneath. The stipules may be obsolete or, if well grown, semi-cordate, acute and serrate.

The numerous catkins appear before or at the same time as the leaves. The staminate catkins are up to 1 inch long, sessile, yellow, and narrowed at the base. The pistillate catkins are ¾ to 1¼ inches long and nearly sessile when in flower, but as much as 3 inches long and lax when in fruit, and terminal on bracted or leafy, densely hairy peduncles ½ to ¾ inch long. Staminate flowers contain 2 stamens with slender filaments, which are free. The capsules, which are lanceolate and taper to a long beak, stand on slender pedicels, but the styles are almost obsolete and the stigma lobes are entire to deeply cleft. The scales in both catkins are lanceolate to oblong, mostly pale yellow but reddish at the tips, and densely to thinly long-hairy. The catkins are in flower during the early half of May, and fruit matures in late May and early June.

Distribution.—The Beak Willow grows in moist but not swampy situations from Newfoundland to Alaska and south to New Jersey, Pennsylvania, eastern South Dakota and central California. In Illinois, it is abundant in the extreme northeastern corner, whence it ranges westward across the state, becoming rare in Jo Daviess County.

SALIX TRISTIS Aiton

Dwarf Pussy Willow Dwarf Upland Willow

The Dwarf Pussy Willow, fig. 6, is a low shrub, generally 12 to 18 inches, very seldom more than 2 feet, high with spreading, decumbent branches and crowded, small, heathlike, hairy leaves. The leaf blades are narrowly oblanceolate, ½ to nearly 2 inches long by ⅛ to ⅜ inch wide, acute at the tip and tapered to the petiole. They are dark green and pubescent to glabrate above but glaucous and woolly beneath, and the margins are entire, undulate or undulate-serrate, and strongly revolute. The short petioles are about ⅛ inch long and generally pubescent like the leaves. The early deciduous stipules are minutely pubescent. Twigs and branches are slender to moderately stout, terete, at first puberulent and green, but glabrous and yellow, reddish brown, or nearly black in age. The reddish-brown, blunt buds are ovate, finely and often sparsely puberulent, and

often stand collaterally in pairs appressed to the stem. The
are one-sixteenth to ⅛ inch long.

The catkins are numerous and crowded, and appear in advanc
of the leaves. They are small, broadly oblong, three-sixteent
to ⅜ inch long, spreading, sessile or at the most short peduncle
and without bracts. Pistillate catkins become ¾ inch long i
fruit. The catkin scales are minute, reddish with reddish-brow
tips, and lanate-hairy. Staminate flowers have 2 stamens, th
filaments of which are free and glabrous, and pistillate flowe
have very short, entire styles capped by short, entire or divide
stigmas. The mature capsules are lanceolate-ampuliform, pu
bescent, generally red tinted at the base, ⅛ to five-sixteent
inch long, and are raised on pedicels about one-sixteenth inc
high.

Distribution.—The Dwarf Pussy Willow, which prefe
sandy uplands, roadsides, and thicket borders, ranges fro
Massachusetts to North Dakota and south into Florida i
the east, Tennessee and Missouri, eastern Nebraska, an
South Dakota in the west. It should be found in suitab
situations throughout much of Illinois, although its occurrenc
has been established only in Cook, Kankakee, Peoria and S
Clair counties.

SALIX SERICEA Marshall

Silky Willow

The Silky Willow, fig. 7, is a low shrub 3 to 8 feet tall, wit
clustered stems and dark green leaves that are brightly silvere
beneath with close, silky hair. The narrowly lanceolate t
lanceolate leaf blades are 2 to 3 or, rarely, 4 inches long b
½ to ¾ inch wide, acuminate at the tip, acute or rounded a
the base, dark green and puberulent to glabrous above, glaucou
and densely shiny-silvery pubescent beneath. The veinlets abov
and below become finely netted in age, and the margins ar
finely serrate. The petioles on which the leaves stand are slen
der, ¼ to ⅜ inch long, light to dark brown, and puberulent t
glabrous. The linear-lanceolate to semicordate, usually earl
deciduous, stipules are glaucous beneath and have serrate mar
gins. The slender, terete twigs range from light to dark brow
and from puberulent to glabrous. They bear blunt, ovat
flattened or plump, reddish-brown, appressed buds that ar

FIG. 7

Salix candida
Salix subsericea
Salix sericea
Salix capraea

puberulent or glabrous and small, ⅛ to three-sixteenths incl long.

Numerous catkins appear in the spring before the leaves They are sessile or very nearly so and are either destitute o bracts or have only 2 or 3 small bracts on their very shor peduncles. The staminate catkins are ovoid to oblong and ⅜ to ¾ inch long, and the pistillate catkins are ½ to 1 inch lon in flower and up to 1¼ inches long in fruit, when they ar narrow and cylindrical. The catkin scales are obtuse, ovate dark brown, and covered by long hairs. Staminate flowers bea 2 stamens, the filaments of which are free and glabrous, an pistillate flowers have very short, though frequently divided styles, which are capped by very short, notched stigmas. Th capsules when mature are blunt, ovoid to oblong, silvery pu bescent, and ⅛ to three-sixteenths inch long. They stand o a distinct pedicel which may be as much as one-sixteenth incl long.

DISTRIBUTION.—The Silky Willow prefers moist and bogg situations and grows in such places from New Brunswick westward into Michigan and south into South Carolina and southeastern Missouri. In Illinois, it should be found in suitabl situations throughout the state, but thus far its occurrence ha been established only near Lake Michigan and in the Wabash valley.

SALIX SUBSERICEA (Andersson) Schneider

This willow, fig. 7, too little known to have a common name, is a large, widely branching shrub that attains 8 or 10 feet of height in the best specimens. Generally it is considerably smaller and is similar in many ways to *S. petiolaris*. Its narrowly lanceolate to oblanceolate leaves, which are ½ to 2 inches long by ¼ to ½ inch wide, stand on petioles less than ¼ inch long. The leaf margins are serrate to entire and slightly revolute. Young leaves are finely hairy, both above and below, and the hairs are silvery or often distinctly tawny. Eventually they become glabrous. The slender, glabrous branches are reddish to purple and provided with fine, longitudinal ridges. They are at first hairy like the leaves and after the first year bear distinctly raised leaf-scars ¼ to ½ inch apart. The ovate, pointed buds, which are appressed or, less often, a little divergent, are eddish to purple, finely hairy on the lower half, and about ⁄8 inch long.

Catkins appear at about the same time as the leaves. They tand on short, leafy pedicels, especially the pistillate ones, which re ¾ to 1¼ inches long and erect in fruit. The catkin scales re light brown, obovate, and thinly to densely fine-hairy. The tyles of the pistillate flowers are short, spreading, and divided, vith 2 long, spreading stigmas. The capsules at maturity are anceolate, at first finely hairy but at maturity nearly glabrous, nd stand on pedicels about one-sixteenth inch high.

Distribution.—This unusual willow is known in Illinois nly through collections of E. J. Hill at West Pullman, Cook County, and from the Barrens near Kankakee.

SALIX CANDIDA Fluegge

Sage Willow Hoary Willow

The Sage Willow, fig. 7, is a low, very branchy shrub generally to 10 inches, rarely 3 feet, high, with long, narrow, densely vhite-tomentose leaves. The leaf blades are linear-oblong or arrowly oblanceolate, ⅜ to ¼ inch wide by 1½ to 4 inches ong, and acute at the apex and at the base. They have revolute, onspicuously glandular margins that usually are entire but ccasionally are crenulate. They are dark green and dull, nearly labrous to thinly tomentose, with sunken veins above, and ensely white-tomentose beneath. The petioles, about ⅛ to ⁄4 inch long, are more or less whitened with tomentum. The noderately slender, round branches are divaricate, at first vhite with dense tomentum, later glabrous and yellowish, red rown or even darker, with buds spaced ⅛ to ¼ inch apart, nd often marked by distinct, fine ridges which are decurrent rom the leaf-scars. The buds are red brown to red, ovate, lunt and rounded, often flattened, rather closely appressed, labrous to tomentulose, and one-sixteenth to ⅛ inch long.

Catkins appear at about the same time as the leaves and re nearly sessile, or the pistillate ones may have leafy bracts nd peduncles. They are ½ to 1½ inches long in flower, and he pistillate catkins become ¾ to 2 inches long in fruit. Scales re brown, obovate, and thinly hairy. Staminate flowers bear stamens with slender, glabrous filaments; and the styles of istillate flowers are short, reddish, entire or divided, and capped by short, spreading, notched stigmas. The mature ca sules are about ¼ inch long, lanceolate, and whitened wit tomentum. They stand on short pedicels that hardly excee the height of the floral glands.

Distribution.—The Sage Willow is a shrub of the far nort It ranges from Newfoundland and Labrador westward acro subarctic North America to British Columbia and southwar into the New England states, New Jersey, northern Ohio an Indiana, and thence westward to the Rocky Mountains, whe it again ranges southward as far as Colorado. Throughout th region it is an inhabitant of cold bogs in glaciated regions. I Illinois, it occurs most abundantly in the tamarack and spha num bogs of Lake County and in lake shore and dune bog near Lake Michigan. It may, however, be found rarely in othe parts of the state, as is evidenced by collections made years ag by Dr. Frederick Brendel in Tazewell County. The Tazewe County records are southern points for the Sage Willow.

SALIX CAPRAEA Linnaeus

Goat Willow Sallow Willow

The Goat Willow, fig. 7, a native of Eurasia, introduced int America as an ornamental, is widely cultivated in Europe. I is often a small tree or, with us, a treelike shrub with larg coarsely subdentate leaves and moderately slender to larg branchlets. The leaves, which are 3 to 6 inches long, vary i shape from narrowly ovate to rather broadly oblong-orbicula They are dark green and glabrous and marked by conspicuou yellowish to brown midveins and whitish, prominent or obscur veinlets above, whitish or grey tomentose beneath with promi nent, netted, brown veins and veinlets. The apex of the blad is acute or abruptly pointed and the base is rounded to th petiole, or subcordate, and the margins are revolute, subdentat to crenulate, and without glands. The leaves stand on stou petioles ⅜ to ⅝ inch long, which are more or less pubescen to tomentose and glandless. The terete twigs are moderate t coarse, tomentose when young but glabrate in age, and bea bark that is somewhat wrinkled to smooth, yellowish brow to dark red. The rather large, subconical buds are red to re brown, somewhat appressed, ⅛ to ¼ inch long, and eithe puberulent or glabrate. The early deciduous stipules are sub cordate, somewhat crenulate, about ¼ inch long, and pubescent.

Catkins appear before the leaves, and both sorts of catkins are sessile. The staminate catkins are ¼ to 1½ inches long and very showy, and the pistillate catkins are at first ¾ to 1 inch long but in fruit become 2 to 3 inches long and stand erect on hairy peduncles ¼ to ½ inch high. Staminate flowers have two stamens with very long, yellow, glabrous filaments, and pistillate flowers bear short, usually undivided styles capped by 2 long, spreading, bifid stigmas. The scales are brown, lanceolate, and tomentose. The capsules at maturity are about ¼ inch long, lanceolate, and tomentose, and stand on long, tomentose pedicels which exceed the floral disk by three to four times.

DISTRIBUTION.—The Goat Willow is a native of Eurasia, but it has been widely used as an ornamental tree in Europe, where its leaves are considered ideal food for cows, goats and horses, and it has been transplanted to this country. In America, it is known chiefly by the pendulous or weeping varieties, which have been extensively planted. In Illinois, it is an occasional escape from cultivation.

MYRICACEAE

The Sweet Gale, or Bayberry, Family

This is a family of monoecious or dioecious shrubs that bear flowers in short, scaly catkins and produce alternate, resinous-dotted, and often fragrant leaves. Female flowers develop, from the one-celled ovaries, a drupelike nut for fruit. There are but two genera in the family, the following occurring in Illinois.

COMPTONIA L'Héritier

Sweetfern

This genus has the general characteristics of the family. The flowers occur in catkins or aments, and each flower, placed under a scale or bract, possesses a pair of bractlets. Staminate catkins are ellipsoid to cylindrical, and pistillate catkins are ovoid or globular. Both sorts arise from axillary, scaly buds. Staminate flowers have 2 to 8 stamens, the filaments of which tend to be joined toward the base, and 2-celled anthers. Pistillate catkins ripen into globular to subcylindric, small nuts.

There are four North American species of this family, the Sweet Gale, native in the north and much used in decorative planting; the Wax Myrtle, the nuts of which are coated with wax; the Bayberry of the eastern coast; and the Sweetfern which alone is native in Illinois.

COMPTONIA PEREGRINA (Linnaeus) Coulter

Sweetfern

The Sweetfern, fig. 8, is a low, twiggy, mat-forming, sweet scented shrub a little over 1 foot to nearly 3 feet high, with long, narrow, cut-edged, ferny leaves. Its branches are slender pubescent, and bear alternate, linear-lanceolate leaves 1 to · or occasionally 5 inches long by ½ to ¾ inch wide. The blades characteristically deeply cut into 20 or more rounded lobes o teeth, are dark green above, paler and pubescent beneath and on the midrib and margin above, and covered more or less densely on both faces with resinous glands. The apex usually i acute and the base is rounded to the very short petiole. The early deciduous stipules are small and half-cordate.

The flowers are generally dioecious, though occasionall

FIG. 8
Comptonia peregrina

monoecious. The staminate catkins, about ¾ inch long, clustered together on the ends of branches, fall about the middle of May. The globular pistillate catkins stand at the end of hort, lateral branches. They become burlike at maturity and as a rule are 4-seeded. In the pistillate flower the ovary is urrounded by 8 long, narrow, awllike, persistent, pubescent cales or bracts that eventually surround and nearly conceal he light brown nut, which is only about ⅛ inch long.

DISTRIBUTION. — More widely distributed than the other species of the family, the Sweetfern ranges from Nova Scotia westward to Saskatchewan, southward in the east to North Carolina and in the west into northern Indiana, northeastern llinois, and Minnesota. In Illinois, it is known to occur only n the extreme northeastern corner of the state, growing in sandy open woods and swamps.

BETULACEAE

The Birch Family

The birch family consists of monoecious or occasionally dioecious trees and shrubs with flowers generally in catkins. Staminate flowers always are in catkins, but pistillate flowers may be clustered or arranged in spikes. The leaves, subtended by early deciduous stipules, are alternate, simple, and straight veined. The fruit is typically a 1-celled or 1-seeded nut, which s borne free or inclosed in a foliaceous, sometimes woody, involucre.

This is a small family of about 5 genera, some trees and ome shrubs, all of which occur in Illinois. *Ostrya*, the Hop Hornbeam, *Carpinus*, the Hornbeam, and the tree birches have been described among the trees of the state. The shrubby orms include hazelnuts, alders and small birches.

Key to Shrubby Genera

Staminate flowers in catkins, pistillate flowers in clusters; nuts large, inclosed in a leafy, somewhat lignified involucre . . . . **Corylus**, p. 62

Both staminate and pistillate flowers in catkins; the seedlike nutlets free and winged.

Fruiting catkins membranous; winter buds sessile . . **Betula**, p. 64

Fruiting catkins woody, miniature cones; winter buds stalked . . . . **Alnus**, p. 66

CORYLUS (Tournefort) Linnaeus

Hazelnuts Filberts

This is a genus of shrubs or, in other lands, small trees, which bear alternate, thin, doubly toothed, broad-bladed leaves. The staminate catkins arise singly or in fascicles from scaly buds on year-old twigs, and the staminate flowers bear 8 stamens and 2 scaly bractlets attached to the inner face of the catkin scale. The pistillate flowers emerge, several together, from a scaly bud on the tip of an early, leafy shoot. The ovary in the flower is tipped with the short limb of the adherent calyx scales. One of its 2 ovules is sterile. The style is short, with 2 red, elongated slender stigmas. The fruit, an ovoid or globose nut, is inclosed in a cup made up of 2 enlarged, leafy or woody bracts.

This genus is, in America, represented by two native species. The filbert of commerce is a Japanese species.

Key to Hazelnut Species

Twigs and petioles glandular-bristly, fruit husk open to the top of the nut, its bracts toothed . . . . **C. americana**

Twigs and petioles not glandular-bristly, fruit husk densely bristly, closed, and prolonged into a narrow, tubular beak . . . . **C. cornuta**

CORYLUS AMERICANA Marshall

Hazelnut American Hazel

The Hazelnut, fig. 9, is a small, branched shrub generally 3 to 5 feet high, or occasionally of ranker growth and 15 or more feet tall. Its alternate, simple, 2-ranked leaves, often as much as 6 inches long by 4 inches wide but usually 3 by 2 inches, vary from nearly orbicular to the more usual ovate and have acuminate tips, slightly obliquely cordate bases, doubly serrate margins, and teeth that are short and blunt. The upper surface is more or less pubescent, the lower thickly so, and the veins and veinlets are at times more or less densely overgrown with stalked glands. The rather stout petioles are ⅛ to 1 inch long, pubescent, and more or less covered with glandular hairs. The gray or brown, zigzag branchlets, at first pubescent and also covered by green or reddish glandular hairs, the latter often persisting, are moderately stout or slender, terete, and contain continuous, pale, somewhat 3-sided pith

The solitary, alternate buds are round to ovoid, obtuse, gray-pubescent, ⅛ inch long, and have 4 distinctly exposed scales. They are sessile and seated somewhat obliquely above rather

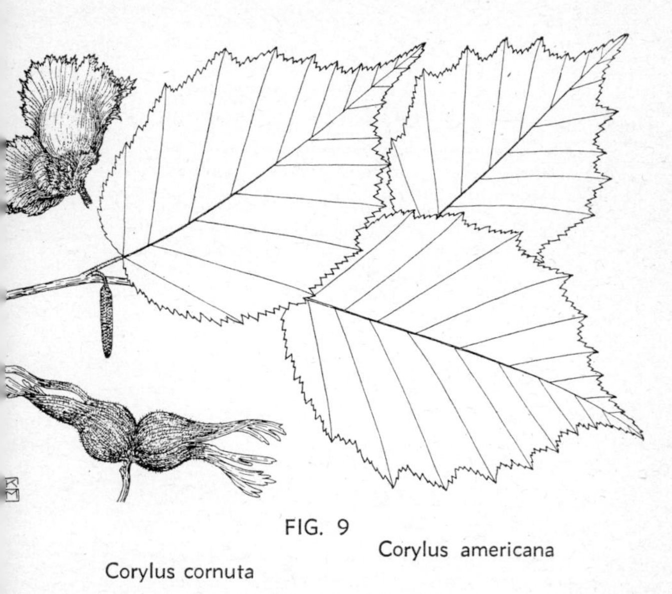

FIG. 9

Corylus americana

Corylus cornuta

small, half-round to triangular and somewhat raised leaf-scars, each marked by 3 bundle traces and flanked by elongated stipule scars.

The graceful, ashen staminate catkins, pendulous at the ends of branches or in leaf axils near branch ends, are up to 2½ inches long. They develop in the fall and flower the next spring. They may be single, or 2 to 5 may occur together. Their scales are pubescent, and each scale subtends a stamen. Pistillate flowers occur in inconspicuous, budlike tufts at the ends of branchlets and in axils of upper leaves on the current year's growth. These mature in the fall into shell-covered nuts, each inclosed by 2 enlarged, more or less pubescent and glandular-hairy bracts. The nuts, which occur in groups of 2 to 4, are globose and light brown, and the shell inclosing them is large, bony, and pubescent at the base. The mature nuts are ¼ to ¾ inch in diameter.

Distribution.—The American Hazel ranges, in a variety o soils and situations, throughout the temperate part of eastern North America, from Maine westward to Saskatchewan an southward to Florida and Oklahoma. In Illinois, it grow through most of the state, although it has not thus far bee widely collected or reported. It flowers in March and April and the fruit ripens from July to September.

The Beaked Hazelnut, *C. cornuta* Marchant, fig. 9, has bee reported, possibly erroneously, in Morgan and Pike counties This species differs from the foregoing in that the twigs, at firs covered only with scattered long hairs, become glabrate, and in that the bracts that surround the fruit are united and pro longed into the tubular, bristly beak for which the species i named.

BETULA (Tournefort) Linnaeus

The Birches

The birches are trees and shrubs which bear alternate, broad bladed, toothed leaves, and produce both staminate and fertil flowers in catkins. In the staminate catkins there are 3 flower to each scale, and each flower has 1 calyx scale and 4 stamen with 1-celled anthers. In the pistillate catkins there are 2 or flowers per scale, each of which has a naked ovary with 2 spread ing stigmas but without a calyx scale. The ovary ripens into winged, scalelike nutlet. The buds on the birches are sessil and scaly. The staminate catkins are sessile also, may be ter minal or lateral, and are formed in the summer and expan the following spring. The pistillate catkins stand at the end of short, 2-leaved, lateral branchlets.

In Illinois, the shrubby birches are represented by the on following species.

BETULA PUMILA Linnaeus

Dwarf Birch

The Dwarf Birch, fig. 10, is a relatively low shrub 3 to 10 feet high, with reddish-brown, smooth bark, characteristic birch shaped leaves, and, in late summer, catkins, which are to pro duce flowers the succeeding year. The leaves are oval, obovat or nearly orbicular, and vary considerably in size, ranging fron

FIG. 10
Alnus rugosa
Betula pumila
Alnus incana

¾ to 1½ inches in length on fruiting branchlets and nearly 2½
inches in length on sterile branchlets. They are wedge shape
at the base, more or less rounded, though occasionally acute, a
the apex, closely serrate on the margin, and at first hairy o
both surfaces but later glabrous or nearly so. The twigs, pu
bescent when young, remain more or less so for a year or mor
and become reddish brown or, later, somewhat grayish.

The pistillate catkins are usually about ½ inch long and ½
inch wide and stand on stalks about ¼ inch long. Their scale
are lobed to about the middle, the middle lobe being generall
the largest, the lateral ones more or less spreading and some
what ciliate on the margin. The nutlets and the wings ar
variable, the nutlets being ovate to slightly obovate and th
wings generally not so wide as the nutlets.

Distribution.—The Dwarf Birch, a northern shrub, range
from Newfoundland to Saskatchewan and south to northern In
diana and southeastern Minnesota. In Illinois, it occurs only i
the extreme northeastern corner of the state, in Cook and Lak
counties, in its typical habitat of bogs, swamps and lake shores

A variety, *glandulifera* Regel, is sometimes distinguished o
the basis that in *glandulifera* young twigs are more or les
abundantly dotted with glands. The typical form and thi
variety may be found in the same habitat and are so likely t
intergrade that the distinction is made with considerabl
difficulty.

ALNUS B. Eberhart

The Alders

The alders are shrubs or small trees, which bear alternate
broad-bladed, toothed leaves and produce stalked but few-scaled
solitary or raceme-like clusters of catkins. The pendulous stami
nate catkins have 4 or 5 bractlets and 3 or 6 flowers clustere
at the base of each short-stalked scale, each flower having
3- to 5-parted calyx and a similar number of stamens, th
anthers of which are 2 celled. The scales of the pistillate cat
kins are fleshy and each covers 2 flowers and 2 small, adheren
scalelets. In fruit they are woody.

The alders are shrubs of stream banks, riverbottoms an
swamps, as well as of high mountainous regions. Of about 2
species, 9 are North American and 2 occur in Illinois.

Key to the Alder Species

Leaves conspicuously doubly serrate, the teeth sharp and rather coarse, the under surface glaucous; mature cones pendant; nutlets with a narrow, thick, marginal wing.........**A. incana**

Leaves not conspicuously doubly serrate, the teeth small and rather blunt, the under surface green; mature cones erect; nutlets without a marginal wing....................**A. rugosa**

ALNUS INCANA (Linnaeus) Moench

Speckled Alder

The Speckled Alder, fig. 10, is a low, stooling shrub with gray-dotted, reddish-barked stems that rise, at an angle of 20 to 40 degrees from the vertical, to a height of 8 to 10 feet. The broadly ovate leaves, 2 to 4½ inches long and nearly as wide, are at first pubescent on both surfaces but become glabrate above with age and eventually nearly glabrous and distinctly glaucous beneath. The leaf tip is acute or shortly acuminate, the base broadly rounded or subcordate and often a little asymmetrical. The margins are doubly and sharply serrate, and the veins, beneath, are prominent, parallel, and pinnately arranged so as to terminate in the tips of the large teeth. The twigs are pubescent and grayish at first but become smooth and turn to golden or reddish brown marked by many dark specks. They are terete to slightly triangular, contain small, continuous 3-sided pith and bear rather large, 3-scaled, ovate, puberulent, stalked, gummy, red-brown buds ¼ inch long, which are set singly above somewhat raised, half-round leaf-scars dotted with 3 bundle traces and flanked by narrow, inconspicuous stipule scars. The early deciduous stipules are conspicuous, foliaceous, lanceolate, entire, pubescent, and about ½ inch long.

The slender staminate catkins occur in groups of 3 or more. Each is 2½ to 3 inches long when in flower and stands on a peduncle ¼ to ⅜ inch long. The pistillate catkins occur in clusters of 2 to 7 near the end of branchlets. They are oval, about ½ inch long by ⅜ inch wide in flower but become woody and looser in fruit. The minute, reddish-brown to chestnut-colored nutlets are ovoid and flat, and the edge of the shell extends outward slightly into a narrow, thick margin or wing.

DISTRIBUTION.—The Speckled Alder grows in cold swamps and on low ground along streams from Newfoundland southward into New York and westward into Saskatchewan and

Nebraska. In Illinois, which lies on the southern boundary of its range, it is to be found only on the moorland north of Waukegan, in Lake County, where it is rare.

ALNUS RUGOSA (Du Roi) Sprengel

Hazel Alder

The Hazel Alder, fig. 10, is an erect shrub, usually 12 or 14 feet high but often in its larger growth somewhat treelike with flexuous, ascending branches and distinctly obovate leaves 2½ to 4 inches long and about two-thirds as wide, which are dark green above and lighter green, glutinous, and often shiny beneath. They are pubescent on both surfaces when young but become glabrate in age. The veins beneath remain, however distinctly brown and hairy. The margins are finely toothed with minute, divergent, bluntly pointed teeth, each of which forms the end of 1 small veinlet. The leaf apex is rounded with at times a small point, and the base slopes in a wedge shape to the petiole, which is of moderate size, pubescent, and ½ to ¾ inch long. The stipules are quickly deciduous. The main branches and trunk are fluted, or angled, and covered with thin, nearly smooth, gray or, on younger growth, reddish to brown bark. The twigs are slender, straight, fluted or angled dark reddish brown on all but the newest growth, and glabrous but new growth is pubescent with brown hair. The blunt pubescent, narrowly ovate, brown buds, about ⅛ inch long, are raised on stout stalks nearly as long as the buds. The leaf-scars are small, little or distinctly raised, narrowly to broadly oval and marked with 3 distinct bundle traces.

Staminate catkins are borne at the end of new growth. They are pendulous, stout, and 1½ to 5 inches long in flower. The pistillate catkins, formed the previous fall, are globular to ovate in shape, woody, conelike, ⅜ to ¾ inch long, and stand erect on the end of branches in clusters of 2 to 5.

Distribution.—The Hazel Alder ranges throughout most of the eastern half of the United States, from Maine to Florida and west to Minnesota and Texas, preferring throughout this territory the margins of streams, wet woods, and cold swamps. Its general distribution, however, is patchy, and large territories apparently are avoided. In Illinois, it occurs in practically all parts of the state, though it is more common northward.

The European Alder, *A. glutinosa* (Linnaeus) Gaertner, has escaped from cultivation in Du Page County.

ULMACEAE

The Elm Family

The elm family consists of trees and shrubs, which bear simple, 2-ranked leaves that are asymmetrically oblique at the base and monoecious, polygamous, or perfect greenish flowers arranged in cymes or racemes. There are 3 to 8 sepals, which are more or less united at the base, no petals, and there are 3 to 8 stamens opposite the sepals. The 2 pistils are united into a 1- or 2-celled, superior ovary, which develops into a 1-seeded samara, drupe or nut.

The more than 150 species in this family, ascribed to about 15 genera, are widely distributed through the world, except in the very far north and the very far south. In Illinois, the family is well represented by elms and hackberries, but only 1 shrubby species occurs in the state.

CELTIS (Tournefort) Linnaeus

The Hackberries

The hackberries are shrubs or trees with thin, smooth or corky-ridged bark and usually serrate, 2-ranked, membranous leaves that are oblique at the base. The axillary flowers are monoecious, the staminate being either solitary or clustered and the pistillate usually solitary. There are 4 or 5 deciduous sepals, the same number of stamens, and a 1-celled ovary, which develops into a globose or elliptic drupe containing a small amount of pulp and a bony stone.

There are about 60 species of hackberries widely distributed in temperate regions in the northern hemisphere and in the tropics. Besides two native tree species, the following shrubby species occurs in Illinois.

CELTIS PUMILA Pursh

Shrubby Hackberry

The Shrubby Hackberry, fig. 11, is usually a low shrub 5 or 6 feet tall, less frequently a small tree up to 12 feet tall, with thin, smooth, gray bark and twigs that are hairy at first but become smooth or nearly so by autumn. The leaves are broadly to narrowly ovate, 1½ to 4 inches long, rounded or somewhat cordate and oblique at the base, and taper pointed to acuminate at the apex. The leaf margins are entire or, rarely, bear a few teeth

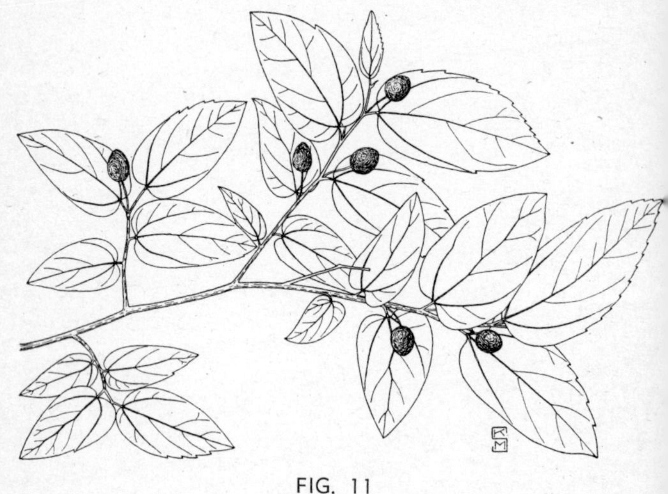

FIG. 11
Celtis pumila

near the middle, and the blade is thick, smooth above at maturity, and generally more or less pubescent along the veins beneath. The globose to elliptical fruit, which matures in late autumn, is usually orange or light cherry color at first, later dark cherry red.

Distribution.—The Shrubby Hackberry ranges from Pennsylvania to Illinois and south to Florida and Arkansas, where it usually grows on dry sandy soils and rocky slopes. In Illinois, it is apparently widely distributed but is rare and local in occurrence. It has been recorded in the northeastern corner of the state, apparently as an extension from the dunes of northern Indiana, but there are no intervening records between this and southern Illinois, where it has been reported in White, Johnson and Williamson, Union and Jersey counties. There is also a solitary record from the vicinity of Oquawka in Henderson County.

LORANTHACEAE

The Mistletoe Family

The mistletoes are small, shrubby plants, which live as parasites upon larger, woody plants and inhabit especially the branches of trees. In America the family is represented by two genera, one of which inhabits evergreen trees, the other deciduous trees. The latter, alone, occurs in Illinois.

PHORADENDRON Nuttall

The American Mistletoes

The American mistletoes are shrubs parasitic on deciduous trees. They have opposite, leathery, flat leaves, usually jointed, brittle twigs, and small, bracted flowers that are dioecious and arise in axillary spikes. Both staminate and pistillate flowers are provided with a generally 3-lobed, globose or ovoid calyx, but have no corolla. The fruit is a globose to ovoid, fleshy berry.

There are in the neighborhood of 100 species in this genus. All of them are inhabitants of America, but only 6 or 7 grow within the limits of the United States and only 1 grows in Illinois.

PHORADENDRON FLAVESCENS (Pursh) Nuttall

American Mistletoe Mistletoe

The American Mistletoe, fig. 12, is a small, evergreen shrub that lives as a parasite on many kinds of deciduous trees. Its branching stems, which are glabrous or slightly pubescent, are not often longer than 12 to 18 inches, and its rather stout, terete twigs are brittle, especially at the base. Both branches and leaves are opposite. The leaves are almost sessile, oblanceolate to obovate, and ¾ to 2 inches long by ¼ to ¾ inch wide. They are rounded at the tip and narrowed at the base to the very short petiole, and their margins are entire. They are quite thick and smooth at maturity and marked by 3 to 5 nerves. Pistillate plants can be told from staminate plants by the fact that their leaves are dark green.

The dioecious flowers arise in spikes from the leaf axils, coming into blossom about the last of October. The small

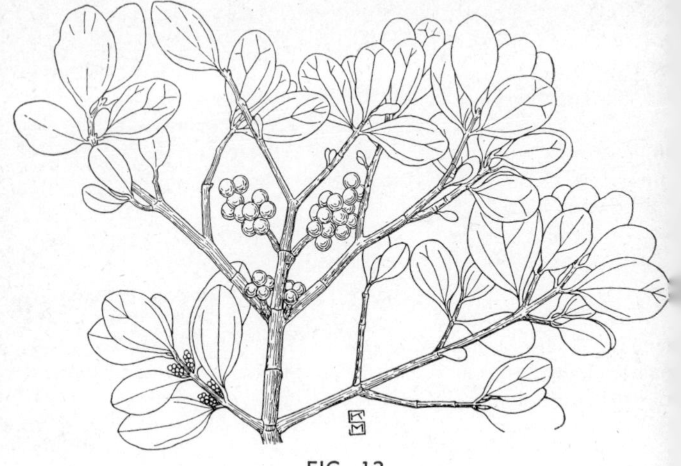

FIG. 12
Phoradendron flavescens

globose berries, scarcely more than 1/8 inch in diameter, mature in late November, and each contains a single seed surrounded by a whitish, sticky mass, which causes it to stick to trees to which it is spread.

DISTRIBUTION.—The American Mistletoe ranges from New Jersey westward into Missouri and southward to Florida and Texas. In Illinois, it is southern in occurrence, at present rare, but nevertheless interesting, partly because of its parasitic habit on trees and partly because of its botanical relationship to the holiday mistletoe. And indeed this shrub, where it grows, is used for holiday decoration. In Illinois, it appears to prefer American elm and black gum as hosts but it occurs also on many other species. In this state, it inhabits especially the Wabash and Ohio river bottoms, coming up the Wabash as far as Wabash County and up the Mississippi into the bottomlands of Union County.

ARISTOLOCHIACEAE

The Birthwort Family

The birthworts are a family of low herbs or twining vines with alternate, mostly cordate leaves and perfect flowers which have a conspicuous, lurid calyx joined at the base to the 4- to 6-celled ovary. The fruit is, in our species, a many-seeded, 6-celled capsule. The flowers lack petals and contain 5 to many stamens, which are more or less united with the style.

Although chiefly South American, this family is widely known in our climate by the Wild Ginger and the decorative vine commonly called Dutchman's Pipe.

ARISTOLOCHIA (Tournefort) Linnaeus

Birthwort Pipe Vine

The twining birthworts are extensive vines with alternate, mostly petioled, entire leaves, which are ovate or cordate and palmately nerved. The flowers are characteristic because of the striking, bent and colored calyx, which is adnate to at least the base of the ovary and extends as a narrow tube that usually is inflated around the style and contracted at the throat, beyond which the 3 lobes are either spreading or reflexed.

Of the three twining species of this genus in Illinois, only the following is woody.

ARISTOLOCHIA TOMENTOSA Sims

Woolly Pipe Vine

The Woolly Pipe Vine, fig. 13, is a twining vine with persistently woolly or tomentose twigs, petioles and leaves, and with strikingly curved, yellowish-green, large flowers that somewhat resemble the Dutchman's Pipe. The alternate, simple leaves are ovate to nearly orbicular, 3 to 6 inches long or, generally, somewhat wider, rounded at the apex, and tending to be cordate at the base. They are quite veiny, with 3 primary veins that are conspicuous and plainly visible above, and the margins are entire. The woolly-tomentose petioles are rather stout and 1 to 3 inches long.

The flowers, which usually are few, occur singly on the stems opposite the leaves, and the peduncles on which they are borne generally are longer than the opposite petioles. The long calyx tube is divided at its tip into 3 parts that spread or are recurved, and are yellow above the purplish throat. The oblong, dry capsule, 2 to 2½ inches long, is more or less tomentose and usually has 6 prominent longitudinal ridges alternating with 6 less prominent ridges. The numerous seeds are flat, triangular, and 1/4 to 3/8 inch long.

Distribution.—The Woolly Pipe Vine grows near streams and the backwaters of rivers from North Carolina and Florida westward into Kansas and Alabama. In Illinois, it is limited

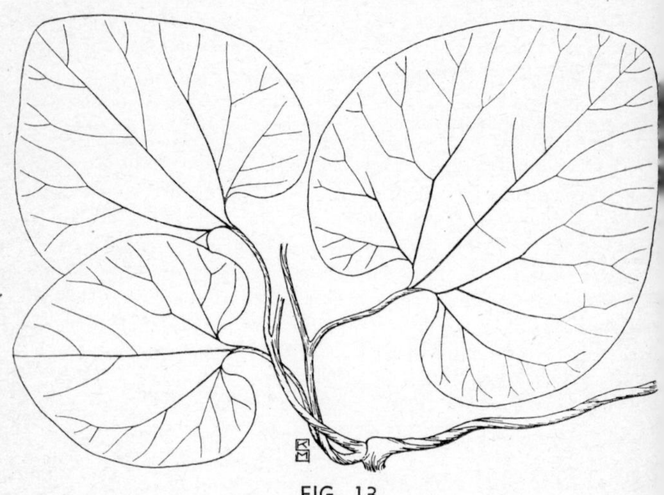

FIG. 13
Aristolochia tomentosa

to the southern part of the state, where it occurs in its usual habitat, following the Wabash River northward as far as Wabash and White counties and coming up the Mississippi into Jackson county.

Another species, *A. durior* Hill, the Dutchman's Pipe, widely used as a decorative vine, ranges from Pennsylvania to Minnesota and from Georgia to Tennessee and Kansas. It has been reported in the Wabash valley in southeastern Illinois, but no specimens have been seen to substantiate the report.

RANUNCULACEAE

The Crowfoot Family

The crowfoot family consists of herbs or climbing vines, which bear alternate or opposite, simple or compound leaves vithout stipules, and regular or irregular flowers with 3 to .5 sepals and with or without as many petals. There usually .re many stamens, and the numerous carpels are distinct and - to 2-celled. The fruit may be an achene, a follicle or a erry.

This very large family, which includes the crowfoots and uttercups, contains nearly 1,200 species which are widely disributed in temperate and cool regions on both sides of the quator and occur even at high altitudes in the tropics. Alhough the family is represented in Illinois by many common nd well-known herbs, only the following genus is woody.

CLEMATIS Linnaeus

Virgin's-Bower Clematis

The virgin's-bowers are climbing vines with opposite, pinately compound leaves, the leaflets of which may be entire or oothed, and short cymes of perfect or dioecious flowers that ack petals. The small sepals are white and resemble petals. There are many stamens and several to many pistils, each of which develops into a 1-seeded achene, on which the elongated style remains as a silky or plumose tail.

Although there are more than 200 species in this genus, widely listributed in temperate parts of the northern hemisphere, only the following occurs as a woody vine in Illinois.

CLEMATIS VIRGINIANA Linnaeus

Virginia Virgin's-Bower Traveler's-Joy Love Vine

The Virginia Virgin's-Bower, fig. 14, is a climbing vine with nore or less woody stems as much as 18 or 20 feet long, which bear opposite, compound leaves, white flowers in axillary, eafy panicles, and plumose heads of seeds. The leaves are either ternately compound, with 3 leaflets, or, rarely, pinnately compound, with 5 leaflets, which are ovate, 2 to 4 inches long, acuminate at the apex, and rounded to subcordate at the base. The margins are coarsely toothed, and both surfaces are glabrous to nearly so. The dull-white flowers, which are dioecious and about 1 inch in diameter, are borne in few-flowered axillary, leafy panicles. The sepals are obovate to spatulate, and petals are lacking. Each ovary develops into a hairy achene tipped with the long, hairy or plumose, persistent style, and the achenes of 1 flower make a plumose head fully 2 inches in diameter.

DISTRIBUTION.—The Virginia Virgin's-Bower, a vine of shrubby thickets, ranges from Nova Scotia to Manitoba and

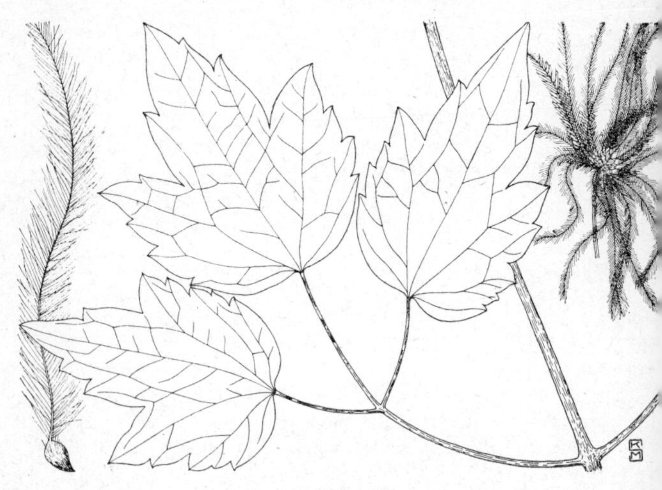

FIG. 14
Clematis virginiana

south to Georgia and Tennessee. In Illinois, it has been recorded in almost every heavily wooded section of the state, with the exception of Jo Daviess County in the extreme northwest. It is not, however, truly woody except in the most southern part of the state.

MENISPERMACEAE

The Moonseed Family

The moonseed family consists chiefly of woody climbers with palmate or peltate leaves arranged alternately on the stems without stipules. The sepals, 4 to 8 in number, and the petals 6 to 8 in number, are similar and are arranged in 3 or 4 rows. The dioecious flowers are small and bear 6 to many stamens or 3 to 6 ovaries which develop into oval, fleshy, 1-seeded drupes.

Although principally tropical, the moonseed family is represented in Illinois by three species, belonging to three genera, each of them at times woody and all vines.

Key to the Genera

Flowers with both sepals and petals, anthers 4-celled, seeds in the shape of a large crescent or ring.
- Parts of the flower, *i.e.,* stamens, petals and sepals, 6 each . . . . . **Cocculus**, p. 77
- Parts of the flower variable in number; sepals 4 to 8, petals 6 to 8, and stamens 12 to 24 . . . . . **Menispermum**, p. 78

Flowers without petals, anthers 2-celled, seeds hollowed so as to be saucer-like . . . . . **Calycocarpum**, p. 80

COCCULUS De Candolle

Coral Bead Moonseed Littleberry Vine

The coral beads are slender, twining vines, perennial and occasionally woody, that bear alternate, petioled leaves, which are ovate or cordate and entire or lobed but not peltate. The flowers are usually dioecious but may be polygamous and occur in axillary cymes or panicles. Both sepals and petals are in two series, and the flowers contain 6 stamens, which are more or less reduced in the pistillate flowers, or 3 to 6 pistils. The fruit is a somewhat flattened drupe, which contains a reniform or horseshoe-shaped stone.

The coral beads, otherwise Asiatic and African, are represented in North America by the single species described below.

COCCULUS CAROLINUS (Linnaeus) De Candolle

Carolina Moonseed Coral Bead

The Carolina Moonseed, fig. 15, is a slender, twining vine with stems up to 25 feet long, from which alternate, more or less 3-pointed leaves arise on long petioles. The leaves are broadly ovate or deltoid, cordate at the base, palmately 3- or 5-veined, sometimes 5-lobed, and 2 to 4 inches long. Mainly they are glabrous above but densely pubescent beneath. The slender petioles are 1 to 4 inches long. The small staminate flowers arise in axillary and terminal panicles, 1 to 5 inches long, that are loose but not drooping. The pistillate flowers, otherwise similar to the staminate ones, occur in simple racemes. Both kinds have sepals and petals that are rough, or erose, at the apex. The laterally flattened fruit is red, and 1/8 to 1/4 inch in diameter. It contains a kidney-shaped or horseshoe-shaped stone.

DISTRIBUTION.—The Carolina Moonseed grows in woods and thickets from Virginia to Kansas and south to Florida and Texas. In Illinois, it occurs only in the extreme southern part where it ranges along the Mississippi, Ohio, and Wabash rivers, reaching its most northern occurrence in the Wabash valley near Little Rock Ferry, Wabash County, and running northward into Jackson County along the Big Muddy River and near Grand Tower. Apparently it does not pass north of the Ozarks except along the rivers on either side.

MENISPERMUM (Tournefort) Linnaeus

The Moonseeds

The moonseeds are climbing vines with alternate, peltate or cordate leaves that may be either lobed or entire and with flowers that are dioecious and that grow in panicles. Each flower has 4 to 8 sepals arranged in two series and 6 to 8 petals that are shorter than the sepals. There are 12 to 24 stamens and, in the fertile flowers, 2 to 4 pistils, each of which matures as a fleshy, 1-seeded, blackish drupe containing a single crescent-shaped seed, for which the vine is named.

There are two species of moonseed vines, one native in eastern North America, the other native in Asia.

MENISPERMUM CANADENSE Linnaeus

Moonseed Vine Canada Moonseed

The Moonseed Vine, fig. 15, is a climber of considerable length, ranging from 6 to 25 feet or more, with twining, slightly pubescent stems and with cordate and entire or 3- to 7-lobed or angled, alternate leaves set on slender petioles. These leaves are glabrate above and pubescent beneath, and measure 4 to 8 inches in width. Rarely, the petiole is set in near the margin so as to make the leaf somewhat peltate. The greenish-white flowers occur in loose panicles, which arise from the axils of the leaves and develop oblong, bluish-black drupes; within the pulp of each a crescent-shaped seed is buried.

DISTRIBUTION.—The Moonseed, a relatively infrequent vine

FIG. 15

Calycocarpum Lyoni

Cocculus carolinus

Menispermum canadense

of woods along hillsides and streams, ranges from western Quebec to Manitoba and south to Georgia and Arkansas. In Illinois, it grows throughout the length and breadth of the state, avoiding only purely prairie regions where there are neither woods nor thickets to furnish the necessary shade.

CALYCOCARPUM Nuttall

Western Moonseed Cupseed

The cupseed genus is a monotypic one, confined to the south-central United States. It has the distinguishing characteristics of its one species, which is described below.

CALYCOCARPUM LYONI (Pursh) Nuttall

Cupseed Western Moonseed

The Cupseed, fig. 15, is a high-climbing vine reaching to the tops of trees by twining stems, which bear large, petioled, palmately veined, lobed leaves. The leaves are thin, cordate at the base, strikingly 3- to 7-lobed, and 5 to 8 inches long, with acute to acuminate lobe points. They are glabrous above but more or less pubescent, at least on the veins, beneath. The dioecious flowers stand in slender axillary panicles and are provided with 6 sepals arranged in two rows, but lack petals. There are 12 stamens, imperfect in the pistillate flowers, and 3 pistils, each of which develops into a black, fleshy drupe nearly 1 inch long, containing in its thin flesh a round or oval, cup-shaped stone.

Distribution.—The Cupseed vine, a plant of woody regions along streams, ranges from Kentucky into Kansas and southward into Florida and Louisiana. In Illinois, it is the rarest of the moonseed vines and occurs only in the extreme southern part of the state, in the valleys of the Wabash, Ohio and Cache rivers. Flowers appear in May and June, but the fruit does not become ripe until August.

BERBERIDACEAE

The Barberry Family

The members of the barberry family are shrubs with yellow wood and inner bark, which bear alternate, simple or pinnately compound, spine-toothed leaves, and racemes or panicles of small, yellow flowers with sepals in two rows above 2 or 3 small bracts, 6 petals arranged in two rows, and 6 stamens. The 1-celled ovary, capped by a shield-shaped stigma, develops into a few-seeded, usually juicy berry.

There are more than 250 species in this family, with a wide distribution in temperate regions north of the equator and southward into the Andes in South America. Only the following occurs in Illinois.

BERBERIS (Tournefort) Linnaeus

The Barberries

The barberries, shrubs with the characteristics of the family, are armed with simple or branched spines formed by the transformation of primary leaves. The foliage consists of fascicles of secondary leaves developed in axils of the first. Flowers are borne in simple, drooping racemes, and the sour, red berries, which have no bloom, are edible.

Of more than 150 species in this genus, perhaps as many as 50 have been introduced into cultivation, and 1, the Japanese Barberry or *Berberis Thunbergii* De Candolle, is widely planted at the present time in Illinois. The following species was early introduced and became widespread and naturalized.

BERBERIS VULGARIS Linnaeus

Common Barberry

The Common Barberry, fig. 16, is an erect shrub 5 to 10 feet or more tall, with gray stems and yellowish or yellowish-red branchlets, which are strongly grooved and bear many 3-parted spines along their length in place of primary leaves. Secondary leaves, developed in the axils of the transformed primary leaves, are elliptic to oblong or obovate, ¾ to 1½ inches long, obtuse or rarely somewhat pointed at the tips, and narrowed at the base into a petiole ¼ to ½ inch long. The leaf margin is serrate, and the teeth are pointed with small, weak spines. The inflorescence, a raceme which terminates short, lateral branches, is many flowered, 1 to 2 inches long in flower, and 3 to 4 inches long in fruit. The flowers are yellow and ¼ inch broad or more. The berries at maturity are oblong or elliptic, sour, and bright scarlet.

Distribution.—The Common Barberry is a native of Europe and Asia, where it is widely used as a decorative shrub. It was brought to New England by early colonists and later was

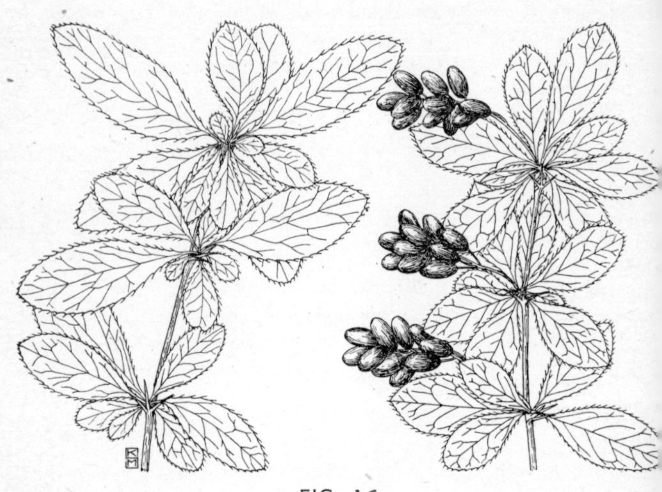

FIG. 16
Berberis vulgaris

planted throughout the northeastern states. The berries are attractive to birds, which scattered seeds so extensively that the shrub became an established, naturalized species. However, it is now doomed to extinction, through the efforts of the Barberry Eradication campaign, which proposes, by destroying it, to remove one of the hosts of black stem rust.

LAURACEAE

The Laurel Family

The laurel family consists of aromatic shrubs or trees with alternate, non-stipulate, and usually glandular-punctate leaves. The monoecious flowers have 4 to 10, most often 6, sepals arranged in two series, but no petals. The stamens, more numerous than the sepals, are reduced in the pistillate flowers. In pistillate flowers, the pistils are solitary and the ovary is 1-celled; the fruit is a drupe which contains a solitary seed.

The laurel family, widely distributed in the tropics and comprising more than a thousand species, is most widely represented in Illinois by the very well known weed tree, Sassafras. Among the shrubs, it is represented here only by the following genus.

LINDERA Thunberg

The Spicebushes

The spicebushes are shrubs, or rarely trees, with aromatic, spicy bark and entire, alternate leaves. They bear yellow flowers in umbels, which arise from old leaf axils before the leaves appear. The flowers usually have 6 sepals, rarely 7 to 9, and there are as a rule 9 stamens in the staminate flowers. The fruit, characteristic of the family, is a pulpy drupe.

There are over 60 species in this genus, all of them Asian except 2 that are North American. Some Asian species are trees. Both of the North American species are shrubs and occur in Illinois; they usually are classed in the genus *Benzoin.*

Key to the Spicebush Species

Leaves narrowed at the base; the shrub glabrous throughout .... **L. Benzoin**

Leaves rounded or nearly cordate at the base; twigs and lower leaf surfaces pubescent.................... **L. melissaefolium**

LINDERA BENZOIN (Linnaeus) Blume

Spicebush Spiceweed Benjamin Bush

The Spicebush, fig. 17, is a stout, branching shrub 8 or 10 feet high with stems 1 to 1½ inches in diameter at the base, covered by rough bark interrupted with corky lenticels. Two kinds of leaves are to be found, all of them alternately placed. Those toward the upper parts of the branches are oblong-ovate or nearly oval; those farther down are generally much smaller and oval to nearly circular. The blades, commonly 2 to 5 inches long by 1 to 2½ inches wide, are acute or somewhat short-acuminate at the tip and narrowed to the petiole at the base, green above and paler beneath, and the margins are entire. The petioles of the outer leaves are ¼ to ½ inch long, those of the lower leaves shorter.

Flowers appear before the leaves in April or early in May, in small, stalkless clusters from the axils of the last year's leaves.

FIG. 17
Lindera melissaefolium
Lindera Benzoin

There are generally 3 to 6 bright yellow flowers in a cluster. The pistillate flowers develop into bright red, fleshy drupes, which ripen in October or November, are bluntly oval to nearly spherical, nearly ½ inch long, and stand on pedicels about half as long.

DISTRIBUTION.—The Spicebush, an undershrub in wet woods, ranges from Maine westward to central Michigan and south into Georgia, Mississippi and Kansas. It occurs throughout Illinois wherever a suitable habitat is to be found.

LINDERA MELISSAEFOLIUM (Walter) Blume

Hairy Spicebush

The Hairy Spicebush, fig. 17, is very similar to the common Spicebush in shape and size but is distinguished by the dense pubescence of the young twigs, buds, and lower surface of the leaves. Also, the leaf blades are ovate-lanceolate to oblong, acute or acuminate at the apex, and rounded to subcordate at the base. They are 2 to 4 inches long by ¾ to 1½ inches wide and stand on petioles ⅛ to ¼ inch long. The fruit develops from the pistillate flowers and is about ½ inch long and oval.

DISTRIBUTION.—The Hairy Spicebush inhabits swamps and wet soil from Missouri to North Carolina and south to Alabama and Florida. Throughout its range it flowers in February and March. In Illinois, it is rare and occurs only in the southern tip of the state.

HYDRANGEACEAE

The Hydrangea Family

The hydrangea family consists of shrubs, trees and some vines, which bear opposite leaves without stipules and perfect flowers arranged in cymes. The flowers may have 4 to 10 sepals and the same number of petals, and there may be 8 to many stamens and 2 to 5 or, rarely, 10 united pistils per flower. The ovary is partly or wholly inferior, and the styles arising from it may be distinct or united. The fruit, when developed, is a capsule.

There are some 16 genera and 80 species in the family, but in Illinois it is represented only by the two wild, native hydrangeas and by the introduced, sometimes escaped, Mock Orange or Syringa. These may be distinguished as follows.

Key to the Genera

Flowers with small petals and 8 to 10 stamens, the hypanthium ribbed in fruit.................................**Hydrange**
Flowers with large petals and 12 to 16 stamens, the hypanthium in fruit not ribbed.............................**Philadelphu**

HYDRANGEA (Gronovius) Linnaeus

The Hydrangeas

The hydrangeas are shrubs with opposite leaves and perfec flowers borne in cymes. The flowers have 4 or 5 sepals, minut except in the sterile flowers, where they are enlarged and petal like. There are 4 or 5 petals and 8 or 10 stamens. Each inferio ovary consists of 2 to 4 united carpels and has the same numbe of cells. Styles are wanting, but there are 2 to 4 stigmas. Th capsule is membranous walled and open at the top and contain numerous seeds. The genus is represented in Illinois by th following species.

Key to the Hydrangea Species

Leaves glabrous or with only scattered hairs.....**H. arborescen**
Leaves densely grayish-tomentose on the underside.....**H. cinere**

HYDRANGEA ARBORESCENS Linnaeus

Hydrangea Smooth Hydrangea

The Smooth Hydrangea, fig. 18, is a shrub which grows i clumps, generally to about 3 feet, seldom as much as 6 feet, high Its old stems are covered by shreddy bark and its pubescen branchlets bear opposite, rather large leaves which are ovat or nearly orbicular. The leaf blades, supported on slende petioles 1 to 4 inches long, are short-acuminate at the apex, cor date or rounded at the base, 3 to 6 inches long by nearly a wide, and sharply dentate or serrate on the margins. The uppe surface often is more or less sparsely pubescent, the lower sur face more or less pubescent on the main nerves and lighter gree than the upper.

The small flowers appear in the latter part of June and i July, standing in terminal cymes or cymelike, white clusters The flowers in the clusters are of two kinds, fertile and sterile the sterile being generally fewer and on the outer margins o the clusters. Fertile flowers develop small, 2-celled capsules

FIG. 18
Philadelphus coronarius
Hydrangea arborescens
Hydrangea cinerea

ripe in the autumn, which are glabrous, a little broader tha
long, and generally prominently ribbed. Each contains man
seeds, which also are longitudinally ribbed.

Distribution.—The distribution of the Smooth Hydrange
is from New York west to Missouri and Oklahoma and sout
to Georgia and Alabama. With us, it is a plant of wet, shad
ravines, and in this habitat it lives throughout the southern two
thirds of Illinois, the most northern record being Starved Roc
in La Salle County.

HYDRANGEA CINEREA Small

Ashy Hydrangea

The Ashy Hydrangea, fig. 18, is a spreading shrub 3 to 6 fee
high that bears large, round or ovate to elliptic leaves, th
blades of which are acuminate at the tip, rounded or cordate a
the base, and serrate along the margins. They are 3 to 6 inche
long and as a rule somewhat thicker and heavier than those o
the preceding species, green on the upper side and nearly gla
brous, but tomentose beneath. The cymes of flowers are roun
topped rather than flat topped, as in the Smooth Hydrangea
and commonly 1 to 4 inches broad. Sterile flowers, often calle
ray-flowers, are usually present, and the mature capsule is 1/
inch long or less and not quite so wide. Flowers appear in Jun
and July, and fruiting heads with their conspicuous, whitene
ray-flowers are mature in late summer and early fall.

Distribution.—The Ashy Hydrangea grows in mountainou
regions from North Carolina west to Missouri and southwar
into Georgia and Alabama. In Illinois, it occurs only in th
Ozark region in the extreme southern part of the state, th
present records of occurrence being limited to the vicinity o
Vienna in Johnson County and to Dixon Springs, Golconda an
Brownfield in Pope County. This species is sometimes consid
ered a variety of the preceding species and then is known a
H. arborescens var. *Deamii* St. John.

The Silverleaf Hydrangea, *H. radiata* Walter, has been re
ported from two counties in the state, Washington and Ver
milion. Both of these are very old records and are, quit
obviously, misidentifications. The record in both cases undoubt
edly applies to one of the hairy varietal forms of the ordinar
species, *arborescens*.

PHILADELPHUS Linnaeus

Mock Oranges Syringas

The mock oranges are branching shrubs with toothed or en-
ire, opposite leaves and perfect flowers borne singly or in cymes
t the end of short, leafy branches. There are 4 or, rarely, 5
epals in the flowers, which are persistent, and 4 or, rarely, 5
hite or yellowish-white petals. The stamens are usually nu-
ierous, that is, from 25 to 60, and the 4-celled ovaries are about
wo-thirds inferior. The mature fruit is a capsule which is
nore or less woody, and contains numerous seeds, the coats of
hich are netted.

PHILADELPHUS CORONARIUS Linnaeus

Syringa Mock Orange

The Syringa, fig. 18, is a 6- to 12-foot shrub characterized
y brown, glabrous bark, which exfoliates in flakes during the
econd season. The apparently 3-nerved leaf blades are ovate
r oval, denticulate along the margins, glabrous, or pubescent
eneath, and 2 to 4 inches long. They are acute or acuminate
t the tip and rounded or narrowed at the base, and the teeth
n the margins are rather distantly spaced. The creamy white,
ery fragrant flowers are arranged in racemes at the end of the
ranches, and are about 1 to 1½ inches broad. There are 5 to
flowers in each raceme.

DISTRIBUTION.—The Syringa is an introduced shrub that has
scaped somewhat sparingly from cultivation in Illinois. The
ppearance of the flowers, which bloom in May and June, gives
ise to the occasionally used name Orange Flower Tree.

A single native species, *P. verrucosus* Schrader, has been
eported in literature as being found on rocky talus below high
luffs on the Ohio River near Golconda in Pope County. This,
ie only record of its occurrence in Illinois or elsewhere, needs
ubstantiating.

ITEACEAE

The Virginia Willow Family

The Virginia willow family is a small family of shrubs and
mall trees with simple, alternate leaves without stipules and

with perfect flowers borne in terminal racemes. The calyx tub
is 5-lobed and adnate at the base to the ovary, and the 5 peta
are linear. There are 4 stamens and a 2-celled ovary, whic
develops into a 2-valved, several- to many-seeded capsule.

The one genus in this family contains perhaps 10 species, a
native in southeastern Asia with the exception of the followin
which is North American. The genus is, by some botanist
included in the Saxifragaceae.

ITEA (Gronovius) Linnaeus

Sweetspire Virginia Willow

The Sweetspires are deciduous or, occasionally, evergree
shrubs or trees with small, superposed buds and alternate, se
rate leaves without stipules. The flowers are white, small, an
perfect and are borne in terminal or axillary racemes or pan
cles. The calyx tube, which consists of 5 sepals, is persisten
There are 5 stamens, and the 2-celled, superior ovary develop
into an elongated, 2-grooved capsule which contains many fla
tened seeds.

ITEA VIRGINICA Linnaeus

Virginia Willow

The Virginia Willow, fig. 19, is an upright shrub 3 to 9 fe
tall, with slender, wandlike branches, which are pubescen
while young but become glabrate when old. The simple, alte
nate leaves, which stand on petioles about 1/4 inch long, are e
liptic to oblong, acute to short-acuminate at the tip, usual
cuneate at the base, and 1 3/4 to 4 inches long. The margins a
serrulate, and the surface is glabrous above but often spa
ingly pubescent beneath. The small, fragrant, white flower
which are in bloom in July and August, are borne in dense, u
right, pubescent racemes 2 to 6 inches long. The fruit develop
as a narrow, pubescent capsule about 1/4 inch long.

Distribution.—The Virginia Willow is a shrub of we
places, in which it ranges from New Jersey to Missouri an
southward to Florida and Louisiana. In Illinois, where
approaches the northwestern limits of its range, it is a rare an
localized species found only in the extreme southern tip of th
state, where it is recorded from the Sandusky Swamp and

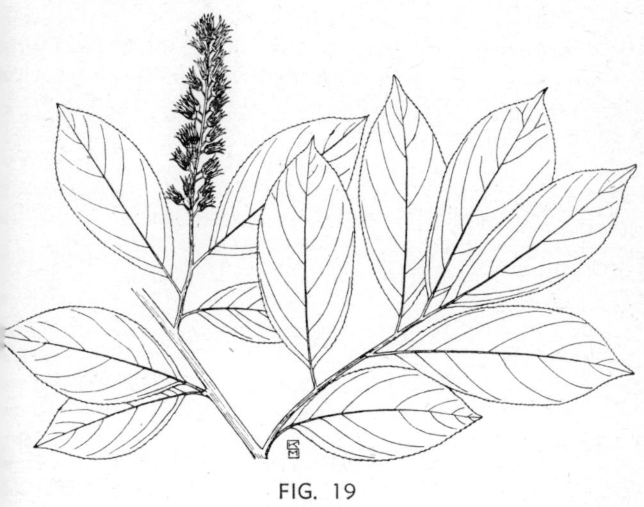

FIG. 19
Itea virginica

Cache River cypress swamp in Alexander County, from a swamp near Karnak in Pulaski County, and from swamps near Rago in Johnson County.

GROSSULARIACEAE

The Gooseberry Family

The gooseberries are shrubs with simple alternate leaves that are triple or palmately nerved and with flowers having sepals, petals, and stamens numbering as a rule 5 but occasionally 4. The ovary is inferior, and the fruit is a berry. This family is made up of two distinct kinds of plants, closely related, and much used for their fruit as well as for decoration—the gooseberries and currants. They are distinguished as follows.

Key to the Genera

Unarmed shrubs with racemes made up of 5 or more flowers; bractlets of the flowers linear; fruit pedicel jointed beneath the fruit..**Ribes**, p. 92

Shrubs armed with spines at the nodes; the flowering racemes having clusters of only 1 to 4 flowers as a rule; bractlets smaller and sheathlike; fruit pedicel not jointed beneath the fruit..............................**Grossularia**, p. 94

RIBES Linnaeus

The Currants

The currants are unarmed shrubs with alternate, palmatel veined and usually also palmately lobed leaves. The inflores cence is several to many flowered, the flower pedicels ar jointed, and a small pair of bractlets often is present at th nodes. The shrubs bear perfect flowers and these develo into thin-skinned berries that never are spiny and may have o be without glands. The fruit disarticulates from the pedice at the joints.

The currants are represented in Illinois by a single nativ species.

RIBES AMERICANUM Miller

American Black Currant

The American Black Currant, fig. 20, is an erect shrul growing 1 to 2½ feet high, with branches which bear neithe spines nor bristles. The leaves are nearly orbicular in outlin but 3-lobed, with the lower lobes sometimes so deeply cut tha the leaves appear 5-lobed. They are 1 to 3 inches wide, some what pubescent, and resinous dotted on the underside. Th margins are dentate-serrate, and the lobes are acute.

Flowers are borne in pendulous, rather loose, pubescen racemes, which arise from the axils of leaves on short fruitin spurs. These flowers are greenish yellow and about one-thir inch long, and each has a linear, small bractlet. They stan on pedicels that are much shorter than the flowers. The caly lobes are about as long as the tube of the corolla, oblon rounded at the apex, and more or less pubescent. The peta and the stamens are a little shorter than the sepals. The frui matures in July and August from the flowers which appeared i May. The berries are globose, black, smooth, and about ¼ inc in diameter.

Distribution.—The American Black Currant is a wood inhabiting plant that grows from Nova Scotia to Manitoba an south to Virginia, Iowa and Nebraska. In Illinois, it is mos frequent in the woods of the northern part of the state, inhabi ing there the boggy places along streams. Probably it grow throughout the state but is rare southward.

FIG. 20
Ribes americanum Grossularia cynosbati
Grossularia missouriensis

GROSSULARIA (Tournefort) Miller

The Gooseberries

The gooseberries are spreading or upright shrubs that nor mally are armed at the nodes with simple or 3-forked spine and that bear rounded or kidney-shaped leaves which usually ar 3 to 5 cleft and crenate or dentate on the margins. The flower arise in few-flowered racemes from the axils of leaves on shor fruiting spurs. The flower pedicels are not jointed. The frui is a berry with, in most species, a smooth but, in some, a glandu lar hispid or spiny skin.

Gooseberries have been widely cultivated, both for their frui and because of their decorative value. Although gooseberrie are distributed throughout the temperate zone, the bulk of th species occur in the United States, and in Illinois the followin are to be found.

Key to the Gooseberry Species

Calyx lobes shorter than the tube of the flower; the ovary and the berry prickly........................**G. cynosbati**, p. 9

Calyx lobes longer than the tube of the flower; the ovary and the berry without prickles.

- Spines at the nodes about ¼ to ¾ inch long; the anthers of the flowers exserted................**G. missouriensis**, p. 9
- Spines at the nodes about ¼ inch long; the anthers not exserted..............................**G. hirtella**, p. 9

GROSSULARIA CYNOSBATI (Linnaeus) Miller

Pasture Gooseberry Dogberry

The Pasture Gooseberry, fig. 20, is a spreading or, rarel erect shrub seldom more than 2 feet high, with spines at th nodes and, on younger branches, generally covered more o less densely with long, reddish prickles. The leaves are near orbicular in outline but 3-lobed, with the lower lobes som times more or less lobed also, cordate or truncate at the bas and acute or obtuse at the lobe point. They are 1 to 2 inche wide and about as long, and their margins are crenate-dentat or incised. They stand on slender, generally pubescent petiol ½ to 1½ inches long.

There are 1 to 3 green flowers on the peduncled racemes, su ported by slender pedicels. These flowers, ¼ inch or a litt longer, are characterized by oblong calyx lobes which ar shorter than the tube of the flower, and the stamens are not exserted beyond the tube. The berries, which are one-third to ½ inch in diameter, mature from the last of July on into September from flowers that appeared in April or May. They are reddish purple, covered with few to many prickles, and vary considerably in size on the same bush.

Distribution.—The Pasture Gooseberry grows in rich, moist soil from New Brunswick westward to Manitoba and southward to North Carolina and Missouri. It occurs in suitable habitats throughout Illinois, but it is not to be searched for in the prairie regions and has not been recorded south of the Ozarks.

GROSSULARIA MISSOURIENSIS (Nuttall) Coville & Britton

The Missouri Gooseberry

The Missouri Gooseberry is larger than the common Pas-ure Gooseberry and more nearly erect, reaching commonly a height of 4½ feet. Spines, 1 to 3 in number, are generally present on the nodes, and are somewhat larger than those of the other species. The white or whitish younger branches are sometimes covered by prickles. The blades of the leaves, ¾ to ½ inches long, are nearly orbicular but 3-lobed, the lower obes being sometimes more or less lobed also. The leaf bases are subcordate, truncate, or even somewhat rounded, and the obes are generally obtuse, though sometimes acute, at the tip. The leaf margin is closely and irregularly crenate-dentate, and he leaf surface is pubescent when young, but smooth or nearly o at maturity above and always pubescent beneath. The leaves tand on pubescent petioles.

The flowers, which appear in April or May, are greenish and occur in clusters of 1 to 3 on each peduncle. Both peduncles and pedicels are pubescent and sometimes also glandular, and he bractlets are sheathing and glandular ciliate. In the flowers, both stamens and styles are longer than the calyx lobes and ap-pear exserted. The fruit, which matures from July to Septem-ber, is purplish, smooth on the surface, and nearly ½ inch in iameter.

Distribution.—The Missouri Gooseberry is a shrub which prefers the wooded banks of streams or the steep slopes of ravines. It is to be found from Michigan west to South Dakota and south to Tennessee and Oklahoma. In Illinois, it is widely distributed but has been collected and recorded a relatively small number of times.

The Low Wild Gooseberry, *G. hirtella* (Michaux) Coville & Britton, an erect shrub generally somewhat less than 3 feet high, with few or no nodal spines and pinkish to cherry-colored or sometimes purplish to black fruit less than ½ inch in diameter, has not to our knowledge been found in the state. It is a plant characteristically inhabiting tamarack bogs and swampy places in woods and along streams. Since northern Ohio and Indiana are on the southern boundary of its range, it may possibly be found in northeastern Illinois.

HAMAMELIDACEAE

The Witch-Hazel Family

The witch-hazel family consists of shrubs or trees which bear alternate, simple leaves and flowers which may be perfect polygamous or monoecious. There are 4 or 5 sepals in each flower and the same number of linear or spatulate petals, or the petals may be wanting. The stamens may be 4 to many, with distinct filaments. The ovary consists of 2 united carpels and is 2-celled. It is partly inferior and is capped by 2 styles. The ovules are solitary in each carpel. The members of the family develop as fruit a woody or coriaceous capsule which is elastically dehiscent.

The witch-hazel family consists of some 13 genera and about 40 species, which are natives of North America, Asia and South Africa. In North America, 2 genera, both shrubs, are native and 1 is native in Illinois.

HAMAMELIS Linnaeus

The Witch-Hazels

The witch-hazels are shrubs with alternate leaves and yellow bracted flowers which appear in late summer or in autumn. The calyx of the flower is made up of 4 sepals which are persistent and adnate to the lower part of the ovary. There are also elongated, linear, persistent petals, which are wanting in the staminate flowers. The stamens are 4, and the ovary is 2-celled and capped by 2 short styles. The fruit is a woody capsule, which is at length 2-valved at the summit and contains an oblong, shining seed.

There are three known species in this genus, two of which occur in Japan. The third is native in eastern North America.

HAMAMELIS VIRGINIANA Linnaeus

Witch-Hazel Spotted Alder

The Witch-Hazel, fig. 21, is a shrub, or less often a small tree, reaching at the most a height of about 20 feet, with slightly scurfy or glabrous twigs and short-petioled, ovate or broadly oval leaves that are pointed to obtuse at the apex and somewhat cordate and asymmetrical at the base. Bright yellow flowers occur in axillary clusters late in the season. The leaves are stellate pubescent, at least when young, 2 to 5 inches long, thick, and repand-dentate.

The flowers are nearly sessile and have narrow petals about one-sixteenth inch wide and ½ to ¾ inch long. The lobes of the calyx are spreading or recurved, oval, and ciliate and pubescent on the outer surface. Capsules mature during the second season.

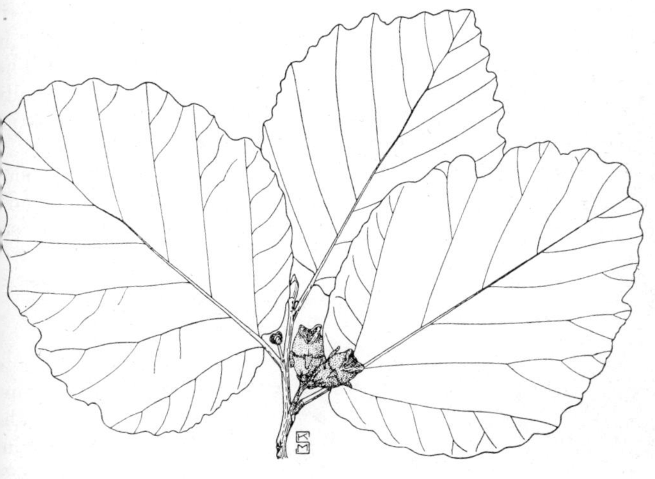

FIG. 21
Hamamelis virginiana

They are beaked by the 2 persistent styles, are densely pubescent, and are ¼ to one-third inch high. They at length burst open and reveal the bony, oblong, black seeds, which are not quite so large as the capsule.

DISTRIBUTION.—The common Witch-Hazel, a plant of ravine slopes and low woods, grows from Nova Scotia to Ontario and Minnesota and south to Florida and Texas. It is found in Illinois wherever a suitable habitat occurs, although it is not to be looked for in purely prairie regions.

This is the shrub from which the witch-hazel used in medicine is derived. The bark and leaves are the source of the drug. It is the plant that furnished the forked hazel branches used by early settlers to search for underground water.

ROSACEAE

The Rose Family

The rose family is an exceedingly large one, made up of herbs, shrubs and trees, all of which bear alternate, simple or compound leaves and, generally, stipules. The flowers of all members of the family are regular, usually having 5 sepals and 5 petals. The stamens are commonly numerous, and the fruit is usually a follicle or an achene.

With more than 75 genera and more than 1,200 species, this family is very widely distributed over the world. Many of its members furnish food and many of them also are valuable as ornamentals. It has, therefore, great economic importance.

Key to the Shrubby Genera

Shrubs with unarmed stems.
- Shrubs with simple leaves and white or rose-colored flowers.
  - Shrubs with branches which curve down, corymbose inflorescence, and carpels united at the base and in maturity inflated, opening by 2 sutures . . **Physocarpus**, p. 9
  - Shrubs with erect or ascending branches, paniculate inflorescence, and carpels free at the base and in maturity not inflated, opening by only 1 suture . . . **Spiraea**, p. 10
- Shrubs with compound leaves and yellow flowers . . . . **Potentilla**, p. 10

Shrubs with stems armed with prickles or bristles, sometimes with both.
- Flowers white or purple; the fruit an aggregate of fleshy carpels, edible . . . . **Rubus**, p. 10
- Flowers rose colored; the fruit a more or less fleshy hip, not commonly eaten . . . . **Rosa**, p. 11

PHYSOCARPUS Rafinesque

The Ninebarks

The ninebarks are shrubs with exfoliating bark, which bear alternate, 3- to 5-ribbed and more or less lobed leaves usually pubescent with more or less stellate hairs. The flowers occur in terminal corymbs and have 5 persistent sepals and 5 white or pinkish petals, 20 to 40 stamens, and 1 to 5 pistils, which are more or less united at the base. The fruit at maturity is a more or less inflated capsule which opens along both sutures, and the shiny, bony-coated seeds are obliquely pear shaped.

Key to the Ninebark Species

Leaves ovate, carpels usually 5 and glabrous........**P. opulifolius**
Leaves suborbicular, carpels 3 or 4 and finely pubescent ....**P. intermedius**

PHYSOCARPUS OPULIFOLIUS (Linnaeus) Maximowicz

Common Ninebark

The Common Ninebark, fig. 22, is a much-branched and spreading shrub, reaching occasionally 9 or 10 feet in height; the old bark exfoliates in long, thin strips. The branchlets and the upper branches are more or less pubescent. The leaves are ovate to nearly orbicular and more or less definitely 3-nerved, sometimes also 3-lobed, and for the most part cordate or truncate at the base. They are glabrous, 1 to 2 inches long on the fruiting branches and on the sterile branches often almost twice as large. The margins are irregularly and doubly crenate, and at maturity the surface is smooth or nearly so above but more or less pubescent beneath, at least on the main nerves.

The white flowers occur in terminal corymbs in May or early June, 25 or more in a cluster. The sepals are ovate, acute, and pubescent inside and out, and the petals are broadly ovate to nearly orbicular and more or less pubescent on both sides. The fruit, which matures from the last of July into September, consists of 3 to 5 follicles ¼ to ½ inch long, which are glabrous and shining, obliquely awl tipped, and about twice as long as the calyx. The glossy, very light brown seed is obliquely ovate and hardly one-sixteenth inch long.

Distribution.—The Common Ninebark is a shrub of

FIG. 22

Physocarpus intermedius
Physocarpus opulifolius

Spiraea tomentosa
Spiraea alba

marshes and low woods. It is to be found in such situations from Quebec westward into Iowa and south to Georgia and Tennessee. It occurs in suitable habitats throughout the state of Illinois, but has been reported much more frequently in the northern part than in the southern, where it evidently is rare and perhaps definitely localized.

PHYSOCARPUS INTERMEDIUS (Rydberg) Schneider

Illinois Ninebark

The Illinois Ninebark, fig. 22, is a shrub very similar in general appearance, foliage, and flowers to the Common Ninebark. It may be distinguished, however, by the fact that its leaves are mostly narrower and narrowed to the petiole at the base. Also, the calyx is densely stellate pubescent and the follicles, 3 or 4 per flower, are abruptly acuminate and permanently stellate pubescent. It is a lower shrub than the Common Ninebark, seldom more than 4½ feet tall.

Distribution.—The Illinois Ninebark ranges from New York westward into South Dakota and southward into Missouri and Arkansas. In Illinois, it is a relatively rare shrub that has been infrequently recorded, mostly in the southern and southeastern part of the state.

By some authorities, this second species is believed to be merely a variety of the first, distinguished entirely on the basis of its permanently pubescent follicles. Material collected in Illinois does not show the intergrading, in this respect, that Deam has observed in his probably much more numerous Indiana collections.

SPIRAEA (Tournefort) Linnaeus

The Meadowsweets Spireas

The meadowsweets are shrubs with alternate, pinnately veined and usually simple leaves but no stipules. The flowers are perfect, with 5 sepals, 5 white to red petals, 15 to 70 stamens and 5 or, rarely, as few as 3 or as many as 8 distinct pistils. The flowers are variously aggregated into racemes, corymbs or panicles. The fruits are leathery follicles which are not inflated and which open along 1 suture and contain, usually, 4 seeds which taper at both ends.

There are over 80 species of meadowsweet, all natives of the north temperate zone. In North America some 18 species occur, but only 2 are native in Illinois. The Bridal Wreath, Thunberg Spirea, and others are commonly cultivated, because of their decorative value, and are familiar to almost everyone.

Key to the Meadowsweet Species

Leaves not tomentose beneath, flowers white .... **S. alba**
Leaves tomentose beneath, flowers pink or purplish . . . **S. tomentosa**

SPIRAEA ALBA Du Roi

Meadow Spirea Narrow-Leaved Meadowsweet

The Meadow Spirea, fig. 22, is an erect shrub that grows generally about 3 feet high, but may become 6 feet tall, with light brown branches and stems and narrowly oblanceolate leaves. The leaf blades are 1 to 2½ inches long and ½ to ¾ inch wide, acute or, rarely, rounded at the apex, wedge shaped at the base, and smooth or sparingly pubescent both above and below. The leaf margins are sharply serrate. Sometimes upper leaves are almost sessile and lower leaves have petioles up to ⅛ inch long.

The flowers occur in terminal panicles, which may be 1½ to 5 inches long. The peduncle and calyx of the flowers and the branches of the panicle are more or less densely pubescent. The white flowers appear in July and August, and the fruit, which matures in the autumn, consists, for each flower, of 5 smooth follicles containing 2 to 5 seeds less than ⅛ inch in length.

Distribution.—The Meadow Spirea, which is almost always an inhabitant of low ground, is distributed from Ontario westward to Saskatchewan and southward to South Carolina and Mississippi. Its range includes the entire state of Illinois, and it is to be found throughout the state in suitable situations, although it is rare south of the Ozarks.

SPIRAEA TOMENTOSA Linnaeus

Hardhack Steeplebush

The Hardhack, fig. 22, is an erect, tomentose shrub, generally about 3 feet tall, with ovate-lanceolate leaves, which are dark green above and densely white or rusty tomentose below

The narrowly oval leaf blades are 1 to 2 inches long and ½ to 1 inch wide, acute or blunt at the apex, and narrowed at the base to the short petiole. The leaf margin is coarsely crenate-serrate, and the upper surface may be more or less puberulent.

The pink or rarely purplish, still more rarely white, flowers are borne in narrow, tomentose panicles 4 to 7 inches long. The calyx lobes are about the length of the floral tube, acute and, at maturity, reflexed. The fruit consists of 5 follicles from each flower; the follicles are tomentose or, in age, somewhat bare at the summit, and there usually are 4 to 7 seeds in each follicle.

DISTRIBUTION.—The Hardhack is a shrub of low grounds and is said to occur only on acid or sour soils. It is therefore local in occurrence, although where it does occur thousands of plants together may occupy considerable areas. Its range is from Nova Scotia to Manitoba and south to Georgia and Kansas. In Illinois, it is recorded only from the northeastern section of the state, notably near Chicago in Cook County, in wet sandy swales in Lake County, in Kankakee County, and also in Iroquois County, near the town of St. Anne. This would indicate a preference in Illinois for a sandy habitat. The shrub should be found, however, in many other parts of the state, if persistent search is made.

The report of *S. latifolia* (Aiton) Borkhausen in Richland County may refer to either of the foregoing species, but it probably refers to *S. alba*.

POTENTILLA Linnaeus

Cinquefoils Five-Fingers

The cinquefoils are, with a few shrubby exceptions, annual or perennial herbs with rootstocks, pinnately or digitately compound leaves, and paniculate inflorescences. The flowers commonly have 5 sepals and 5 petals and are bractless. The stamens are generally not more than 20 in number and there usually are numerous pistils attached to a hemispheric or conic receptacle. The seeds are contained within individual carpels.

There are more than 300 species in this genus, almost all of them distributed in the north temperate zone. About 125 are American, and in Illinois, besides a number of herbaceous species, there occurs the following shrub.

POTENTILLA FRUTICOSA Linnaeus

Shrubby Cinquefoil

The Shrubby Cinquefoil, fig. 23, is a small, more or less erect shrub, which commonly grows 1 to 3 feet high and is much branched. The stem is covered by light reddish-brown shreddy bark, and the branches are densely covered with long hair. The leaves are pinnately compound and consist generally of 5 but sometimes of 3 or 7 sessile leaflets, which are oblong or oblong-ovate, acute at the tip, narrowed at the base, and silky pubescent on both faces. The margin of the leaflet is entire and revolute.

Flowers appear from July to September, and vary in color from light yellow to orange. The fruit is a head, consisting of many carpels or achenes less than one-sixteenth inch long, which are dry and hard and covered with long hairs.

Distribution.—The Shrubby Cinquefoil, typically a bog or marsh plant, ranges from Labrador to Alaska and south to New Jersey and California. Although it often has been collected in Illinois, its distribution seems definitely limited to the northeastern corner of the state, including Cook and Lake

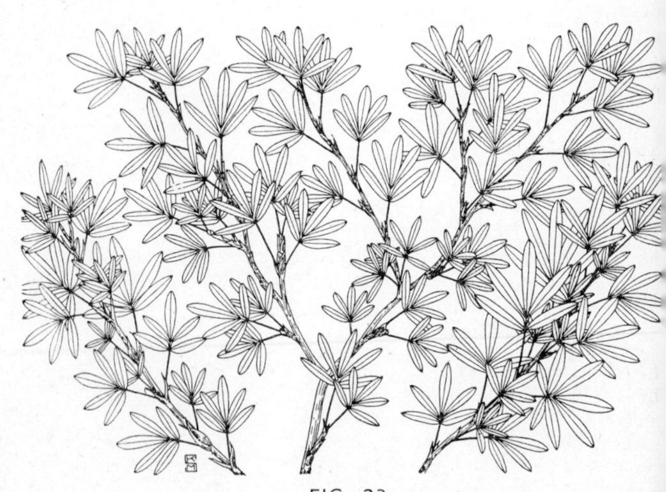

FIG. 23
Potentilla fruticosa

counties, and to the Apple River Canyon in the extreme northwestern corner of the state. Formerly, it must have been very abundant near Chicago, Ravenswood, Elgin and Waukegan. Probably it has been largely destroyed and now may be a fairly rare plant.

RUBUS (Tournefort) Linnaeus

The Brambles: Raspberries, Blackberries, Dewberries

The brambles are chiefly shrubs with trailing, erect, or curved branches. A few are herbaceous. The woody forms are perennial and have stems armed with prickles or bristles, or both. The stems are biennial, simple and unbranched the first year but the second year develop side branches which bear fruit. The leaves are alternate and may be either simple or compound and composed of 3 or 5 leaflets. Flowers are borne in racemes or corymbs and are chiefly white, with 5 green sepals and 5 petals. The stamens and the ovaries are many, and the fruit is an edible aggregate of fleshy carpels.

Between 1,500 and 2,000 species have been described in this genus, which is world wide in distribution. But there is much overlapping of species, with resultant confusion in characteristics, so that professional opinion varies greatly, both as to what may constitute a species and as to the number of species properly recognizable.

The brambles are divisible into three general groups which are relatively easily recognized: raspberries, the ripe fruit of which separates as a hollow shell from the receptacle on which it is borne; blackberries, the fruit of which does not separate from its receptacle; and dewberries, which have the same kind of fruit as the blackberries but which have stems that, in their second year, are trailing, rather than erect or curving.

Key to the Bramble Species

Leaves simple, but usually more or less lobed . . . **R. odoratus**, p. 106
Leaves compound, consisting of 3 to 5 leaflets.
  Leaves white-tomentose beneath, fruit parting from the receptacle (raspberries).
    Stems prickly and glaucous, fruit black . . **R. occidentalis**, p. 108
    Stems bristle armed, not glaucous, fruit red.
      Plants not glandular-hispid; inflorescence finely villous . . . . **R. idaeus**, p. 108

Plants glandular-hispid, especially the inflorescence .... **R. strigosus**, p. 109

Leaves green beneath; prickles on the angles of the stems; fruit adhering to the receptacle.

Old stems erect, curving or arching (blackberries).

Inflorescence densely glandular, glands stalked .... **R. allegheniensis**, p. 110

Inflorescence not glandular or the stalks sessile.

Leaves glabrous beneath .... **R. canadensis**, p. 110

Leaves pubescent beneath.

New canes deeply channeled between prominent angles .... **R. argutus**, p. 112

New canes terete or nearly so ...... **R. frondosus**, p. 113

Old stems prostrate and trailing (dewberries).

Leaves green above and below, stems sparsely retrorse-prickly .... **R. flagellaris**, p. 114

Leaves dark green above, paler beneath; stems densely retrorse-bristly .... **R. hispidus**, p. 116

RUBUS ODORATUS Linnaeus

Flowering Raspberry Thimbleberry

The Flowering Raspberry, fig. 24, which grows 3 to 5 feet high, is distinct among raspberries because of its simple leaves which are digitately ribbed and lobed, and its relatively tall stems with more or less shreddy bark, which are essentially unarmed, though glandular-hispid in the young parts, and villous. The broadly cordate leaf blades are 3- to 5-lobed with triangular or ovate, abruptly acute lobes which are irregularly serrate, 5 to 7 inches long and almost as wide, and pubescent both above and below.

The flowers, which appear from about the middle of June to the middle of July, are grouped in terminal panicles and have rose-purple, orbicular petals. The sepals and the long flower pedicels are densely glandular-hispid. The flattened spherical, reddish fruit, which matures in midsummer, is dry and hardly pleasant to eat.

Distribution.—The Flowering Raspberry is naturally an inhabitant of rocky soil in woods and is distributed from Nova Scotia westward to Michigan and south to Georgia and Tennessee. In Illinois, essentially a prairie state with few rock-covered regions, it has been known as a rare shrub. If it is not now extinct, it should be found on wooded rocky slopes along streams, especially in the hilly Ozark region of the state and southward.

FIG. 24
Rubus idaeus
Rubus occidentalis

Rubus strigosus

Rubus odoratus

RUBUS OCCIDENTALIS Linnaeus

Common Blackcap Raspberry

The Common Blackcap Raspberry, fig. 24, is a shrub with canelike stems sometimes 10 or 12 feet long, which arch and recurve so that the tips often root in the soil. It is sparingly armed with strong, recurved prickles. Old canes are purplish and more or less glaucous, and new canes are so glaucous as to be whitish. The leaves are 3-foliate, or rarely on new canes some are 5-foliate. The leaflets are ovate, generally 2 to 3 inches long, and abruptly acuminate at the apex, and the terminal leaflet is rounded or cordate at the base. Leaflet margins are doubly serrate and the blades are smooth or nearly so above but white-tomentose beneath. Both the petioles and the leaflet stalks are glabrous or only slightly pubescent.

The corymbs of flowers are either terminal or axillary and consist of only a few flowers, which bloom from early May until early June. The petals are white, and the sepals, which are tomentose on both sides, are reflexed at flowering time but close about the ripening fruit, which is matured from the last of June until the last of July. It is black, hemispheric, variable in size, more or less tomentose, about ⅜ to ⅝ inch in diameter, juicy and quite edible.

Distribution.—The Common Blackcap occurs in both moist and dry habitats in open woods and clearings and on the borders of streams and lakes. In these situations, it ranges from New Brunswick westward to Minnesota and southward to Georgia and Colorado. In Illinois, it is the most common of the raspberries and is to be found in almost all parts of the state. Its fruit, in season, is commonly picked and eaten.

RUBUS IDAEUS Linnaeus

European Red Raspberry

The European Red Raspberry, fig. 24, is a shrub with erect, light-colored, finely tomentose stems, which are armed with bristles or weak prickles. The leaves of 1-year-old canes are pinnately 5-foliate, and those on the flower-bearing branches are 3-foliate. The terminal leaflets are broadly ovate, rounded or cordate at the base, short-acuminate at the tips, and doubly serrate along the margins. They are 2 to 4 inches long and ark green above but white-tomentose beneath. Lateral leaflets re ovate and somewhat smaller than the terminal ones.

The flowers are grouped in short racemes which are terminal r arise from the upper axils. The peduncles and pedicels are nely tomentose and armed with small, recurved prickles. The blong or conical fruit is commonly dark red but sometimes ellowish to whitish. It is variable in quality and size, but sually edible.

Distribution.—This is the common cultivated Red Raspberry. It is native in Eurasia and has been widely introduced nto North America as a cultivated plant valuable for its fruit. n Illinois, as elsewhere, it has escaped to some extent from ultivation, and one may expect to encounter it in any part of he state.

RUBUS STRIGOSUS Michaux

merican Red Raspberry   Common Wild Raspberry

The American Red Raspberry, fig. 24, a shrub which grows to 6 feet high, has more or less bristly, but not tomentose, rownish or reddish stems. The leaves on new shoots are pinately 5-foliate and those on the flowering branches are 3-foliate. The ovate terminal leaflet is 2 to 4 inches long, doubly serrate, bruptly acuminate at the apex, rounded or cordate at the base, nd sometimes 3-lobed. Lateral leaflets are obliquely ovate and maller. The leaf blades are dark green and short-hairy to labrate above but white-tomentose beneath. The narrow stiples are deciduous.

The flowers are borne in terminal and axillary, few-flowered acemes on slender pedicels which are curving in fruit. The etals are white, and the sepals are spreading, acuminate, mostly ispid, and velvety. The fruit when ripe is elongate-hemispheric, right red or, rarely, white, and edible.

Distribution.—The American Red Raspberry generally refers moist soil rich in humus and is therefore found often n old bogs and marshes that are being invaded by timber. It anges from Newfoundland westward to British Columbia and outhward to Virginia and Wyoming. In Illinois, it is undoubtedly much more widespread than the records for Joliet, Cass nd Hancock counties indicate. Taxonomically, it is perhaps etter to regard the American Red Raspberry as a variety,

rather than as a species; it would then be known as *R. idaeu*
var. *strigosus* (Michaux) Maximowicz.

RUBUS ALLEGHENIENSIS Porter

Blackberry Allegheny Blackberry

The Allegheny Blackberry, fig. 25, is a relatively erect shru with canes that when old attain a length of 3 to 6 feet and ar recurved in the upper part. The lower part of the stem i terete, but the upper part is angled and sparsely clothed wit straight, or in the inflorescence recurved, prickles. The erec angled new canes bear leaves which are either 3- or 5-foliat Petioles, leaf stalks and midribs are villous and glandula Leaflets are ovate, doubly serrate, abruptly acuminate, pilos above but softly pubescent beneath, and ¾ to 4 inches long.

The flowers are borne in May in elongated racemes of 6 t 20 or more flowers, which extend well beyond the leaves. Th pedicel of each flower arises from the axil of a bract. The petal are white, and the sepals are reflexed while the plant is in flowe The pedicels on which the flowers stand are long and spread a a wide angle from the midstalk of the racemes. Fruit begin to mature in July. It is black, ¼ to ½ inch long, hemispheric and tart.

Distribution. — The Allegheny Blackberry prefers moist rich soil and frequently occurs on cut-over woodland, in ope woods, and along fences and roadsides. It is perhaps the com monest blackberry in Illinois and grows everywhere in th state. It is the original wild form from which many of th cultivated blackberries have been selected.

RUBUS CANADENSIS Linnaeus

Wild Blackberry

This Wild Blackberry, fig. 25, is a shrub with erect stem which reach a length of 3 to 12 feet and are grooved, roun angled, and glabrous. Sometimes they are unarmed or are pro vided with a few weak, straight prickles. The leaves on ne shoots are 5-foliate, those on old shoots 3-foliate. The thin dark green leaflets are glabrous or nearly so, sharply serrate abruptly long-acuminate at the tip, rounded or subcordate a the base, and 2 to 6 inches long. Leaflets on flowering branche

FIG. 25

Rubus argutus

Rubus canadensis
Rubus allegheniensis

Rubus frondosus

are oval, less acuminate, and 1¼ to 4 inches long. The flowe occur in lax racemes commonly 3 to 6 inches long, at the ti of branches and in the axils of old leaves. The oval petals a about ½ inch long and the lanceolate sepals are acuminat The flowers, which blossom in May and June, develop late into black and very pulpy fruits about ½ inch long.

Distribution.—This blackberry inhabits thickets and woo and grows from Newfoundland west to Minnesota and sout ward as far as North Carolina. In Illinois, it is a rare shru reported definitely only from Cahokia, south of East St. Loui Possibly this report is erroneous.

RUBUS ARGUTUS Link

Highbush Blackberry Tall Blackberry

The Highbush Blackberry, fig. 25, is an erect or somewh nodding shrub with canes that when old reach a length of to 6 feet and have at least the upper part deeply furrowed an prickly. It is characteristic that the prickles are flattened the base. They are straight or recurved, the recurved one more abundant toward the tip of the stems. The new cane which usually are smooth but sometimes pubescent or sprinkle with sessile red glands, are deeply channeled on the sides. Th leaves of new canes are usually 5-foliate. Terminal leaflets a acuminate at the apex, rounded or subcordate at the base an generally about 3 inches long by 1½ inches wide. The blade slightly pubescent above and definitely pubescent beneath, espe cially along the veins. The margins are more or less doubly an sharply serrate. The leaves of old canes are almost entirel 3-foliate, with leaflets similar to those on the new canes, excep that they are smaller and are gradually rather than abruptl acute at the apex.

The inflorescence is a short raceme, consisting commonly o 6 to 10 flowers, its peduncle pubescent and armed more or les with recurved prickles. It may be terminal or arise from th axils of leaves. The white flowers, which bloom in the earl part of June, have round to oval petals about ½ inch long an ovate sepals with abrupt tips, which are strongly reflexed a fruiting time. The pedicels of the flowers are strongly ascend ing, about ½ to 1 inch long, pubescent, and sometimes prickl Fruit ripens from late July to about the middle of August. I s glabrous, oblong, about $\frac{1}{2}$ to $\frac{3}{4}$ inch long by half as wide, weet, and reddish when it becomes dry.

DISTRIBUTION.—The Highbush Blackberry seems to prefer hard, moist soil, frequently a clay soil, and in such habitats anges from Nova Scotia southwestward to Kansas and Iowa. n the east its southern limit is North Carolina. In Illinois, it ccurs throughout the southern part of the state and has een reported rather frequently from the vicinity of Chicago. Although there are straggling occurrences in the north, the orthern limits of abundance are probably Vermilion County n the east and Pike County in the west. This species, as epresented in Illinois, might possibly be better regarded as R. *ostryifolius* Rydberg; it has, however, been most often lassified under the name used here.

RUBUS FRONDOSUS Bigelow

Leafy-Flowered Blackberry

The Leafy-Flowered Blackberry, fig. 25, is a shrub with erect oung stems and with old canes that usually recurve strongly ut do not root at the tip. The stems are terete or nearly so, generally 3 to 6 feet long, and bear few prickles, most of which are somewhat flattened at the base, and short and straight or only partly recurved. Sometimes the upper parts of new canes have wide, shallow channels. Most leaves on new canes are 5-foliate, and the terminal leaflet is broadly ovate, abruptly hort-acuminate at the apex, and rounded or cordate at the base. The leaf surface is sparingly short-pubescent above and densely so beneath, and the margins are doubly serrate with ovate teeth. Most leaves on the old canes are 3-foliate and doubly serrate with ovate teeth, and the terminal leaflet is rhombic-oval or obovate, about $1\frac{1}{4}$ to 2 inches long, acute at the apex, and generally wedge shaped at the base.

The inflorescence is a very short raceme, generally of fewer than 10 flowers, which open about the first of June. The ovate sepals, which have abrupt short tips, become strongly reflexed at fruiting time. The flower pedicels are ascending, densely pubescent, and $\frac{1}{4}$ to $\frac{1}{2}$ inch long. The black, glabrous fruit, which begins to ripen in July, is globose or slightly elongated, juicy, tart, and edible.

DISTRIBUTION.—The Leafy-Flowered Blackberry appears to

prefer drier land than other blackberry species and range from Ontario westward to Iowa and south to Virginia an Kansas. It is a relatively common shrub throughout most o the northern two-thirds of Illinois. The southernmost record are Wabash and Marion counties.

RUBUS FLAGELLARIS Willdenow

Northern Dewberry

The Northern Dewberry, fig. 26, is a low, trailing shru with stems that when old are prostrate, 3 to 9 feet long, gla brous, and armed more or less with weak, recurved prickles which put out lateral branches 4 to 12 inches long. The nev canes, which soon become prostrate, are smooth or, rarely, ar sparsely covered with long hairs or sessile red glands. Prickle on the stems usually are flattened at the base; and the branchlet and petioles are more or less pubescent and prickly, sometime also covered with sessile red glands and glandular hair. Leave on new canes are usually 3-foliate, rarely 5-foliate, and thei leaflets vary in shape. The terminal leaflet is ovate to nearl orbicular, acuminate at the apex, and sharply and irregularl doubly serrate. The blades are more or less pubescent abov and beneath, and occasionally covered with sessile red gland or glandular hairs on the underside.

The inflorescence, placed toward the end of branchlets, con sists as a rule of 1 to 5 flowers, which arise singly in the axil of upper leaves or bracts or, often, 2 or 3 are grouped together terminating the branch. The flowers bloom from early in Ma to past the middle of June. The sepals are ovate, acute, an sometimes more or less leaflike, tomentose within and pubescen and sometimes glandular on the outside. The narrowly ellipti to ovate petals are about ½ inch long, and the stamens generall are shorter than the sepals. The black, juicy fruit, which ma tures from late June into early August, is hemispheric or slightl elongated, usually about ½ inch long, and glabrate to hairy.

Distribution.—The Northern Dewberry grows on almos any kind of soil, although it prefers poor or acid soils, an ranges from southern Maine to Minnesota and south to Vir ginia and Oklahoma. It occurs throughout all of Illinois frequently invading abandoned fields, disturbed soil along roadsides, and other waste places.

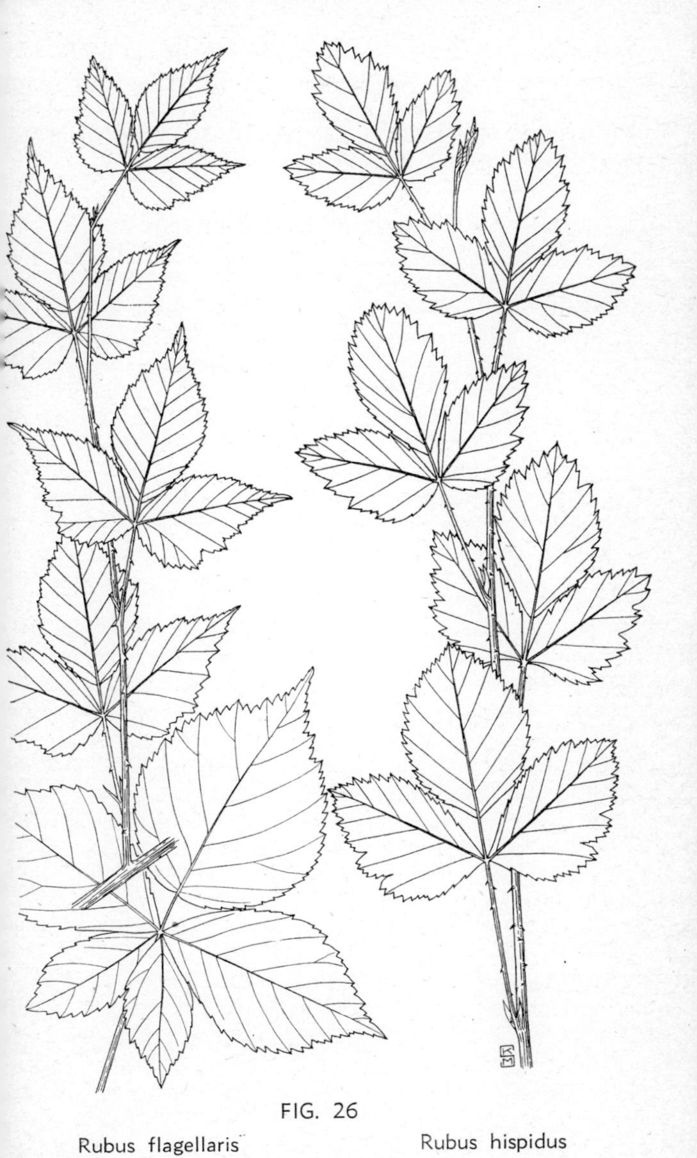

FIG. 26

Rubus flagellaris Rubus hispidus

The Northern Dewberry is extremely variable, and taxono
mists have separated several of its forms as species. All of thes
are included here under the one name. This shrub, beside
yielding great quantities of wild fruit, is the species from whic
nearly all cultivated dewberries have been derived.

RUBUS HISPIDUS Linnaeus

Swamp Dewberry

The Swamp Dewberry, fig. 26, is a low shrub with slende
prostrate, trailing stems, which, although glabrous, are clothe
more or less densely with recurved or straight bristles, all c
which are tipped with glands. The branchlets are erect, usuall
3 to 6 inches long, and bear 3-foliate or, rarely, 5-foliate leave
with nearly smooth or occasionally pubescent petioles more o
less covered with bristles similar to those of the stem. Th
blades are firm and sometimes persist through the winter. The
are obovate, or the lateral ones may be rhombic-ovate to nearl
orbicular, generally ¾ to 2 inches long, nearly acute at th
apex, and rounded at the base. The margin is doubly serrate
except the lower third, which may be entire. The upper surfac
is glossy and smooth, and the lower surface is smooth witl
frequently, pubescent veins.

The flowers occur in groups of 2 to 6 at the end of branchlet
and there also may be 1 or 2 from the axils of upper leave
The white blossoms open from early June to the last of Augus
They stand on pubescent, sometimes bristly pedicels. Sepals ar
ovate, nearly acute or sometimes obtuse, and pointed with
gland. They are densely pubescent on the outside and tomentos
within, are reflexed at flowering time and do not close on th
fruit. The white petals are obovate. The fruit, which usuall
matures in August or later, is reddish purple and consists o
a few glabrous, sour drupelets. Because of its small size an
acidity, it has little food value.

Distribution.—As its name indicates, the Swamp Dewberr
grows near lakes and marshes, especially at the base of woode
slopes. In such habitats it ranges from Nova Scotia to Georgi
and west to Minnesota and Kansas. All of Illinois lies withi
its range, and it may be expected in suitable habitats anywher
within the state. It has not been widely reported, howeve
Present records indicate its occurrence only in Cook County

n old sand regions in Kankakee County, and in Pulaski County n the extreme southern part of the state.

Additional Bramble Species.—Besides the above important r relatively abundant species, others have been recorded occa-ionally. One, *Rubus pubescens* Rafinesque, is herbaceous and s sometimes called the Dwarf Raspberry. It bears globose, dible, dark red fruit and is a low, unarmed perennial some-imes slightly woody at the base. It has been extensively col-ected in a few northeastern counties, the only part of the state n which it is known to occur. Rare collections of southern pecies have been recorded from the southern part of Illinois. among these are *R. betulifolius* Small, *R. pergratus* Blanchard, ?. *recurvans* Blanchard and *R. rubrisetus* Rydberg. The bram-les of the state have not been completely studied, and both ccurrence and distribution remain to be demonstrated for these nd other species.

ROSA (Tournefort) Linnaeus

The Roses

The roses are a group of erect or widely spreading shrubs vith stems generally armed with prickles, alternate, compound, dd-pinnate leaves, and stipules adnate to the petioles. Flowers ave 5 sepals, which are united at the base and more or less oliaceous, 5 showy petals, and many stamens. The several to umerous pistils develop bony seeds or achenes inside of small, pple-like fruits called hips, which are the fleshy receptacles of he flowers.

The rose genus is represented by great numbers of species videly distributed over the northern hemisphere, and the opularity of the flower has led to its cultivation in an ever-ncreasing number of varieties. Distinctions between even wild pecies are not easily made, and there is perhaps as much dis-greement among authorities concerning the rose species as here is concerning *Rubus* species.

Key to the Rose Species

)ld stems trailing or climbing; leaves on old stems mostly 3-foliate, on new growth 3- or 5-foliate....... **R. setigera**, p. 118

)ld stems essentially erect; leaves on old and new stems 5- to 9-foliate.

Calyx lobes reflexed after flowering, and deciduous.

Prickles stout and strongly recurved.......R. **palustris**, p. 12
Prickles slender and straight.
Leaflet surfaces pubescent beneath.
Leaflets thin..........................R. **Lyonii**, p. 12
Leaflets thick and coriaceous.........R. **rudiuscula**, p. 12
Only the veins beneath pubescent.
Leaflet teeth not gland tipped.........R. **carolina**, p. 12
Leaflet teeth gland tipped.............R. **serrulata**, p. 12
Calyx lobes erect after flowering, and persistent.
Prickles generally absent below the stipules.
Leaflets 9 to 11 per leaf, densely pubescent beneath ....R. **suffulta**, p. 12
Leaflets 5 to 7 per leaf, finely pubescent beneath....... ....R. **blanda**, p. 12
Prickles present below stipules; leaves glabrous......... ....R. **Woodsii**, p. 12

ROSA SETIGERA Michaux

Prairie Rose

The Prairie Rose, fig. 27, is a shrub with arching, climbin stems usually 4 to 12 feet long, which are armed with prickle scattered singly along and around the stem and in pairs belo each leaf on the upper part of the stem. They are recurve or rarely straight, and the lower half is much enlarged an flattened laterally. Both petioles and rachises are more or le covered with stalked glands. The stipules are narrow, adnat for about three-fourths of their length, and marginally studde with glandular hairs. Leaves on old stems generally have leaflets, on new stems either 3 or 5 leaflets. The leaflets ar lanceolate to broadly ovate, or sometimes slightly obovate, an lateral leaflets are nearly sessile. The terminal leaflet is def nitely stalked and is always the largest, and the basal pai when there are 5 leaflets, is always much smaller. Leafle are wedge shaped or rounded at the base, or the termin leaflet sometimes may be subcordate, acute or acuminate the apex, either serrate or doubly serrate. The upper surfa is glabrous, and the lower surface is glabrous or somewh pubescent along the veins.

The flowers, which appear from the middle of June throug July, are borne in terminal corymbs, on pedicels covered wit glandular hairs. The calyx tube and the sepals are glandula hispid, the end of the sepals being reflexed after flowering an later deciduous. The petal color is light to deep rose. Th

FIG. 27

Rosa carolina Rosa setigera Rosa palustris

species is marked by the fact that the styles of the pistils cc
here in a column. The fruit, which is red, matures in autum
and is glandular-hispid, pear shaped to subglobose, and abou
one-third inch in diameter.

DISTRIBUTION.—The Prairie Rose prefers relatively ope
situations along fences and roadsides, in clearings, and in ope
woods. In such places it grows from Ohio to Florida an
west to Kansas. In Illinois, it is common and abundant. I
has been reported from all parts of the state and seemingl
from all kinds of situations except dense woods. It is on
of the most beautiful of the wild roses and is one of th
species from which valuable cultivated climbing roses hav
been derived.

Forms of this rose distinguished by more or less dense pu
bescence on the under surface of the leaves and with leaflet
which are as a rule thicker and have a harsher appearance ar
segregated as the variety *tomentosa* Torrey & Gray.

ROSA PALUSTRIS Marshall

Swamp Rose

The Swamp Rose, fig. 27, is a shrub with erect, smooth stem
generally 2 to 6 feet high that are armed with numerous prickles
which are limited to non-flowering stems on some specimens
These prickles are recurved and generally flattened at the base
sometimes quite eccentric and strongly decurrent on the stems
and arranged singly except on new shoots, where they ofte
occur in pairs below the leaves. Most leaves have 7 leaflets
but sometimes there are 5 or 9. The leaflets are lance-ellipti
to broadly elliptic and up to 3 inches long by 1¼ inches wide
though usually only about half that size. Lateral leaflets ar
sessile or nearly so, but terminal leaflets are supported on
stalk almost ½ inch long. They are narrowed at the base an
generally acute at the apex, though sometimes rounded, and th
margins are finely serrate nearly to the base. The surface i
smooth or nearly so above and hairy beneath, though sometime
only on the veins. Both petioles and rachises are pubescent an
sometimes prickly. The stipules are narrow, commonly wit
involute edges, and ½ to 1¼ inches long.

The flowers, deep rose in color, up to 2 inches wide, whic
blossom from late in June through July, are in corymbs o

ometimes are solitary, and are seated on pedicels up to ¾ inch ong, which are glandular-hispid or, rarely, almost smooth. The ube of the calyx is glandular-hispid and the attenuated calyx obes, sometimes foliaceous at the tip, are glandular-hispid on he back and tomentose on the inside and on the margins. They pread and become reflexed after flowering and are tardily eciduous. The fruit matures in autumn as a red, glandular-ispid, most often depressed-globose but rarely somewhat oblong ip about ⅜ inch in diameter, with seeds attached to the bottom.

DISTRIBUTION.—The Swamp Rose grows in wet places from Nova Scotia south to Florida and west to Minnesota and Mis-issippi. In Illinois, it occurs through much of the state and may e looked for wherever suitably wet habitats occur.

ROSA CAROLINA Linnaeus

Pasture Rose

The Pasture Rose, fig. 27, is a shrub with erect, terete stems p to 3 feet, but generally 1½ to 2 feet, tall, which are smooth, r rarely glandular-hispid, and thickly covered when young with tout, weak prickles. The prickles are arranged singly about ie stem, often in pairs below leaves on the branchlets, and are iore or less deciduous after the first year. They are straight, ecurved, reflexed, or rarely point forward, and sometimes young rickles are flattened at the base. The leaves are made up of to 7 leaflets, which are lanceolate-elliptic to nearly orbicular, nd generally about 1¼ inches long by ¾ inch wide, acute at ie apex or sometimes rounded, and acute or narrowed at the ase. The margins are sharply and closely serrate, and the sur-ice is generally smooth above and glabrous or more or less ensely pubescent beneath. Lateral leaflets are sessile or nearly), and terminal leaflets stand on stalks about ½ inch long. Both etioles and rachises are more or less pubescent, glandular, and rickly, and the stipules, about ⅜ inch long and ⅛ inch wide, enerally have some teeth and some glands on the margin.

The flowers, which bloom from about the first of June until ie middle of August, usually are solitary or in pairs or clusters f 3 at the end of branchlets and may be 2 inches or more in iameter. They stand on more or less glandular-hispid pedicels to 1¼ inches long. The calyx tube is more or less glandular-ispid, and the lobes are lanceolate-cordate and often expanded at the tip, generally about 1 inch long, generally reflexed afte the petals fall, and tardily deciduous. The fruit, which mature in autumn, is pear shaped or depressed-globose, red, about 1/ to ½ inch in diameter, and smooth or more or less glandular hispid. The achenes are attached to its base.

Distribution. — The Pasture Rose prefers relatively ope situations and is to be found on the borders of woods, in ope places in woodlands, or along roadsides from Maine to Wis consin and south to Florida and Texas. It is distribute throughout the entire state of Illinois.

The Pasture Rose sends out long underground stems, fror which aerial stems arise. These tend to die back from year t year, but may be responsible for sizable colonies of the ros The species is an extremely variable one, forms of it havin been segregated both as species and as varieties. It appear to be very sensitive to habitat factors. This rose has been i cultivation since 1826 and is used for borders and shrubber The variety *grandiflora* (Baker) Rehder has been distinguishe on the basis that the leaflets are usually 7 and obovate or ova and the flowers about 2½ inches across. Another variet *glandulosa* (Crépin) Rehder, has doubly and glandularly se rate leaflets and glandular-hispid rachises. *R. Lyonii* Purs described below, is considered by authorities a variety of th species and is then designated as var. *villosa* (Best) Rehder.

ROSA LYONII Pursh

This rose, fig. 28, is a rather low shrub, with round, glabro stems seldom as much as 4 feet long, which usually are brist and covered with slender prickles. The leaves have 5 to elliptic to lance-elliptic leaflets ½ to 2 inches long, which a acute or, rarely, obtuse, serrate along the margins, and du and sparingly pubescent to glabrate above but definitely p bescent beneath. The rachis on which the leaflets stand villous, and the stipules are narrow. The rose-pink flowe stand in groups of 1 to 4 and are 2 to 2½ inches wide. T pedicels and the receptacle are glandular-hispid, or rarely t receptacle may be glabrous. The petals are sometimes sparing lobed. The hip, which matures in the fall, is ¼ to ⅜ inch diameter, and the seeds are attached at its bottom.

Distribution.—This rose ranges from Massachusetts wes

FIG. 28

Rosa blanda

Rosa Lyonii

Rosa serrulata

ward to Minnesota and south to Georgia and Arkansas. Ir Illinois, it is rare, reported thus far only from St. Clair anc Henderson counties.

ROSA BLANDA Aiton

Meadow Rose

The Meadow Rose, fig. 28, is a low shrub generally less thar 3 feet high, with glabrous canes that when old are sometime covered more or less densely with short, straight, or curve weak prickles. The branches and branchlets are also smootl or rarely armed with a few prickles. There are 5 to 7, o rarely 9, oval to obovate or oblong leaflets per leaf. Latera leaflets are sessile or stand on very short stalks, and termina leaflets stand on stalks sometimes 1½ inches long. The leaflet are up to 1 inch wide and nearly 2 inches long, acute or rounde at the apex, narrowed or rounded at the base, and coarsel serrate on the margins. The upper surface is dull, smooth or rarely, slightly pubescent, and the under surface is more or les pubescent. Petioles and rachises are more or less densely wooll pubescent and, rarely, glandular-hispid also. The stipules ar generally pubescent above and beneath, or sometimes glabrou except on the margins, which are entire and ciliate or more o less glandular-hispid.

The pale or bright pink flowers, which appear about the firs of June, are solitary or in pairs or small clusters of 3 to 5 a the end of branches. They stand on glabrous pedicels ¼ to ¾ inch long. The calyx tube is glabrous, and its lanceolate, cau date lobes are slightly dilated at the tip, about ½ inch long, an glandular-hispid on the back, and erect and persistent. Th fruit, which matures in autumn, is scarlet, nearly globose c oval, and smooth, and the seeds are attached at the bottom c the seed receptacle.

Distribution.—The Meadow Rose ranges from Newfoun land west to Saskatchewan and south to Pennsylvania ar Illinois. In Illinois, it is an abundant rose in the norther counties, but becomes rarer southward and has not been o served at any point south of the Ozarks.

A tall, swamp-inhabiting form of this species growing northeastern Illinois counties appears identical with *R. acic larioides* Schuette, a Wisconsin species.

ROSA SERRULATA Rafinesque

This rose, fig. 28, is a shrub with slender arms 1 to 3 feet .igh, which bear straight, round prickles in pairs below the tipules, and it usually has 5, or sometimes 3 or 7, leaflets per eaf. The leaflets are lance-elliptic or, rarely, oval, glabrous n both sides or slightly pubescent on the veins beneath, and lso pale beneath. The margins are sharply, often doubly, serate and the teeth are gland tipped. The flowers are solitary nd first open in early May. The fruit matures in late autumn nd reaches a size of about ¼ inch. The seeds are attached at he bottom of the fruit.

DISTRIBUTION.—This rose, which grows especially on high and, is distributed from Massachusetts westward to Ontario nd Iowa and south to Florida and New Mexico. In Illinois, : is rare and has been taken definitely only in Lawrence County. 'erhaps it is, as authorities believe, identical with *R. carolina* ar. *glandulosa* (Crépin) Rehder.

ROSA RUDIUSCULA Greene

This rose, fig. 29, is an erect shrub generally 2 to 3 feet high, ith short and ascending branches. The stems are terete, smooth, nd more or less covered with prickles and bristles when young ut sparsely so when old. The prickles are round, straight, ometimes curved, slightly reflexed, or on some of the branches ot reflexed at all. For the most part, the leaves have 5 to 7 aflets, though rarely 9. The leaflets are subcoriaceous, elliptic, val, or oblong, and generally ¾ to 1¼ inches long by about ½ inch wide. They are acute or rounded at the apex and narowed at the base, and the margins are sharply serrate except t the base, there being generally 10 to 15 teeth on each side of e leaf. The blade is glabrous above, paler and pubescent all ver the lower surface or only along the midrib, and the midrib often reddish. The rachis of the leaf is pubescent and often ears a few prickles or bristles and some stalked glands. Lateral aflets are nearly sessile, but terminal leaflets are seated on alks nearly ¼ inch long. The stipules are lanceolate to oval, nd smooth to densely pubescent above and beneath, with marins which are pubescent and entire, or sometimes glandularentate.

FIG. 29
Rosa Woodsii
Rosa suffulta Rosa rudiuscula

The flowers stand solitarily at the end of the branches, or n twos or threes, on pedicels about 1/4 inch long, which are ;enerally glandular-hispid but sometimes smooth. The calyx ube is often glandular-hispid, and its lobes are lanceolate and audate, reflexed, and deciduous. The fruit, which matures in .utumn, is generally depressed, 1/4 inch wide or a little larger, .nd bright red.

Distribution.—This rose is a prairie species which ranges rom Indiana westward into Missouri and from Wisconsin and owa south to Oklahoma. It grows throughout the prairie egion of Illinois and is to be looked for especially along road-ides. The reddish foliage and the thicker leaflets serve as a eady means of distinguishing it from the Pasture Rose.

ROSA SUFFULTA Greene

This rose, fig. 29, is a shrub with erect, generally simple tems, which reach a height of 18 to 30 inches and are covered nore or less densely with straight prickles. The leaves are made .p commonly of 9, but sometimes of 7 or 11, obovate or broadly val leaflets, which are bluntly or acutely rounded at the apex nd narrowed at the base. Their margins are bluntly and ather coarsely serrate, and the blades at maturity are generally mooth above but pubescent beneath. Petioles and the rachises re woolly pubescent and sometimes glandular-prickly. The tipules are pubescent and dilated, and their margins are more r less erose or dentate and studded with glands.

The flowers stand in corymbs at the top of the stems and are upported on smooth pedicels 1/4 to nearly 1/2 inch long. The alyx tube is glabrous, and its lobes are caudate, often expanded t the tip, glandular on the back, and tomentose within and on he outer margin. After flowering they are generally erect and ersistent. The red, globose or, rarely, pyriform fruit matures 1 the autumn and is not quite 1/4 inch in diameter. The seeds re attached to the bottom and near the base of the interior.

Distribution.—This rose is a prairie species generally as-ociated with typical prairie land. Its natural range is from lberta to Manitoba and south to Texas and New Mexico. llinois stands almost on the eastern border of its range, and is known to occur in northern, central and western, but not ne southeastern, sections of the state.

ROSA WOODSII Lindley

Woods's Rose

This rose, fig. 29, is an erect shrub with terete, glabrou
stems 1½ to 6 feet high, which are armed with numerou
straight or slightly recurved prickles. The leaves are mad
up of 5 to 7 obovate leaflets, which are wedge shaped at th
base, glabrous on both sides, and glaucous beneath. They ar
¼ to ½ inch long, or rarely longer, and serrate around th
upper part of the margin. The stipules are glabrous, usuall
without glands, and entire or a little toothed on the margins
The sepals are glabrous or slightly glandular on the back and
after flowering, stand erectly together and are persistent o
the fruit. The flowering period is from May to July. Th
glabrous, red fruit is globose, only slightly more than ⅛ inc
in diameter at maturity, and it ripens in the autumn.

Distribution.—This rose is an inhabitant of river bank
and thickets from Manitoba to North Dakota and south t
Kansas and westward. As a plains species, it occurs rarel
in Illinois, being actually reported only in Jo Daviess County
in the northwest corner of the state, and in Pope County, i
the extreme south.

MALACEAE

The Apple Family

The apple family consists of shrubs or trees which bear simpl
or pinnately compound, alternate, stipulate leaves and perfect
regular flowers with a well-developed hypanthium adnate to th
ovary, which in maturity becomes fleshy and constitutes a par
of the fruit. The sepals and petals are for the most part 5 i
number; the stamens are distinct and numerous and inserte
on the margins of the receptacle; and the ovary consists o
1 to 5 united pistils, the cells being 5 and the correspondin
styles distinct or sometimes partly united. The fruit is mor
or less fleshy, apple-like, and generally is called a pome.

The apple family, sometimes considered not distinct from th
rose family, consists of some 20 genera and more than 50
species, which are widely distributed in Europe, Asia and Nort
America and extend southward to Mexico and into Sout
America along the Andes. The family is noted for the useful

ness of its members, especially the apple and pear. There are four shrubby genera found in Illinois.

Key to the Shrubby Genera

Leaves compound . . . . **Sorbus**, p. 129
Leaves simple.
  Shrubs without spines.
    Leaf margins serrate and teeth gland-tipped; stalked glands on the midrib above . . . . **Aronia**, p. 130
    Leaf margins serrate but the teeth not gland-tipped; no stalked glands on the midrib above . . . **Amelanchier**, p. 133
  Shrubs with spines . . . . **Crataegus**, p. 134

SORBUS (Tournefort) Linnaeus

Mountain-Ash

The mountain-ashes are shrubs or trees, which bear alternate, pinnately compound leaves consisting of serrate leaflets, deciduous stipules, and perfect, regular flowers in terminal, compound ymes. The flowers have 5 erect, or spreading, deciduous sepals, white, spreading petals, many stamens, and an inferior ovary dnate to the hypanthium. The styles are 3 and usually distinct, nd the 3 cells of the ovary each contain 2 ovules. The fruit is mall, berry-like and, in our species, red and very acid.

There are about 10 species, all of them natives of the north emperate zone, and at least 4 are native in North America. The cultivated mountain-ash, noteworthy for its decorative, range-yellow fruit, is a member of the genus. There is only ne shrubby species native in Illinois.

SORBUS SUBVESTITA Greene

Western Mountain-Ash

The Western Mountain-Ash is an erect shrub, or more rarely small tree, with branchlets which are at first long pubescent ut soon become smooth. Its leaves, which are 4 to 6 inches ong, stand on petioles ½ to 1½ inches long and consist of 13 17 leaflets arranged in pinnate pairs along the rachis. The aflets are lanceolate or oblong, up to 1¾ inches long by ½ inch r a little more wide, acute at the apex, rounded and very asymmetrical at the base, the upper half being the shortest. The margins are singly and sharply serrate to near the base, or the ower side may be serrate only to about the middle. Both surfaces are long pubescent at first, but the upper surface soo becomes glabrous or nearly so and the lower surface remain pubescent until maturity. The rachis is usually long pubescent channeled above, and bears a cluster of glands in the channe at the base of each leaflet. Lateral leaflets are sessile, or nearl so, and terminal leaflets stand on a stalk ¼ to ½ inch long The stipules are obovate and glandular-serrate, and the uppe margin is elongated and tipped with a bristle-like gland.

The white flowers appear late in May in terminal cyme The calyx tube is pubescent at first but soon becomes glabrou The fruit, which matures in late August or September, is small, globose, bright red pome a little less than ¼ inch i diameter, which as a rule contains 1 seed.

Distribution.—The Western Mountain-Ash is an inhabitar of the far north with a natural range which extends from Lab rador to Minnesota and south to Pennsylvania and Iowa. It occurrence in Illinois at the present time is to be doubted, a though two specimens collected in Lake County nearly half century ago show that it was a member of the state's flora.

ARONIA Medicus

Chokeberry Chokepear

The chokeberries are low shrubs which bear simple, alternat serrate leaves, small, deciduous stipules, and small, perfect flow ers in terminal, compound cymes. There are 5 distinct sepal 5 white or pink, spreading petals, numerous stamens, and a 3- 5-celled ovary capped by 3 to 5 basally united styles. The fru is a small, globose pome capped by a persistent calyx.

This genus consists of only three species, all restricted North America. The following occur in Illinois.

Key to the Chokeberry Species

Branchlets, calyx and pedicels more or less pubescent........
....**A. prunifol**
Branchlets, calyx and pedicels glabrous..........**A. melanocar**

ARONIA PRUNIFOLIA (Marshall) Rehder

Purple Chokeberry

The Purple Chokeberry, fig. 30, is a shrub which grows 3 to feet high, with smooth or somewhat roughened bark somewh

FIG. 30

ronia prunifolia

Amelanchier humilis

Aronia melanocarpa

like the bark of cherries. The branches are smooth and generall grayish, and the branchlets more or less woolly-pubescent an light or reddish brown. The obovate or sometimes oval leave usually ¾ to 1 inch wide and 2 to 3 inches long, are generall abruptly short-acuminate or acute and taper to the petiole a the base. They are smooth above and more or less woolly pubescent beneath and stand on petioles seldom more than ½ inch long.

The flowers, which appear in the latter part of May, usuall stand in clusters of 12 or fewer, on peduncles ¼ to ½ inc long. The calyx is generally densely woolly-pubescent on th outside, and the lobes are triangular, always woolly on the ir side, and may have a few red glands on the margins. The petal which are about ⅛ inch long, are broadly ovate to oval. Th fruit, which matures after the middle of August and on throug the fall, is variable in shape and size, and lustrous. It is even tually purplish black, dry, spherical, and a little less than ½ inch in diameter.

Distribution.—The Purple Chokeberry grows in old tama rack bogs and similar situations and in such habitats range from Newfoundland west to Minnesota and south to Florid In Illinois, it is to be sought only in the old bogs in the nort eastern corner of the state. Early maturing fruit is much large than that matured later, very juicy, and somewhat astringent.

ARONIA MELANOCARPA (Michaux) Elliott

Chokepear Black Chokeberry

The Chokepear, fig. 30, is an upright shrub sometimes much as 12 feet high, with obovate or ovate, short-petiole glabrous leaves which may be obtuse, acute, or abruptly ac minate at the tip, and are narrowed or wedge shaped at t base. The leaf margins are finely dentate, and the blade dark green above and pale beneath. Both calyx and pedice are glabrous. The flowers bear petals less than ¼ inch lon which are ovate to obovate, and the fruit is globose or ov purplish black or black, ¼ to one-third inch in diameter, a it falls early.

Distribution.—The Black Chokeberry grows near ponds in low woods, rarely on drier soil, and ranges from No Scotia to Ontario and south to Florida and Illinois. In Illino it occurs in suitable habitats throughout the entire northern third of the state, and one rare report of it comes as far south as Clark County.

AMELANCHIER Medicus

Shadblow Serviceberry Shadbush

The shadblows are shrubs or trees with alternate, simple, petioled leaves that may be either serrate or entire. The unarmed branches bear racemose or, rarely, solitary, white flowers, which have bell-shaped calyx tubes more or less adnate to the ovary, 5 narrow, reflexed, persistent sepals, 5 petals, and many stamens. The 2 to 5 styles are united at least at the base, where they are also pubescent. The at least partly inferior ovary has twice as many cavities as there are styles, and 1 ovule in each cavity. The hoary, gray pome is hollow, very light, and 4- to 10-celled.

The shadbushes, a group of about 25 species, are all north temperate zone plants. Perhaps 18 or 19 are natives of North America, where they are well known because of their beauty and because of legends regarding them in the New England states. Only the following occurs in Illinois.

AMELANCHIER HUMILIS Wiegand

Low Shadblow Low Shadbush

The Low Shadblow, fig. 30, is an erect shrub with stems 16 inches to nearly 5 feet high, which arise from stolons. The branchlets are generally pubescent at first but become smooth and reddish brown by the end of the season. They bear broad, oval or oval-oblong leaves, 2 to 4 inches long by ¾ to 2 inches wide, which are rounded at the apex or sometimes subacute, and mostly rounded or subcordate at the base. The margins are coarsely and somewhat irregularly dentate to the middle or lower, leaving the basal part entire or very shallowly toothed. The teeth often are double. When young, the leaves are folded together and slightly pubescent above, but at length become dark green. They are densely tomentose beneath when first unfolded but become glabrous at maturity. The 7 to 13 pairs of veins are conspicuous above and beneath. At maturity, the petioles, ⅛ to ⅜ inch long, are pubescent at least above.

The flowers are borne in short, erect racemes, which may be either terminal or lateral, and contain usually 5 flowers. Flowering occurs from early to late May, and the blossoms are white, with obovate or oblanceolate, small petals. The juicy, edible fruit matures in July. It is at first cherry red but turns purple black, and at maturity is nearly globose, glaucous, and about ¼ inch in diameter. The sepals are persistent and stand erect on the fruit.

Distribution.—The Low Shadblow, a shrub of slopes and hills, ranges from Vermont westward to Nebraska and northward perhaps to the Mackenzie River. In Illinois, it should be found, on careful search, throughout much of the northern part of the state, but up to the present it is definitely recorded only in Hancock County.

CRATAEGUS Linnaeus

Haw Hawthorn

The hawthorns are shrubs or small trees usually armed with thorns or spines. They bear alternate, petioled, simple, toothed, usually more or less lobed leaves, and terminal, cymose clusters of flowers, which have 5 sepals that are reflexed after blossoming, 5 white or pink, spreading, rounded petals, and 5 to 25 stamens with slender, incurved filaments. The ovary is inferior and consists of 1 to 5 carpels capped by 1 to 5 distinct stigmas. The fruit, a globose, pear-shaped, or ellipsoid pome, which may be yellow, red, blue or black, contains 1 to 5 bony carpels, each of which bears 1 seed.

There are perhaps 300 species of hawthorns. Most of them are natives of the north temperate zone but they range southward by way of the table lands of Mexico into the Andes. The center of distribution is said to lie in the eastern United States, and many of the named species have been described from material collected in Illinois. The naming of hawthorns is exceedingly difficult. Taxonomic botanists have named more than 1,000 species from the United States alone, but the consensus is that many of these are hybrids.

Hawthorns are abundant in almost all parts of Illinois; but, in spite of many collections and careful study in two limited sections of the state, they are by no means well known. There is record of the occurrence of 105 species in Illinois, but neither the distribution nor the abundance of more than a few is known. Forty-seven species have been described and named from original Illinois material, but most of these and many of the others are known only from isolated or limited collections. The 26 species given in the following key, without distinction as to tree or shrub forms, are known to have either wide distribution or local abundance and are those most apt to be encountered.

Among the hawthorns there is much variation in the obvious characters relied upon, in other groups, for species identification. Species normally treelike often assume a shrubby habit. Leaf shape may vary greatly, even on the same branch; and variations in finer characters, such as lobing, serration, pubescence, twig color, and size, texture and color of fruit, add confusion.

Major characters used in distinguishing species are, in the order of their commonly recognized importance, (1) the color of the anthers, (2) the number of the stamens, (3) the pubescence character of the corymbs at flowering time, and (4) the general shape of the leaf. Broader characters used in the grouping of species include (1) leaf serration and lobing, (2) leaf texture, (3) leaf veining, (4) foliage color, (5) size, shape and color of the fruit, and (6) the number and shape of the nutlets.

Accurate naming of a hawthorn is a task that taxes even the discriminative judgment of an experienced taxonomist. Careful and prolonged observation of the unknown plant must be coupled with keen appreciation of characteristics as they appear or change from season to season. For any but the most common species, the help of an expert should be sought, and one should submit for examination an adequate series of specimens showing the full growing season's changes from flowers to ripe fruit.

Key to Common Hawthorn Species

A. Leaf veins extending only to the points of lobes or teeth; leaves usually only slightly, if at all, lobed.
  B. Leaf widest at or beyond the middle, the base wedge shaped.
    C. Widest part of the leaf beyond the middle.
      1. Leaves lustrous; veins not deeply impressed above.
        2. Thorns 3 to 4 inches long, midrib greenish (fig. 31) .... **C. Crus-galli** L.
        2. Thorns 1 to 2 inches long, midrib yellow........ .... **C. arduennae** Sarg.

FIG. 31

Crataegus Margaretta
Crataegus Crus-galli

Crataegus illinoiensis
Crataegus rotundifolia

1. Leaves dull; veins deeply impressed above.
   3. Thorns up to 7 inches long; leaves glabrous above.............. **C. cuneiformis** (Marsh.) Egglest.
   3. Thorns up to 2 inches long; leaves pubescent .... **C. punctata** Jacq.

C. Leaf blade widest at the middle.
   4. Leaf veins deeply impressed above.
      5. Leaves thin; thorns 1½ to 2 inches long.................................... **C. tomentosa** L.
      5. Leaves leathery, thorns up to 2½ to 4 inches long.
         6. Leaves elliptic, acute at both ends.............................. **C. succulenta** Schrad.
         6. Leaves broader, mostly rounded at the apex.
            7. Calyx lobes edged with stipitate, bright red glands (fig. 31) .... **C. illinoiensis** Ashe
            7. Calyx lobes bearing only minute, dark glands .... **C. macracantha** Lodd.
   4. Leaf veins not deeply impressed above.
      8. Margins of calyx lobes glandular.
         9. Leaves leathery, 1½ to 2 inches long, midrib green (fig. 31)............ **C. rotundifolia** Moench
         9. Leaves firm, 1 to 1¼ inches long, midrib yellow (fig. 31)...................... **C. Margaretta** Ashe
      8. Margins of calyx lobes glandless.
         10. Thorns up to 1 inch long; midrib yellow below............................. **C. viridis** L.
         10. Thorns 1 to 1½ inches long; midrib red below.................. **C. nitida** (Engelm.) Sarg.

B. Leaf widest toward the base.
   D. Calyx lobes entire; leaves relatively small.
      11. Leaves glabrous above, blue green; fruit hard and covered with bloom.
         12. Fruit green until nearly ripe (fig. 32)............................... **C. pruinosa** (Wendl.) K. Koch
         12. Fruit orange red, green blotched, dark dotted .... **C. conjuncta** Sarg.
      11. Leaves pubescent or scabrous above; fruit soft and without bloom.
         13. Leaf teeth tipped with bright red glands.................................... **C. lucorum** Sarg.
         13. Leaf teeth lacking such glands.
            14. Fruit subglobose.
               15. Fruit reddish purple, pale dotted.................................. **C. cyanophylla** Sarg.
               15. Fruit scarlet, not conspicuously dotted .... **C. sextilis** Sarg.
            14. Fruit obovoid, bright reddish purple .... **C. apiomorpha** Sarg.
   D. Calyx lobes toothed; leaves larger (1 to 4 inches long).
      16. Mature leaves glabrous.
         17. Calyx not enlarged on the fruit.

FIG. 32
Crataegus mollis
Crataegus pruinosa Crataegus Phaenopyrum

18. Thorns 1 to 1½ inches long; midrib yellow ....**C. assurgens** Sarg.
18. Thorns up to 2½ inches long.
19. Midrib greenish; petioles up to 1½ inches long; fruit obovoid, crimson, pale dotted ....**C. Hillii** Sarg.
19. Midrib yellow; petioles 1½ to 3 inches long; fruit subglobose, bright red, pale dotted ....**C. sertata** Sarg.
17. Calyx much enlarged on the fruit....... ....**C. coccinioides** Ashe
16. Mature leaves pubescent or tementose below (fig. 32).....................**C. mollis** (T. & G.) Scheele
A. Leaf veins extending both to lobe points and to sinuses.
E. Leaves triangular-ovate; sepals deciduous (fig. 32) ....**C. Phaenopyrum** (L. f.) Med.
E. Leaf bases cuneate; sepals persistent.
20. Leaves with 3 to 5 short, broad, serrulate lobes ....**C. Oxyacantha** L.
20. Leaves with 3 to 7 long, narrow, entire lobes ....**C. monogyna** Jacq.

AMYGDALACEAE

The Plum Family

The plum family consists of trees or shrubs which bear alernate, simple leaves, deciduous stipules and, in the American pecies, perfect flowers that have 5 sepals, 5 petals and 10 or nore stamens. The pistils are usually solitary and develop into single-seeded fruit known as a drupe, of which the plum is ypical.

The family is widely distributed in the north temperate zone nd contains some 120 species, divided into about 10 genera. Among the important species are the edible and cultivated lums, the peach, the apricot and the cherries. The family is epresented in Illinois by both native tree and shrub forms.

PRUNUS (Tournefort) Linnaeus

Plums and Cherries

These are shrubs or trees with alternate, deciduous leaves vhich usually are toothed on the margin and can be definitely ecognized by the presence of glands on the petioles near the ase of the leaf blades. The flowers, which are perfect, are olitary, umbellate, or in corymbs at the end of leafy branches, or arise from scaly, lateral buds. There are 5 sepals, 5 petal and 15 to 30 stamens with distinct, filiform filaments. Th drupe has a fleshy covering, is often white with bloom, an contains within its pulp a bony, smooth stone which incloses th seed.

Key to the Shrubby Species

Flowers produced in umbel-like clusters, appearing before or with the leaves on branchlets produced the preceding year.
 Leaves mostly lanceolate and folded together; calyx lobes ciliate; fruit red when ripe........... **P. angustifolia,** p. 14
 Leaves mostly oblanceolate and flat; calyx lobes not ciliate; fruit black when ripe..................... **P. pumila,** p. 14
Flowers produced in racemes, appearing after the leaves on branchlets of the present year............ **P. virginiana,** p. 14

PRUNUS ANGUSTIFOLIA Marshall

Chickasaw Plum

The Chickasaw Plum, fig. 33, is an erect, bushy shrub ofte 12 or more feet high, with stems as much as 2½ inches in d ameter. The branches are many, usually crooked or zigza and some of the shorter ones tend to become thornlike. Th branchlets are slender, glabrous and reddish, and bear lance late to oblong-lanceolate leaves, some or all of which have th upper surface folded together. These leaves are 1 to 2½ inch long by ¼ to ¾ inch wide, acute at the apex, and narrowe or rounded at the base. The margins are finely and minute glandular-serrate, and the blade is glossy and smooth abov but paler and smooth beneath or pubescent beneath along th midrib. The petioles, which are variable in length but shor are pubescent above and generally bear 2 glands near the bas of the leaf blade.

The flowers, which appear before or with the leaves in Ma stand in umbels of 2 to 4 on smooth pedicels ⅛ to ¼ inch lon They are white and a little less than ¼ inch wide. The caly lobes are oblong, obtuse, and entire but ciliate on the margin The petals are obovate. The fruit, which ripens the latter pa of June or early in July, is bright red, not covered by bloom, globose, and about ¼ inch in diameter. Its pulp clings to th stone, which is round, and roughened on the surface.

Distribution.—The Chickasaw Plum is a shrub we adapted to poor soil, especially clay and sand, and grows fro

FIG. 33

Prunus virginiana

Prunus angustifolia

Prunus pumila

Delaware to Florida and west to Texas and Nebraska. It has been widely cultivated for its fruit. In Illinois, it is reported by numerous collections from the southern half of the state but there is no record of it in northern Illinois elsewhere than at Castle Rock.

PRUNUS PUMILA Linnaeus

Sand Cherry

The Sand Cherry, fig. 33, is an erect shrub, generally 2 to 9 feet high, with characteristically nearly erect leaves, bark resembling that of a cultivated cherry tree, and strongly angled reddish-brown to gray branches. The branchlets, green and glabrous at first, become reddish brown by the end of the season. The leaves are mostly oblanceolate or spatulate, and usually 1¼ to 2½ inches long by ¼ to ¾ inch wide, though often larger on vigorous shoots and seedlings. The blade is acute at the apex or, rarely, bluntly rounded, and is long tapered to the petiole at the base. The margins are serrate with short gland-tipped teeth to somewhat below the middle of the leaf, often farther down on one side than the other, and the surface is smooth above and beneath and much paler beneath. The petioles, which are ⅛ to ¼ inch long, generally have 1 or 2 glands near the base of the leaf blade. The stipules, which are soon lost, are linear and glandular-serrate.

The white flowers appear before or with the leaves in late May, generally 2 or 3 together, rarely 4, in sessile umbels. The calyx is glabrous, and the calyx lobes are very short, obtuse, and glandular-serrate on the margins, which usually are rose colored. The obovate or ovate petals are about one-sixteenth inch long. Fruit begins to ripen in late July and is mature shortly after the middle of August. For the most part it is nearly globose and a little over ¼ inch in diameter, or it may be somewhat elongated and about ¼ inch wide and ⅜ inch long. When ripe, it is black and not bloom covered, is purplish red, juicy, and tasty. The stone is ovoid to oblong, rounded at one or both ends, or sometimes pointed at both ends, and has a definite, narrow ridge on the back. Its surface is marked with slanting grooves which point outward from the dorsal groove.

DISTRIBUTION.—The Sand Cherry prefers sandy situations, where it may grow alone or in association with other shrubs and trees. Where the habitat is favorable, it may be found from New Brunswick west to Manitoba and south to Pennsylvania, Indiana and Illinois. In Illinois, it has been widely collected from the sandy regions in Cook and Lake counties, occasionally in Kankakee County, and near Oregon, where dry sand from sandstone rocks favors its growth. Forms with broad leaves are segregated as var. *susquehanae* (Willdenow) Jaeger.

PRUNUS VIRGINIANA Linnaeus

Chokecherry Common Chokecherry

The Chokecherry, fig. 33, is a small or large, erect shrub up to 18 feet high, with stems as much as 3 inches in diameter and smooth, reddish-brown branches and greenish branchlets which turn reddish brown. Its oval to obovate leaves with blades up to 3 inches long and 1¾ inches wide are narrowly acute and short pointed at the apex, and narrowed, rounded, or subcordate at the base. The margins are sharply serrate or often doubly serrate, and the surface is smooth above, and smooth but definitely paler beneath or with pubescence along the midrib or in the axils of the principal veins. The petioles, which are ¼ to nearly ½ inch long, generally bear 2 glands near the base of the blade.

The flowers, which appear from early May to early June, occur in terminal racemes arising from short, lateral branchlets of the season. These racemes, which have glabrous stalks, are from 1¾ to 3 inches long and each has about 25 white flowers, which are less than ¼ inch wide. The calyx lobes are deciduous, cut along the edges, and mostly tipped with glands. The fruit, which begins to ripen during the last of August, is at maturity nearly black, globose, and ⅛ to ¼ inch in diameter. The stone within is smooth and varies from oblong-ovoid to nearly orbicular. It is slightly compressed laterally and the dorsal suture is broad, while the ventral one is acute.

Distribution.—The Chokecherry is a northern shrub which is distributed from Labrador to Hudson Bay and south to North Carolina, Kentucky and Kansas. It prefers moist, alluvial soil along lakes and streams but may occasionally occur along roadsides and fences. In Illinois, though by no means a common shrub, it is widely distributed over the northern half of the state and is especially abundant in the northeastern corner. Southward it becomes rare, and has not been reported south of Jefferson and St. Clair counties.

Forms of this cherry which occur in the northeastern part of the state, especially on the sand near Lake Michigan, are referred to the variety *demissa* (Nuttall) Torrey, which differs in having the underside of the leaves woolly-pubescent and the leaf blades more or less cordate at the base. Also, the branchlets are puberulent and the rachis and pedicels of the inflorescence are pubescent.

LEGUMINOSAE

The Pea Family

The pea family includes herbs, vines, shrubs and trees, all of which bear alternate and for the most part compound, stipulate leaves and irregular but mostly perfect flowers in spikes, heads, racemes or panicles. The calyx in this family is 4- to 5-toothed or 4- to 5-cleft, the lobes being either equal or unequal and sometimes 2-lipped. The petals are more or less united and usually consist of a broad upper one, called the standard or banner, 2 lateral ones, known as wings, and 2 front ones which are more or less united to form the keel. The stamens may be monodelphous, diadelphous or sometimes separate. In most genera there are 10; sometimes there are 9, and rarely there are only 5. The pistil is simple and generally there is only 1 per flower. The ovary is superior and for the most part 1-celled, and the style is simple and unbranched. The fruit, commonly known as a legume, is a 1- to many-seeded pod which opens by 2 valves.

There are over 300 genera and more than 10,000 species in this family. They are most abundant in temperate and warm regions and include a large number of commercially important plants. Although many species of herbs and several trees native in Illinois belong to this family, only two of the native genera are represented by shrubby species. These shrubs are all plants of special habitats, and each occurs only where favorable habitats exist in the state. The local variation in characteristics has given rise to varietal names not recognized below.

Key to the Shrubby Genera

Upright shrubs with glandular-punctate leaves . . . **Amorpha**, p. 145

Twining vines; leaves not glandular-punctate . . . . . **Wisteria**, p. 146

AMORPHA Linnaeus

False-Indigo Shoestrings

The false-indigos are shrubs with alternate, odd-pinnate leaves, which are also glandular-punctate. The flowers are perfect but incomplete and are borne in spikelike racemes. The calyx has 5 lobes and is short, and the blue, purple or white corolla lacks wings and keel. The banner is erect, clawed, and folded around the 10 stamens, the filaments of which are united at the base only. The ovary develops into a short, 1- to 2-seeded, nearly indehiscent pod.

The false-indigos are limited in their distribution to North America and Mexico. There are about 15 species, of which only 2 occur in Illinois as shrubs.

Key to the False-Indigo Species

Tall shrubs, reaching a height of 3 to 12 feet; leaflets ¾ to 1½ inches long . . . . **A. fruticosa**

Low shrubs, generally less than 3 feet high; leaflets mostly less than ¾ inch long . . . . **A. canescens**

AMORPHA FRUTICOSA Linnaeus

Indigobush False-Indigo

The Indigobush, fig. 34, is an erect shrub with gray or brown bark and greenish branchlets, which become glabrous, or nearly so, and light brown by autumn. The leaves are generally 8 to 12 inches long. They stand on petioles ¼ to ¾ inch long and consist as a rule of 9 to 25 entire-margined leaflets which are set in opposite or nearly opposite pairs well separated along the rachis on stalks less than ⅛ inch long. The leaflets are ½ to 1½ inches long, oval or oblong, rounded or narrowed at the base, and rounded and emarginate but mucronate at the tip. At maturity, the surface is more or less pubescent on both sides and is glandular-dotted beneath.

The inflorescences, clusters of spikelike racemes, are borne near the end of the branches. Sometimes the spikes are solitary. The flowers, which open in May or June, are numerous, violet-purple, and about ¼ inch long. The fruit is a glabrous, glandular pod generally ¼ inch long or a little more, which usually contains 2 seeds.

Distribution.—The Indigobush prefers well-drained alluvial soil along streams and in such situations grows from southern Pennsylvania northwestward to Saskatchewan and south to Florida and northern Mexico. In Illinois, it is exceedingly rare, although widely distributed. There are records of it from Winnebago County in the extreme north, Calhoun County in the west, and Pope County in the southeast.

AMORPHA CANESCENS Nuttall

Leadplant

The Leadplant, fig. 34, is a densely white-canescent, erect shrub usually 2 to 3 feet high, without side branches. The leaves, which are 2 to 5 inches long, stand on very short petioles and consist of 21 to 49 nearly sessile leaflets, which are crowded on the rachis in opposite or nearly opposite pairs. The leaflet is ¼ to about ½ inch in length, oval, lanceolate, or oblong, rounded or truncate at the base, and obtuse or acute and mucronate at the apex. The margin is entire. The surface is appressed-pubescent above and woolly-pubescent beneath. The inflorescence consists of a terminal cluster of many-flowered spikes. The flowers appear in June or July and are small and purplish blue. The fruit is a 1-seeded, densely hairy pod about ⅛ inch long.

Distribution.—The Leadplant prefers sandy situations on knolls and ridges and dry places in prairies, especially when they are located in the open. In such situations it ranges from northern Indiana to Manitoba and south to Louisiana and New Mexico. In Illinois, it is widely distributed and abundant throughout the northern half of the state but distinctly localized, because of its definite habitat limitation.

WISTERIA Nuttall

The Wisterias

The wisterias are long, climbing vines that bear alternate odd-pinnately compound leaves, which are subtended by stipules and bear alternate leaflets. The flowers are showy, colored and borne in large terminal racemes. The calyx is somewhat 2-lipped, the upper lobe shorter than the 3 lower ones, and the standard of the corolla is large, reflexed, and clawed, while the wings are oblong and eared at the base. The keel is curved

FIG. 34
Wisteria macrostachya
Amorpha canescens
Amorpha fruticosa

inward and obtuse. The stamens are arranged in 2 groups and the ovary develops into an elongated, leathery pod containing several seeds.

There are seven species of wisteria native in Asia and two native in North America. Only the following occurs in Illinois as a woody vine.

WISTERIA MACROSTACHYA Nuttall

Wisteria

The Wisteria, fig. 34, is a slender, climbing vine with long stems, sometimes 20 to 25 feet in length, bearing sparingly pubescent young branches, which soon become glabrous, and alternate, pinnately compound leaves composed usually of 9 leaflets set alternately but more or less definitely in pairs along the rachis. The leaflets are ovate to elliptic, 1 to 2¾ inches long, acuminate at the tip, and rounded to almost cordate at the base. The margins are smooth and the surface, although pubescent at first, becomes glabrous with maturity or remains only sparingly pubescent.

The lilac to purple, showy flowers are borne in dense racemes 8 to 12 inches long, which, although terminal, are loosely flowered and drooping. Both rachis and lower pedicel are hairy and glandular with cup-shaped glands. The bell-shaped, pubescent calyx has lower teeth at least half as long as the tube. The standard of the corolla is not prominently eared but the wings bear an awl-shaped spur at the base about as long as the claw. The flowers are in blossom from July to August, and the fruit, which ripens in fall, is an elongated pod 2 to 4 inches long, which is narrowed between the seeds and contains several black, shining seeds.

Distribution.—This wisteria is an inhabitant of swampy woods and ranges from southern Illinois to Louisiana and Texas. In Illinois, it is limited to a very small portion of the southern part of the state, not extending north beyond the Ozarks at any point. It has thus far been recorded in Pope, Pulaski and Alexander counties only, in one instance as a fence climber, but elsewhere only as a climbing vine in the rich bottomland forests along the southern rivers. Early reports of *Wisteria frutescens* (Linnaeus) Poiret in Washington and other southern counties are undoubtedly referable to this species.

RUTACEAE

The Rue Family

The rue family consists of trees or shrubs, which are made romatic by secreting glands in the foliage. The leaves are for ie most part digitately or pinnately compound, and the leaflets re not equilateral. The flowers are perfect and polygamous or ioecious. The calyx consists usually of 3 to 5 lobes or sepals, hich rarely may be wanting, and there are 3 to 5 petals. The tamens may be either the same number as the petals or twice s many, and the ovary consists of 1 to 5 or more free or united arpels. The fruit is variable and may be a follicle, a capsule, samara or a drupe.

This large family of more than 100 genera and nearly 1,000 pecies occurs most abundantly in South Africa and Australia. ts 2 North American shrubby genera are both native in Illinois.

Key to the Shrubby Genera

hrubs armed with spines, the leaflets more than 3 .... **Zanthoxylum**

hrubs not armed with spines, the leaflets 3 per leaf .... **Ptelea**

ZANTHOXYLUM Linnaeus

Prickly-Ash

The prickly-ashes are shrubs or trees, usually prickly and vith aromatic bark, that bear alternate, usually pinnate leaves ften provided with stipular prickles. The flowers are mostly in ymes or panicles and are perfect and dioecious or polygamous. The sepals may be 3 to 5, or sometimes wanting, and usually re more or less united. There are 3 to 10 petals and 3 to 5 tamens. The pistils, which are only rudimentary in staminate lowers, number 1 to 5 and develop into 1-celled and usually -seeded follicles. The seeds are oblong, black, and shiny.

Among about 150 species, which are natives of temperate nd near-tropical regions, only 4 occur within the boundaries f the United States and only 1 in Illinois.

ZANTHOXYLUM AMERICANUM Miller

Prickly-Ash Toothache-Tree

The Prickly-Ash, fig. 35, is a much-branched, upright shrub generally 4½ to 10 but sometimes as much as 18 feet high, with

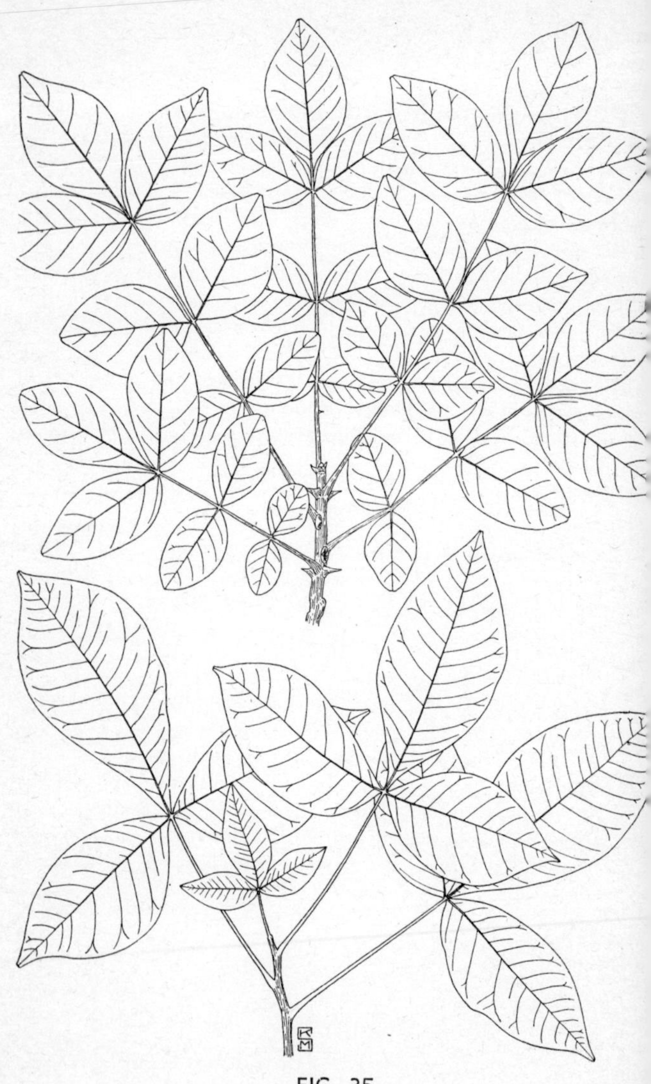

FIG. 35
Zanthoxylum americanum
Ptelea trifoliata

mooth, gray or brownish bark and smooth branches and ranchlets armed, at the base of each leaf, with a pair of traight, sharp spines, which are persistent and much flattened t the base. The odd-pinnate leaves, which are 3 to 10 inches ong, consist of 5 to 11 leaflets set oppositely in pairs along the achis on very short stalks. The narrowly to broadly ovate eaflets, ¾ to 3 inches long and ½ to 1¾ inches wide, taper radually to the apex, where they are obtuse and notched, but t the base they are oblique and either narrowed or rounded. The margin is entire or crenulate, and the surface, pubescent t first, becomes smooth or nearly so above and remains pu-escent beneath. The petiole and rachis are sometimes prickly.

The flowers, which appear before the leaves, stand in small, xillary clusters on the branches of the previous season. They re dioecious and small, the staminate being about one-six-eenth inch in diameter. The fruit, which matures in August nd September, is a reddish, globose or ellipsoid, 1-seeded cap-ule about ⅛ inch long, with a pitted surface. It is strongly romatic, and the seeds are black and shining.

Distribution.—The Prickly-Ash is a shrub which prefers ow woods, especially those growing on flood plains and along anks of streams. In such situations it is distributed from Que-ec and Ontario to North Dakota and south to Georgia and Oklahoma. In Illinois, it is a widely distributed and frequently bserved shrub throughout the northern two-thirds of the tate, but southward it is seldom or rarely encountered. The nost southern Illinois records are Tunnel Hill in Johnson County and Murphysboro in Jackson County.

PTELEA Linnaeus

Hop-Tree Shrubby Trefoil

The hop-trees are unarmed shrubs or trees with alternate r, rarely, opposite, 3-foliate leaves, the leaflets of which are ntire or toothed and translucently dotted. The polygamous owers are produced in corymbose or paniculate cymes and ear 4, 5 or, rarely, 6 sepals and the same number of greenish r yellowish-white petals. There are 4, 5 or, rarely, 6 stamens, which are imperfect in the pistillate flowers. The ovary con-ists of 2 or 3 united carpels, and the fruit is a 2-celled or, arely, 3-celled samara with reticulated wings.

There are only three species of hop-tree, all natives of th United States and Mexico. Only one of them occurs in Illinoi

PTELEA TRIFOLIATA Linnaeus

Wafer Ash Hop-Tree

The Wafer Ash, fig. 35, is an erect, sometimes treelik shrub 5 to 15 feet tall, with smooth, gray or grayish-brow bark, which may be roughened on old specimens, light to me dium brown branches and branchlets, and small, 3-foliate, ash like, compound leaves, which stand on petioles 2½ to 4 inche long. The leaflets are sessile or nearly so and are variable i size and shape. They are ovate to oblong-lanceolate, on fruit ing branches 1¾ to 6 inches long, and on sterile shoots ofte somewhat larger. Lateral leaflets are about two-thirds a large as the terminal one, and all are somewhat inequilatera the lateral ones the more noticeably so. They are short-acum nate and gradually tapered to blunt and often distinctl notched tips and are oblique and narrowed to rounded at th base. The margins, though usually entire, may be undulate o coarsely serrate. The leaf surface at maturity is smooth an shining above and pale and smooth below, and both surface are sprinkled with black dots.

The numerous, small, greenish flowers, which appear i June and early July after the leaves are almost full grown, ar borne in panicled cymes. The fruit, which matures in Augus and September, is a colorless samara about ½ to 1 inch long usually circular but sometimes oval in outline, with a rounde or notched apex and a rounded, subcordate, or sometime somewhat narrowed base. Both of its faces are strongly an coarsely reticulated, and the spaces between veins are sprinkle with resinous glands. The body of the samara is oblong an situated near its center.

DISTRIBUTION.—The Wafer Ash, a shrub of limestone bluff and black alluvial soils along streams, occurs from Connecticu and southern Ontario westward to Wisconsin and south t Florida and northern Mexico. It grows throughout the stat of Illinois, wherever suitable habitats occur.

Individuals with leaflets remaining hairy are segregated a form *pubescens* (Pursh) Fernald; shrubs of wider growth habi and pubescent branchlets as var. *Deamiana* Nieuwland.

INDIGOBUSH *Amorpha fruticosa* Linnaeus

SMOOTH SUMAC *Rhus glabra* Linnaeus

ANACARDIACEAE

The Sumac Family

The sumacs, shrubs or trees with alternate, simple or pinately compound leaves without stipules, bear polygamous, ıonoecious or dioecious flowers in panicles, spikes or racemes. 'he flowers are regular and have 3 to 5 distinct sepals, 3 to 5 etals, and 3 to 5 stamens alternate with the petals. The ovary onsists of 4 to 5 united or nearly distinct carpels, and the yles are likewise either united or distinct. The fruit is a drupe r berry which contains a solitary seed.

There are about 60 genera and 3,000 species in this family. 'hese are most abundant in warm or tropical regions, but the ange of a few extends into the temperate zone. Three genera re native in northeastern North America, but only one grows Illinois.

RHUS (Tournefort) Linnaeus

The Sumacs

The sumacs are shrubs, trees or vines, some poisonous and me not, with alternate, odd-pinnate leaves, which may be enre or toothed. The greenish-white or yellow flowers are lygamous or dioecious and occur in terminal panicles. Sepals, tals and stamens commonly are 5 in number. The ovary is celled, and the fruit is a small drupe containing a smooth one.

Key to the Sumac Species

aflets 3 per leaf.
- Petioles of the leaves generally less than 1¼ inches long, the fruit red and densely hairy......... **R. aromatica**, p. 159
- Petioles generally more than 1¼ inches long, the fruit pale green and usually smooth............... **R. radicans**, p. 159

aflets more than 3 per leaf.
- Branchlets pubescent.
  - Rachis of the leaf winged, leaflets almost entire but sometimes with a few coarse teeth......... **R. copallina**, p. 154
  - Rachis of the leaf not winged, leaflets regularly serrate to the base......................... **R. typhina**, p. 154
- Branchlets smooth.
  - Branchlets angled, leaves serrate, fruit red... **R. glabra**, p. 156
  - Branchlets round, leaves entire or nearly so, fruit pale green to almost colorless................ **R. vernix**, p. 158

RHUS COPALLINA Linnaeus

Shining Sumac

The Shining Sumac, fig. 36, is an erect shrub generally 4 t 7 feet high, with densely short-pubescent branchlets and leave 6 to 18 inches long on long petioles. Both the petiole and th rachis are more or less pubescent, and the rachis is definitel winged between the leaflets. There are, as a rule, 7 to 15 leaf lets per leaf. These are ovate-lanceolate or oblong-lanceolate and usually 1¼ inches to 4½ inches long by ½ to 1¼ inche wide. They are unequilateral at the base, and the lateral ones which are sometimes falcate, are sessile or nearly so, and some what smaller than the terminal leaflet. The leaflet blades ar acute to short- or long-acuminate and oblique and narrowed o rounded at the base, with margins entire or with a few coars teeth. The leaf surface is smooth or nearly so above except o the midvein, where it is densely pubescent, and it is more o less pubescent beneath.

The inflorescence is a terminal panicle 4 to 8 inches long which appears in flower in July and August. The flowers ar greenish yellow or sometimes pinkish, and the margins of th petals are more or less glandular-ciliate. The fruit, which ma tures in September or October, is somewhat asymmetricall spherical in shape, about ⅛ inch in diameter, red, and densel covered with hairs and short-stalked or sessile glands. Th smooth seeds are brown and quite small.

Distribution.—The Shining Sumac, a shrub of dry, sand soil, prefers open places such as abandoned fields, borders c woodlands, and fence rows. In such situations it grows fro New England westward to Michigan and south to Florida an Texas. It ranges throughout the length and breadth of Ill nois but is not, of course, to be expected in purely prair regions.

RHUS TYPHINA Linnaeus

Staghorn Sumac

The Staghorn Sumac, fig. 36, is an erect shrub, sometimes small tree, 5 to 18 feet tall, with densely velvety pubesce branchlets, and compound leaves 8 to 24 inches long on lon petioles. The leaflets, of which there are 11 to 25 per leaf, a

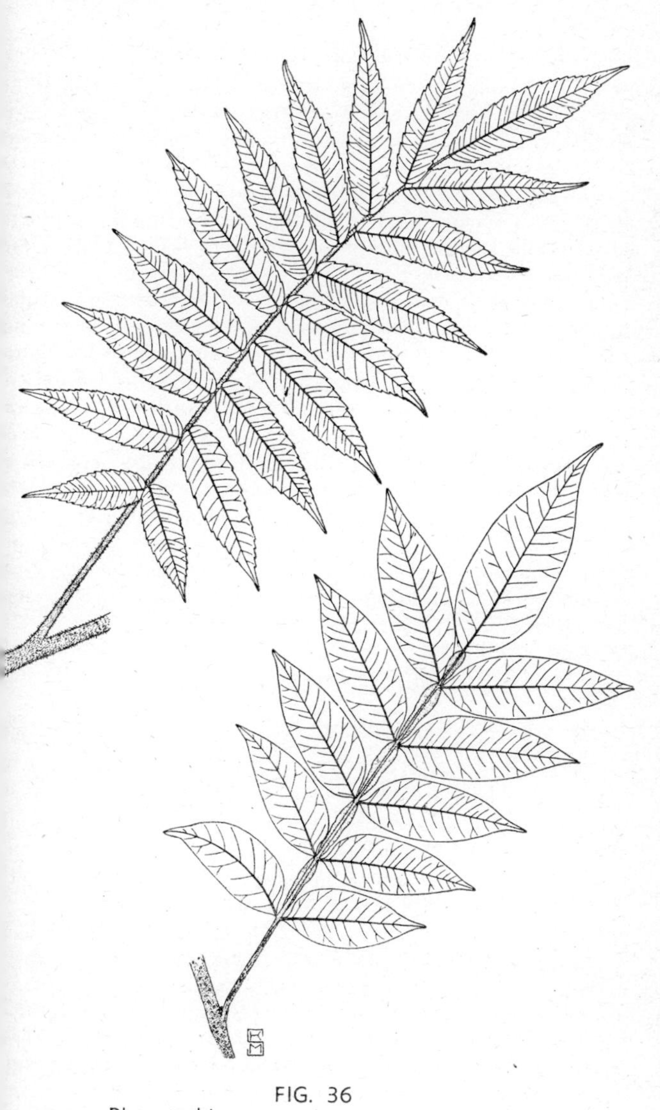

FIG. 36

Rhus typhina

Rhus copallina

sessile, oblong to linear-oblong, often falcate, 1¼ to 5 inche
long, and up to 1¼ inches wide. They are narrowed or rounde
at the base and acuminate at the apex, and their margins ar
finely or coarsely serrate. At maturity they are dark green an
smooth above, or nearly so beneath, except on the midrib an
the main vein.

The inflorescence is a dense, terminal panicle up to 12 inche
long, which comes into flower in June and July. The flower
are greenish yellow, those bearing stamens being about ⅛ inc
in diameter, and the margins of the petals are not glandula
ciliate. The fruit matures in August and September as a smal
bright red drupe densely covered with long red hairs; an
the light brown, slightly flattened seed is smooth and oblique

DISTRIBUTION.—The Staghorn Sumac prefers sandy
gravelly ridges and slopes or bluffs, and sometimes it grows
moist situations about lakes and bogs. It ranges from Ne
Brunswick to North Dakota and south to Georgia and Missi
sippi. In Illinois, it is widely distributed throughout the nort
ern part of the state, being especially abundant in the nort
east in the vicinity of Lake Michigan. Elsewhere it is rare ar
local, and has been recorded at Starved Rock in La Sal
County, in Morgan County, Cass County, Hancock Coun
and along bluffs of the Apple River in Jo Daviess County.

RHUS GLABRA Linnaeus

Smooth Sumac

The Smooth Sumac, fig. 37, is an upright shrub commo
4 to 12 feet high, with branchlets which are, by the end of t
year, more or less keeled below the buds and with compou
leaves 12 to 20 inches long. The leaf rachis is smooth, exce
for a pubescent line above, and the leaflets generally numb
15 to 25. The lateral leaflets are sessile or nearly so, and t
terminal ones are short-stalked. The blades are oblong-ova
to lanceolate-oblong, 2 to 4 inches long by ½ to 1¼ inch
wide, and acuminate at the apex. Terminal leaflets are na
rowed or rounded at the base; lateral leaflets are oblique a
rounded at the base. The margins are rather coarsely serra
and the leaf surface is green and smooth above, except alo
the midvein, and smooth and glaucous beneath.

The inflorescence is a large, terminal, pubescent panicle, a

FIG. 37

Rhus glabra

Rhus vernix

the flowers, which appear in June or July, are greenish yellov
The fruit matures from late August into October, and
slightly flattened, asymmetrically globose, bright red, dense
covered with short, sticky hairs, and sour. The smooth seec
are small, ash colored or light brown, and somewhat wide
than long.

DISTRIBUTION.—The Smooth Sumac grows in dry, sandy
gravelly soil and ranges from Nova Scotia west to North D
kota and south to Florida and Louisiana. It often grows
colonies in open places, on sandy or gravelly ridges, along t
borders of woods, and on fence rows. It is distributed throug
out the state of Illinois.

RHUS VERNIX Linnaeus

Poison Sumac Swamp Sumac Poison Elder

The Poison Sumac, fig. 37, is an erect shrub, or sometimes
small tree, with a widely spreading crown of smooth branch
and branchlets bearing compound leaves 6 to 14 inches lon
The leaf rachis is smooth or nearly so, and the leaflets, of whi
there are 7 to 13, vary greatly in shape and size on the sar
leaf, being obovate-oblong to oval, and 1½ to 4½ inches long
¾ to 2 inches wide. They taper abruptly to a blunt point a
also taper to the petiole. They may be nearly sessile or sta
on short stalks, the terminal leaflets being longer stalked, as
rule, than the others. The margins are entire or somewh
undulating, and at maturity the leaves are dark green a
smooth above; when young they are pubescent but soon becor
smooth or nearly so beneath.

The inflorescence takes the form of an axillary panicle. T
flowers open in June and are greenish yellow. The fruit, whi
matures in August and September, is pale green to almost colc
less and slightly flattened to somewhat asymmetrically globo
The flat, depressed seeds are deeply grooved along the sides a
have about 4 ridges on a side.

DISTRIBUTION.—The Poison Sumac is a shrub that grows
low ground about lakes and tamarack bogs. In such situatic
it ranges from northern New England to Minnesota and sou
to Florida and Texas. In Illinois, it is known only in t
tamarack bogs of Lake County.

Poison Sumac is the most poisonous shrub in Illinois.

oisonous principle is the same as that carried by Poison Ivy, ıt the effect is reputed to be much more severe.

RHUS AROMATICA Aiton

Fragrant Sumac

The Fragrant Sumac, fig. 38, is a low, spreading shrub about feet high or, rarely, an erect shrub up to 12 feet high, with nooth or pubescent branchlets, compound leaves 2 to 5 inches ng, and petioles from ½ to 1¼ inches long. There are 3 vate to rhombic leaflets per leaf, the lateral 2 sessile, the rminal on a short stalk. The terminal leaflet is 1¼ to 3¾ ches long and about ¾ to 2½ inches wide, and the lateral aflets are about three-fourths as large. The blades are acute rounded at the apex, the terminal one narrowed at the base ıd the lateral ones either narrowed or rounded and asymetrical at the base. The margin is closely crenate-dentate, ıd the surface is pubescent both above and beneath, or somenes glabrous.

The inflorescences are in the form of short, crowded, axillary ikes borne on year-old branchlets. The greenish-yellow flowers en, as a rule, before the leaves appear. The fruit, which atures from July on into September, is red, densely hairy, obose, and small, and contains a light brown, slightly flatned, asymmetrical seed.

Distribution.—The Fragrant Sumac prefers ridges and cky bluffs along streams and ravines, where open situations vor its growth. In such habitats, it is distributed from estern Vermont to Minnesota and south to Florida and ouisiana. It grows in suitable situations throughout Illinois. 'hen erect and with leaflets rounded to obtuse at the apex, ore densely pubescent beneath than above, and provided with wer, rounded teeth, shrubs of this species are segregated as r. *illinoensis* (Greene) Rehder.

Toxicodendron

~~RHUS~~ RADICANS Linnaeus

Poison Ivy   Three-Leaved Ivy   Poison Oak

Poison Ivy, fig. 38, is a trailing shrub or climbing vine which ails by underground stems or climbs by aerial rootlets. Its anches are more or less striate and pubescent. The com-

FIG. 38

Rhus radicans Rhus aromatica

pound, 3-foliate leaves are variable in size, shape, texture and pubescence, being generally 6 to 14 inches long and on petioles up to 6 inches long. The blades are ovate to rhombic, and acuminate or short-acuminate at the apex, the lateral ones on short stalks, the terminal one on a definitely longer stalk. The terminal leaflet is rounded at the base or sometimes narrowed; the lateral ones are asymmetrical and oblique, although more or less rounded, at the base; and the margins are either entire or provided with 1 to several coarse teeth. Rarely, the leaflets are lobed. The surfaces are pubescent on unfolding but become glabrous in varying degrees at maturity, remaining pubescent at least on the principal veins.

The greenish flowers appear in loose axillary panicles from he last of May on into June. The fruit, which matures from he last of August on through October, is somewhat flattened-globose, pale green to almost colorless, and usually smooth, though sometimes more or less densely covered with hairs; and ne flattened small seed has a groove near the middle across he shortest diameter.

Distribution.—Poison Ivy is well adapted to almost any ind of habitat and is becoming increasingly common through-ut its range, which extends from Nova Scotia to British Columbia and south to Florida and Mexico. In Illinois, it is n expected and generally abundant vine of deep woods, as well as a common and troublesome weed of roadsides and other waste places.

Persons who suspect, or know, they are susceptible to ivy poisoning should become familiar enough with this plant to e able to avoid it. The white lac in the leaves, stems and ruit contains a poisonous principle known as toxicodendrol, hich causes severe inflammation of the skin. But poisoning ten can be prevented by washing the skin thoroughly with ap and water after exposure. A vanishing cream containing dium perborate is said to give protection if applied to the skin fore it is exposed to the poison.

AQUIFOLIACEAE

The Holly Family

The holly family consists of shrubs or trees with alternate, ten evergreen, leaves without stipules. The flowers are perfect, dioecious or polygamous, and usually are produced i cymes. They are made up of 4 to 6 sepals, which are persisten the same number of deciduous petals, and stamens alternat with the petals. The ovary is compound, consisting of 2 to carpels, and the stigma is usually sessile on the ovary. Th fruit is a drupe with horny or crusty nutlets.

There are only 3 genera but some 300 species in this famil all native in temperate and tropical regions. Two of the gener occur in North America and both are represented by nativ shrubs in Illinois.

Key to the Shrubby Genera

Leaves serrate; petals united at the base; fruit pedicels usually about ¼ inch long .... **Ilex**, p. 16

Leaf margins entire or, rarely, with a few teeth; petals not at all united; fruit pedicels more than ¼ inch long .... **Nemopanthus**, p. 1

ILEX Linnaeus

Holly Winterberry

The hollies are usually glabrous shrubs or small trees wi dioecious flowers. Staminate flowers occur in axillary cluster and pistillate flowers are solitary. The sepals, petals and st mens number 4 to 6, and the petals are united at the bas The fruit is a nearly globose drupe with 4 to 6 or, rarel 7 or 8 nutlets.

There are about 200 species of holly, most of them Americ but some Asian and Australian. About 15 occur in the Unit States, and the 2 following are native in Illinois.

Key to the Holly Species

Lobes of the calyx not ciliate, the nutlets ribbed .... **I. decid**

Lobes of the calyx ciliate, nutlets not ribbed .... **I. verticilla**

ILEX DECIDUA Walter

Possumhaw Swamp Holly

The Possumhaw, fig. 39, is an upright shrub, or less oft a small tree, with gray bark made warty by corky lentice The branches are light gray and the smooth branchlets so become light gray. The leaves, which are borne in crowd groups on the ends of short branchlets, or may be separat

FIG. 39
Nemopanthus mucronata
Ilex decidua Ilex verticillata

on vigorous branchlets, are firm, rather widely to narrowly lanceolate, and 1¾ to 4 inches long by about ¾ to 1½ inches wide. The apex is bluntly acute and the blade usually is tapered from below the middle to the petiole, the margin being crenulate or crenulate-serrate. The blade is smooth above and more or less pubescent beneath, especially on the main veins, and the short petiole is grooved and pubescent above.

The flowers are of two sorts. Those having stamens are borne on pedicels about ⅛ to ¼ inch long, generally in clusters of 3 to 12. Those having pistils stand on shorter pedicels and are solitary or in pairs. The calyx lobes are triangular, blunt and not glandular-ciliate. The fruit, which matures in September and October, is globose, nearly one-third inch in diameter, red, and contains 3 to 4 nutlets, which are moon shaped bony, and ribbed longitudinally.

Distribution. — The Possumhaw prefers the borders o sloughs and bogs and usually grows in swamps and low woods. In such habitats it is scattered from Virginia wes to Illinois and southern Missouri and south to Florida an Texas. In Illinois, its distribution follows chiefly the valley of the Wabash, Ohio and Mississippi rivers, beginning, on th eastern side of the state, at Edwards and Wabash countie and extending south around the lower part of the state an north again to the southern tip of Calhoun County. It is however, reported at an altitude of 900 feet in the Ozark in Union County, and there is an isolated report of its occurrence in La Salle County along the Illinois River.

ILEX VERTICILLATA (Linnaeus) Gray

Common Winterberry

The Common Winterberry, fig. 39, is an erect shrub 5 to 1 feet high, with smooth bark roughened by warty lenticels an with gray to reddish-brown branches. The branchlets ar smooth, and the oval-lanceolate to broadly obovate leaves ar 1¼ to 4 inches long by ¾ to 2 inches wide. They are most acuminate at the tip and narrowed to sometimes rounded a the base, and the margins are serrate or sometimes doub serrate. The leaf surface is glabrous or nearly so above an more or less pubescent beneath, particularly on the main vein The texture of the leaves varies, some being thin, others thic or firm and often very veiny beneath. The petioles are channeled above and thinly pubescent.

The greenish or yellowish-white flowers appear in June and early July and are of two kinds. Those with stamens are clustered in short-peduncled cymes of as many as a dozen flowers. Those having pistils occur 1 to 3 in a place. The calyx lobes are obtuse and definitely ciliate. The fruit, which appears in the autumn, is bright red or orange, globose, about one-third inch in diameter, and contains 3 to 5 nutlets, which are lunate, bone colored, and smooth.

Distribution.—The Common Winterberry is a shrub which prefers low land bordering lakes, marshes and swamps, and in such situations ranges from Nova Scotia west to Minnesota and south to Florida and Mississippi. In Illinois, it divides the state with the Possumhaw, occurring in the northeastern quarter. It has been especially abundant in Cook and Lake counties and ranges southwestward to Oregon and southward into Kankakee County. There is a single report from as far south as Hardin County.

NEMOPANTHUS Rafinesque

Mountain-Holly Catberry

The mountain-hollies are shrubs with ashy gray bark and alternate, deciduous leaves which are glabrous and slender petioled. The axillary flowers appear singly or a few together and are long pediceled and dioecious. Staminate flowers have minute, 4- or 5-toothed calyces, and fertile flowers have none. There are 4 or 5 long, narrow, spreading petals and 4 or 5 stamens per flower. The fruit is a drupe which contains 4 or 5 bony nutlets.

This genus contains but a single species.

NEMOPANTHUS MUCRONATA (Linnaeus) Trelease

Mountain-Holly

The Mountain-Holly, fig. 39, is an erect, branching shrub 4 to 12 feet high, with gray stems and gray branches, which may turn reddish brown, and smooth branchlets. The leaves are oval to oblong-oval and occur in crowded groups on the end of short spurs. The blades are 1¼ to 4 inches long by about ½ to 1¼ inches wide, generally thin, and for the most part blunt and mucronate, although sometimes acute. They are narrowed at the base, and the margins are entire or rarely show a few teeth. Both the leaves and the petioles are smooth above and below.

The flowers, which appear in May, are solitary or in clusters up to 4 in number. They stand on pedicels about 1 inch long. The fruit, which ripens towards the last of July, is crimson red, globose, and generally about ¼ inch in diameter. It usually contains 4 nutlets, which are smooth, moon shaped, and have at least 1 rib on the back.

Distribution.—The Mountain-Holly, like the other hollies in Illinois, prefers swampy places about lakes and bogs. In such habitats it ranges from Newfoundland to Wisconsin and south to Virginia and Illinois. In Illinois, it is so rare as to have been collected only four times within the boundary of the state. Three of these reports are from Cook County, and the fourth is from Starved Rock in La Salle County.

CELASTRACEAE

The Staff-Tree Family

The staff-tree family is made up of shrubs, trees and climbing vines, some of which are spiny, with opposite, whorled, or alternate, simple leaves without stipules. The inflorescences normally are cymose, and the flowers are perfect and polygamous or dioecious. There are 4 or 5 sepals, 4 or 5 petals, 4 or 5 stamens and a compound pistil made up of 2 to 5 ovaries. The style is short or absent, and the ovary is capped by a 2- to 5-lobed stigma. The fruit is a capsule, a drupe or a berry, and the seeds often are surrounded by a brightly colored structure known as an aril.

Of about 45 genera, comprising between 350 and 400 species widely distributed in temperate and warmer regions, 3 occur in the northeastern United States and 2 are native in Illinois.

Key to the Shrubby Genera

Decumbent or upright shrubs with opposite leaves ....
.... **Euonymus**, p. 16
Twining vines with alternate leaves .... **Celastrus**, p. 17

EUONYMUS (Tournefort) Linnaeus

Burning Bush Wahoo

The burning bushes are shrubs or trees, commonly with 4-angled branches and opposite, entire or toothed, deciduous leaves and deciduous stipules. The flowers are solitary or grouped in cymes and have the structure indicated for the family. The fruit is a 3- to 5-lobed capsule, which is angled or winged and at maturity splits down through the middle at the back of each cell. There are 2 seeds in each cavity, surrounded by an orange or scarlet aril.

There are about 120 species in this genus, inhabitants of Europe, Asia, Australia, and North and Central America. Three species are native in Illinois.

Key to the Burning Bush Species

Petioles of the 2 end leaves on the branches more than 1/4 inch long, mature capsules smooth .... **E. atropurpurea**, p. 167

Petioles of the final leaves on the branches less than 1/4 inch long, mature capsules tuberculate.

- Erect or ascending shrubs with ovate-lanceolate terminal leaves and light red capsules .... **E. americana**, p. 169
- Decumbent shrubs which root at the nodes, terminal leaves obovate, capsules scarlet or orange red .... **E. obovata**, p. 170

EUONYMUS ATROPURPUREA Jacquin

Wahoo

The Wahoo, fig. 40, is an erect shrub, or rarely a small tree, up to 25 feet tall, with stems up to 2 inches in diameter and green branches streaked or covered more or less with reddish brown. The green, smooth branchlets are 4-angled and bear oblong-ovate, elliptic, or obovate leaves 1½ to 6 inches long and ¾ to 1¾ inches wide. The leaf blades are acuminate at the apex, narrowed at the base or sometimes rounded, serrulate or biserrulate on the margins, smooth above and finely hairy beneath, and stand on petioles up to ¾ inch long.

The flowers, which appear from the last of May on into early July, are maroon colored, hardly ¼ inch across, and occur 5 to 15 together in cymes arising from the axils of leaves on the current year's growth. The purplish-red fruit, which matures in late September and on through October, is a somewhat flattened, smooth, lobed capsule about ¾ inch wide, made

FIG. 40

Euonymus americana

Euonymus atropurpurea

up usually of 2 to 4 cells. In each cell there are 1 or 2 oblong, light brown nutlets less than ½ inch in length.

DISTRIBUTION.—The Wahoo is a shrub that prefers banks and low ground along streams, although it is found occasionally in other situations. It ranges from New York to Minnesota and south to Florida and Texas. In Illinois, it occurs in all wooded portions and is recorded in many places along small and large streams, where prairie regions are invaded by woods.

EUONYMUS AMERICANA Linnaeus

Brook Euonymus

The Brook Euonymus, fig. 40, is a low but erect or ascending shrub, which reaches a height of only 6 to 12 inches. It is much branched, and the branches and branchlets are greenish gray, 4-angled, and smooth. The leaves are nearly sessile and ovate-lanceolate to broadly oval, and the terminal pair on the branch usually is not so large as other pairs. The leaf blades are acuminate or abruptly acute at the apex, generally narrowed at the base or sometimes rounded or subcordate, and 1 to 4 inches long by ¾ to 1¾ inches wide. The margins are crenulate-serrate and the surface is smooth above and also beneath, except on the midrib, which may be pubescent.

The flowers, which appear in May, are grouped 1 to 3 together in small cymes which arise from the axils of leaves of the present year. The petals are circular or nearly so, with toothed margins, and are usually greenish purple. The fruit matures in September and October as a somewhat flattened 3- to 5-celled and lobed, light red capsule, which is tuberculately roughened. Each cell of the capsule contains 1 to 6 nutlets, which are elliptic and more or less flattened and have the orange color characteristic of bittersweet.

DISTRIBUTION.—The Brook Euonymus prefers low, flat woods. It is a species definitely southern in distribution and ranges from New York west to Illinois and south to Florida and Texas. In Illinois, it has been reported only rarely, but these reports range throughout the length of the state, from Cook County in the northeast to Hancock County in the central west by way of La Salle County, and finally in Pulaski County in the south. It is one of the rare shrubs of the state.

EUONYMUS OBOVATA Nuttall

Running Euonymus

The Running Euonymus, fig. 41, is a decumbent shrub whic roots at the nodes and sends up upright branches to a heigh of 6 to 18 inches. These branches are gray and terete, an the branchlets, at first green, become gray and smooth or rarely, remain somewhat pubescent. Each branch has, as rule, 2 to 4 pairs of leaves, which are either sessile or on shor petioles seldom more than ⅛ inch long. The leaf blades ar obovate to elliptic or oblong, and the terminal 2 leaves on eac branch are definitely the largest. The leaves range from 1½ to 3¾ inches long and from ¾ to 1¾ inches wide an they are abruptly narrowed at the tip to a blunt point an tapered to the petiole below. The margins are crenulate-serrat or sometimes somewhat double toothed, and the leaf surfac is smooth or pubescent on the principal veins above and glabrou beneath.

The flowers, which appear in May, are grouped 1 to together in small cymes. The petals are circular, with shor or indistinct claws, and are greenish yellow on the outer par and maroon colored toward the base. The fruit matures i autumn as a flat, 3-angled, scarlet to orange-red capsule abou ¼ inch wide, which is tuberculately roughened. Each cell i the capsule contains 1 to 2 seeds which are elliptic and mor or less flattened, smooth, and flesh colored.

Distribution.—The Running Euonymus prefers rich, mois soil in woods and grows in dense mats which may cover severa square yards. It ranges from Ontario to Michigan and sout to Pennsylvania and Kentucky. In Illinois, it has been col lected and reported frequently from woody portions of th state, but not from the prairie regions in the central part and it ranges from the northern to the southern and fror the eastern to the western boundaries.

CELASTRUS Linnaeus

Bittersweets Waxworts

The bittersweets are twining vines or shrubs with alternate entire or toothed leaves and minute stipules. The flowers ar borne in axillary or terminal racemes or panicles. There ar

FIG. 41

Celastrus scandens

Euonymus obovata

5 sepals, 5 petals, 5 stamens and a compound pistil consisting of 2 to 4 cells capped by a short, stout style and a 2- to 4-lobed stigma. The capsule is globose or ellipsoid, leathery, and 2- to 4-celled, and at maturity it splits down the back of the middle of each cell. In each cavity there are 1 to 2 seeds surrounded by a scarlet aril.

There are more than 30 bittersweet species, chiefly native in southern and eastern Asia and Australia. The species described here is the only one native in North America.

CELASTRUS SCANDENS Linnaeus

American Bittersweet

The American Bittersweet, fig. 41, is a twining vine with stems up to 6 inches in circumference and as much as 35 feet long. The branches are smooth and gray or brown, and the branchlets, green at first, are smooth and become gray by the end of the season. The leaves are oval, ovate, or obovate with blades up to 6 inches long and half as wide, and petioles which are variable in length and up to ¾ inch long. The leaf blade is acute or acuminate at the apex, usually narrowed at the base to the petiole, though sometimes rounded, crenulate on the margin, and smooth both above and beneath.

The flowers, which appear in May and June, are greenish yellow and stand in racemes or panicles 1¼ to 2 inches long which frequently are terminal on the branchlets. The fruit which matures in late autumn, is a globular, brilliant orange capsule about ¼ inch in diameter, which breaks open by 3 valves to expose the crimson arils which surround the seed Generally, in each aril there are 2 reddish-brown seeds about ⅛ inch long.

Distribution.—The American Bittersweet prefers a rich moist soil, but grows in all kinds of soil and also in dry situations. It ranges from Manitoba southeastward to North Carolina and Tennessee and southwestward into New Mexico It occurs throughout the state of Illinois, excepting only areas that are natural prairie. With the removal of most of the original forest, it has adapted itself to some extent as a fence-row inhabitant. In the fall the fruit of this vine is collected and sold in towns and cities as indoor decoration for the winter months.

STAPHYLEACEAE

The Bladdernut Family

The bladdernut family consists of shrubs or trees with alternate or opposite, compound leaves which have no stipules. The flowers are perfect or polygamous and are borne in racemes or panicles. There are 5 sepals and 5 petals, and the stamens have distinct filaments. The ovary consists of 2 or 3 partly united carpels capped by 2 or 3 distinct or partly united styles. The fruit is an inflated, membranous capsule or a berry, and the seeds may be few or many.

There are about 22 species in this family. They are widely distributed and assigned among 5 genera, of which 1 only occurs in Illinois.

STAPHYLEA Linnaeus

The Bladdernuts

The bladdernuts are shrubs with 3-foliate or odd-pinnate, opposite leaves and perfect, regular flowers, which are produced in axillary racemes or panicles. The carpels are united at the base, and the stigmas are capitate. The fruit is a membranous capsule, which is 2- or 3-celled and 2- or 3-lobed, and seeds are produced singly in each cavity.

There are about six species, all of them inhabitants of the north temperate zone. Two are native in North America, one in California, the other in the northeastern states.

STAPHYLEA TRIFOLIA Linnaeus

American Bladdernut

The American Bladdernut, fig. 42, is an erect shrub 3 to 12 feet high, with stems up to 4 inches in diameter covered by smoothish bark, which may be longitudinally streaked with gray, and smoothish branches also streaked with gray. The branchlets, green at first, are glabrous and turn light reddish brown by late autumn. The leaves, which are opposite, are trifoliate and stand on petioles 1 to 5 inches long. The blades are glabrous or pubescent, mostly oval but quite variable, and up to 2 inches long by ¾ inch wide. The terminal leaflet is the largest. The leaflets are abruptly short-acuminate at the apex and rounded or narrowed at the base, the lateral ones being also somewhat asymmetrical at the base. The margins are closely serrate and the surfaces, almost smooth above on unfolding, become glabrous or nearly so at maturity, although they generally are pubescent beneath. Terminal leaflets stand

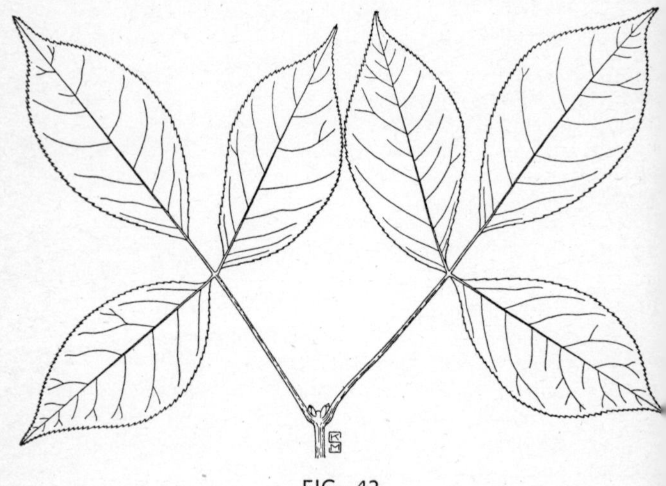

FIG. 42
Staphylea trifolia

on stalks up to 2 inches long, but lateral leaflets are generally sessile or very short stalked.

The flowers, which appear from early in April until about the middle of May, when the leaves are well grown, are developed in drooping racemes 1¼ to 4 inches long, which arise in the axils of leaves at the end of branchlets. Flowers, which are hardly ¼ inch wide, have a white corolla and a greenish-white or pinkish calyx. The fruit, which ripens during October, is an inflated, papery, 3-celled pod, usually obovate but sometimes nearly spherical, and pubescent at flowering time but glabrous or nearly so at maturity. It is variable in size and may be as much as 3 inches long by 2 inches wide. The single seed in each cavity is light brown, smooth, and ¼ inch long.

DISTRIBUTION.—The American Bladdernut is seldom found elsewhere than on slopes and banks along streams. It ranges from Quebec to Minnesota and south to South Carolina and Kansas. In Illinois, it grows from the northern boundary to the southern and from the eastern to the western, and one may expect to encounter it wherever suitable habitats occur, with the single exception that there are no records of its occurrence in the extreme northwestern corner of the state.

HIPPOCASTANACEAE

The Buckeye Family

The buckeye family consists of shrubs or trees which bear alternate, palmately compound leaves without stipules, and racemes or panicles of irregular, showy, polygamous flowers. The tubular to bell-shaped calyx is 5-lobed, and there are 4 or 5 unequal petals and 5 to 9 stamens. The 3 pistils are united into a 3-celled ovary which develops into a leathery, smooth or prickly capsule containing a single large seed.

The 2 genera in this family number about 20 species, natives of Asia, North America and Mexico. Only the following genus is represented in Illinois.

AESCULUS Linnaeus

Buckeye Horsechestnut

The buckeyes are deciduous trees or shrubs with rather coarse branches bearing large winter buds and long-petioled, digitately compound leaves, the leaflets of which are serrate. Showy flowers are borne in upright, many-flowered panicles. The calyx is bell-shaped to tubular and 4- or 5-lobed, and there are 4 or 5 petals with long claws. There are 5 to 9 stamens, and the 3-celled, superior ovary develops into a 1-celled, leathery capsule, containing usually 1 very large seed marked with a round, whitish scar that gives rise to the name buckeye.

There are about 25 species of buckeye or horsechestnut native in eastern Asia, southeastern Europe, and North America. In all species the bark is bitter and astringent, and the seeds contain a glucoside, aesculin, that is poisonous to animals and man. Heat inactivates the poison, however, and the seed can be used as food after being thoroughly roasted. For the most part the buckeyes are trees, but the following species grows as a shrub in Illinois.

AESCULUS PAVIA Linnaeus

Red Buckeye

The Red Buckeye, fig. 43, is a shrub 3 to 8 feet high or sometimes a tall tree with large, erect, smooth-barked branches and glabrous, orange-brown branchlets which become pale brown and are conspicuously marked by numerous leaf-scars.

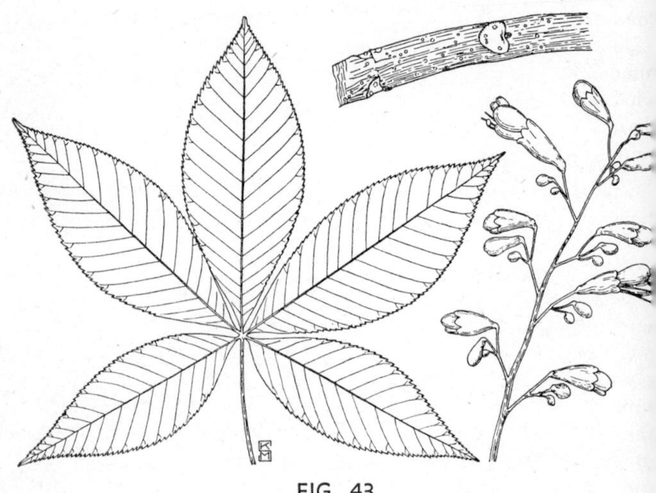

FIG. 43
Aesculus Pavia

The leaves are opposite and digitately compound, being made up of 5 elliptic to oblong leaflets, which are abruptly acuminate at the apex and gradually narrowed and wedge shaped at the base. The leaflet margins are sharply but evenly toothed, and the blades at maturity are glabrous above and beneath, except that there are conspicuous tufts of hair in the vein axils beneath. The leaves are 4 to 6 inches long, and the leaflets have the same length and are from 1¼ to 1¾ inches wide.

The light red flowers, which open in early spring when the leaves are about half grown, stand at the end of branches in narrow panicles 4 to 8 inches long. The tubular calyx is red, and the petals are provided at the base with claws as long as the calyx, the upper pair with claws much longer than the calyx.

Гhe fruit, which ripens late in the fall, is a smooth, pitted, eathery capsule, which contains 1 or 2 seeds, each about 1 nch wide.

DISTRIBUTION.—The Red Buckeye is a shrub or tree of rich iverbottom lands. It ranges from Virginia to southern Illinois ınd southward to Florida and Louisiana. In Illinois, its distribuion is distinctly southern and includes only Union County, in he vicinity of Jonesboro, Pope County, in the vicinity of Golonda, and Alexander County, in the vicinity of Hanging Rock.

The Sweet Buckeye, *A. octandra* Marshall, is relatively ommon in southern Illinois and sometimes assumes a somevhat shrubby growth habit. It may be distinguished from he Red Buckeye by the reddish-brown pubescence on its leaf 'eins.

RHAMNACEAE

The Buckthorn Family

The buckthorn family consists of shrubs or trees with alterıate or, rarely, opposite, simple, usually several-ribbed leaves .nd small stipules. The flowers are greenish, perfect or polygaıous or, rarely, dioecious. There are 4 or 5 sepals and an equal ıumber of petals and stamens. The ovary consists of 2 or 3 ınited carpels which are immersed in the disk of the flower .nd are capped by more or less united styles and stigmas. The ruit may be a capsule, a drupe or a samara.

There are about 600 species in this family, all natives of emperate and warmer regions. They are distributed among ome 50 genera, of which 3 are native in eastern North America nd 2 in Illinois.

Key to the Genera

,eaves pinnately veined, flowers greenish yellow, fruit a drupe . . . . **Rhamnus**, p. 177

,eaves strongly 3-veined, flowers white, fruit a dry capsule . . . . **Ceanothus**, p. 181

RHAMNUS (Tournefort) Linnaeus

The Buckthorns

The buckthorns are shrubs or trees, either unarmed or armed vith spinelike branchlets, which bear alternate, toothed or entire, several-ribbed leaves and early deciduous stipules. The flowers are perfect or polygamous, axillary, and often clustered in various ways. There are 4 or 5 sepals, 4 or 5 petals (the latter sometimes wanting), and 4 or 5 stamens with short filaments. The ovary is 2- or 4-celled, with 2 or 4 styles united at the base. The fruit is a berry-like drupe which contains 3 to 4 nutlets.

Some 90 species of buckthorn are known in temperate and warmer regions. About 15 of them are native in North America and 3 occur in Illinois.

Key to the Buckthorn Species

Flowers with 4 sepals and 4 petals, fruit containing 2 nutlets. .... **R. lanceolata**, p. 178

Flowers with 5 sepals and 5 petals, fruit containing 3 nutlets.

- Pedicels of flowers glabrate, petals absent, nutlets grooved on the back .... **R. alnifolia**, p. 180
- Pedicels of flowers pubescent, petals 5, nutlets not grooved on the back .... **R. caroliniana**, p. 180

RHAMNUS LANCEOLATA Pursh

Lance-Leaved Buckthorn

The Lance-Leaved Buckthorn, fig. 44, is a small or large, widely branching shrub with gray to dark brown branches. The branchlets, at first puberulent, become smooth or nearly so and gray by the end of the season. The ovate-oblong to ovate-lanceolate leaves are 1¼ to 4 inches long by ¾ to 1¾ inches wide, narrowed or rounded at the base, and acute or acuminate at the apex. Their margins are crenulate-serrate; and the upper surface becomes smooth, but the lower surface remains more or less pubescent. The petioles are definite, though short, and variable in length.

The dioecious, yellowish-green, fragrant flowers appear in May with the leaves and stand in sessile clusters in the axils of lower leaves. Generally there are 1 to 3, sometimes as many as 6, flowers in a cluster. The pedicels on which they stand are glabrate and quite short. The black fruit, which matures in August and September, is globose, about ⅛ inch in diameter, and contains 2 nutlets, each with a deep groove on the back.

Distribution.—The Lance-Leaved Buckthorn inhabits many types of habitats from very dry ground to bogs. It ranges from Pennsylvania to Nebraska and south to Alabama and Texas.

FIG. 44
Rhamnus caroliniana
Rhamnus alnifolia
Rhamnus lanceolata

It is the commonest and most abundant of the buckthorns i
Illinois and ranges from the eastern to the western boundar
and from the northern boundary southward at least as far a
St. Clair and Effingham counties.

RHAMNUS ALNIFOLIA L'Héritier

Alder-Leaved Buckthorn

The Alder-Leaved Buckthorn, fig. 44, is a low shrub wit
reddish-brown, smooth bark, which seldom reaches a heigh
of more than 3 feet. The branchlets are at first more or les
pubescent but become smooth and gray by the end of the sea
son. The leaves are oval or slightly obovate, 1¾ to 5 inche
long by ¾ to 2½ inches wide, acute or acuminate at the ape
more or less narrowed at the base, and crenulate-serrate o
the margins. The surface is smooth above, except the midri
and the upper surface of the petiole, and smooth beneath a
maturity, although the main nerves may remain more or les
pubescent. The lower leaves are often smaller than the oute
leaves and more rounded at the tip.

The small, greenish-yellow flowers, which appear in late Ma
and early June, stand alone or in clusters of 2 to 3 in the axil
of lower leaves on short, glabrate pedicels. The black, bloom
covered fruit, which matures in August, is obovoid, about one
third inch long, and contains 1 to 3 more or less tuberculat
nutlets bearing 2 grooves on the back.

Distribution.—The Alder-Leaved Buckthorn prefers bog
and swamps. It ranges from Newfoundland to British Colum
bia and south to New Jersey and Illinois, inland, and norther
California on the western coast. In Illinois, it is at preser
limited to the northeastern corner of the state, where it i
common, although formerly, like a number of other bog plant
it grew in Peoria and Tazewell counties.

RHAMNUS CAROLINIANA Walter

Carolina Buckthorn

The Carolina Buckthorn, fig. 44, is a tall shrub, or occa
sionally a small tree, the branchlets of which are at firs
puberulent and green but later glabrate and gray. The leave
often 6 inches long by 2 inches wide, are broadest beyond th

niddle, acute or acuminate at the apex, and rounded or slightly narrowed to the petiole. The margins are irregularly crenulate-serrate, and at maturity the blades are smooth above and generally more or less pubescent along the main veins beneath. The lower leaves are usually definitely smaller than the upper or outer ones and tend to be more rounded at the apex. The petioles are about 1/4 to 3/8 inch long and at least pubescent above.

The greenish-yellow flowers, which appear in June after the leaves are grown, stand in small umbels of about 12 flowers in the leaf axils. Rarely the flowers may be solitary or in small clusters of 2 or 3. The peduncle, the pedicel and the calyx tube are pubescent. The fruit, which matures in late autumn, is at first red and then black. It is globose, about one-third inch in diameter, and contains 3 nutlets without grooves on the back.

DISTRIBUTION.—The Carolina Buckthorn prefers the sides of wooded hills. It ranges from Virginia to Nebraska and south to Florida and Texas. In Illinois, its occurrence in the southern part of the state is well established, although its exact range is not well known. It was reported years ago from the vicinity of Grand Tower and more recently from Shawneetown and Jackson County. The collection made at Grand Tower has been distinguished as the variety *mollis* Fernald, which is characterized by having leaves that are velvety beneath.

The European Alder Buckthorn, *R. Frangula* Linnaeus, is reported to have escaped from cultivation in northeastern Illinois. This species may be distinguished from the Carolina Buckthorn by its panicled rather than umbeled inflorescence and its entire-margined leaves, which have 8 to 10 instead of 7 to 15 pairs of veins.

CEANOTHUS Linnaeus

The Jersey-Teas

This genus consists chiefly of deciduous or evergreen shrubs which often are somewhat spiny. The leaves are alternate, usually 3-ribbed from the base, and serrate or sometimes entire, and the stipules are small and deciduous. The small, perfect flowers, which have their parts arranged in fives, are borne in small umbels which combine to form terminal spikes or panicle The ovary is 3-celled, and the fruit is usually dry, globose, an 3-lobed at the apex, and separates into 3 nutlets.

There are between 50 and 60 species in this genus, all of the natives of North America and northern Mexico. Only 2 occu in the northeastern United States and these are native also Illinois.

Key to the Jersey-Tea Species

Leaves ovate to ovate-oblong, pubescent beneath; peduncles longer than the leaves from whose axils they arise; capsules crested; seeds smooth .... **C. american**

Leaves elliptic-lanceolate, glabrous beneath; peduncles shorter than the leaves in whose axils they arise; capsules not crested; seeds pitted on the surface .... **C. ovat**

CEANOTHUS AMERICANUS Linnaeus

Jersey-Tea

The Jersey-Tea, fig. 45, is an erect shrub, generally wi several stems rising from a very large, red rootstock to a heig seldom in excess of 3 feet. The stems are somewhat branch and either pubescent or glabrous below. The leaves are ova to ovate-oblong, 1¾ to 4 inches long, ¾ to 3 inches wide, acu at the apex, and generally rounded and somewhat cordate the base. Margins are serrate, and the teeth are tipped wi glands. The surface is more or less pubescent above and ge erally velvety to the touch beneath. The petioles are sho usually less than ¼ inch long.

The small, white flowers, which appear in June and ear July, stand in dense clusters at the end of long peduncl which are either terminal or arise from the axils of leaves the current year. The petals are clawed. The fruit matur in September and October as a 3-celled capsule, each cell which contains one smooth, light brown seed, which is oblo and is flattened on one side.

Distribution.—The Jersey-Tea prefers dry situations a often is found on slopes with black oak, as well as occasiona in prairie regions. It ranges from Manitoba to Maine a south to Texas and Florida. In Illinois, it has been collect in more than a third of the counties and is one of the m widely distributed shrubs in the state.

FIG. 45

Ceanothus ovatus

Ceanothus americanus

CEANOTHUS OVATUS Desfontaines

Inland Jersey-Tea

The Inland Jersey-Tea, fig. 45, is a small, erect shrub wit
stems which are smooth throughout by the end of the seaso
and commonly reach a height of only 12 to 24 inches. Its ver
short-petioled leaves are elliptic to lanceolate, ¾ to 2 inche
long by ¼ to 2 inches wide, obtuse at the apex, rounded o
narrowed at the base, glabrous beneath or at maturity some
what hairy along the veins, and provided along the margin
with gland-tipped teeth.

The tiny, white flowers are grouped in terminal clusters o
short peduncles or sometimes arise from the axils of uppe
leaves. The fruit matures in autumn and is similar to tha
of the Jersey-Tea, except that the capsules are smooth and th
seeds within the capsules are dark brown, somewhat longe
than those of the Jersey-Tea, and covered with pits.

DISTRIBUTION.—The Inland Jersey-Tea ranges from Ver
mont to Manitoba and south to Maryland, Illinois and Texas
In Illinois, it is a relatively rare shrub, apparently limited t
sandy habitats in the northern third of the state. It has bee
reported from Cook, Lake, Whiteside, Jo Daviess and Han
cock counties only.

VITACEAE

The Grape Family

The grape family consists of woody vines which climb b
means of tendrils and bear perfect, polygamous or dioeciou
flowers in axillary racemes. There are 4 or 5 sepals and petal
in each flower, and the 4 or 5 stamens are situated opposite th
petals. The ovary consists of 2 united or, rarely, of 3 distinc
carpels, the styles of which are united and topped by capitat
or peltate stigmas. The fruit is a fleshy berry, which contain
1 or 2 seeds in each of its cavities.

The members of the grape family are widely distributed ove
the world and constitute some 500 species. They are grouped i
about 10 genera, 3 of which are native in northeastern Unite
States and in Illinois. Various native species are in cultivatio
both as ornamentals and as sources of food. The fruits o
certain wild grapes are sought for the making of jellies.

Key to the Genera

.eaves simple.
Pith of the branches interrupted at the nodes; petals not separating at the summit but falling off as a cap; berry spherical, black or bluish black, and edible.....**Vitis**, p. 185
Pith of the branches not interrupted at the nodes; petals separating and expanding before falling off; berry oblate-spherical in shape, bluish, not edible...**Ampelopsis**, p. 194
.eaves compound, the leaflets palmately arranged...**Parthenocissus**, p. 196

VITIS (Tournefort) Linnaeus

The Grapes

The grapes are climbing or trailing vines, mostly with shreddy ark and branched tendrils opposite some or all of the leaves. 'he leaves are alternate and simple but often prominently lobed nd veined, and the stipules are small and early deciduous. The owers are dioecious or, rarely, perfect and possess a minute alyx and early deciduous petals which cling together at the op like a cap. The ovary is 2-celled, and the fruit is a pulpy erry which contains a few pear-shaped seeds.

Grapes are native in warm and temperate regions throughout e world. There are about 50 species, among which possibly) are native in the United States and 6 in Illinois. They often e difficult to identify botanically.

Key to the Grape Species

tendril or a flower cluster opposite every leaf...**V. Labrusca**, p. 186
either a tendril nor a flower cluster opposite every third leaf.
Under surface of the leaves rusty pubescent, glaucous, or covered with cobwebby pubescence......**V. aestivalis**, p. 186
Under surface of the leaves glabrous or pubescent but never glaucous or rusty pubescent.
Leaves either without lobes or with 2 lateral lobes forming wide sinuses.
Under surface of mature leaves more or less densely pubescent..........................**V. cinerea**, p. 188
Leaves glabrous on the under surface or pubescent only along the veins.....................**V. vulpina**, p. 190
Leaves with 2 lateral lobes forming acute sinuses.
Branchlets bright red; berries bloomless..**V. palmata**, p. 191
Branchlets not red; berries bloom covered..**V. riparia**, p. 193

VITIS LABRUSCA Linnaeus

Fox Grape

The Fox Grape, fig. 46, is a long vine with stems that hav more of a tendency to trail than to twine. The branchlets an petioles are covered with dense, rusty or whitish hair and fre quently with upright, stalked glands. The leaves, about as lon as wide, generally are 2 to 6 inches wide and usually have short lateral lobes, which may be either blunt or acute, sepa rated from the blade by broad, rounded sinuses. The blade either deeply and narrowly or broadly V-shaped at the bas acute or acuminate at the apex, and irregularly toothed wit relatively shallow, mucronate teeth. The upper leaf surfa is woolly when the leaf unfolds but becomes smooth or near so at maturity and is then dull and dark green. The unde surface is covered until maturity with a heavy, rusty or whiti tomentum, but at maturity the veins may become smooth. Th petioles are usually about two-thirds as long as the leaf blad

The inflorescence arises from the stem opposite a leaf ar stands on a peduncle ½ to 2 inches long. The flowers bloo about the middle of June, and the berries, which mature fro late August into September, are dark purple to wine re spherical, and about ¼ inch in diameter, and covered wi little or no bloom. Each contains 2 to 4 seeds, which a notched at the large end.

Distribution.—The Fox Grape, which prefers woods alo streams and bodies of water, ranges from New England Illinois and south to Georgia. In Illinois it is, however, rare that there is only one reliable report of its occurrence the state. This report is for Cass County.

The Fox Grape is the wild species from which a considerab number of the American grapes now in cultivation, such as t Concord and Catawba, were derived.

VITIS AESTIVALIS Michaux

Summer Grape

The Summer Grape, fig. 46, is a large, high-climbing vi with large, lobed leaves and small, tough-skinned, black berri Its branchlets, more or less woolly when young, soon beco smooth or nearly so, except the first few internodes, whi

FIG. 46

Vitis Labrusca

Vitis aestivalis

remain densely pubescent. The leaf blades, just about as long as wide, are 2 to 7 inches long and generally 3- to 5-lobed. The lobe tips are acute, and the sinuses are usually rounded, though sometimes acute. The base of the leaf is deeply and narrowly or widely, U-shaped, and the margin is irregularly serrate with low teeth ending in a small point. The leaf is covered above and beneath by white, or rusty, cobwebby pubescence when it unfolds but soon becomes smooth and bright green above while remaining more or less cobwebby and rusty beneath, especially along the veins. The lower surface is for the most part green but may be glaucous or bluish green. The petioles, like the leaves, are covered with cobwebby pubescence and are usually one-third to two-thirds as long as the blade.

The cylindrical or sometimes branched inflorescence arises opposite a leaf, is 2 to 6 inches long, stands on a peduncle sometimes as much as 2 inches long, and is in blossom throughout the month of June. The berries, which mature in September and October, are somewhat more than ¼ inch in diameter, black, and bloom covered, and contain 2 to 4 seeds.

Distribution. — The Summer Grape is an inhabitant of woods and thickets from New Hampshire and Florida westward to Kansas and Texas. It is found in suitable situations practically throughout the state of Illinois and is perhaps the most generally distributed wild grape in the state.

As described here, the Summer Grape includes *V. bicolor* Le Conte, which sometimes is distinguished as a separate species, *V. argentifolia* Munson, or as the variety *bicolor* (Le Conte) Deam, on the basis that the leaves are glaucous beneath and nearly glabrous when old.

VITIS CINEREA Engelmann

Sweet Winter Grape

The Sweet Winter Grape, fig. 47, is a large, high-climbing vine with angled branchlets, large, indefinitely lobed leaves and large, black fruit. The branchlets are densely covered with persistent, gray pubescence and sometimes even appear woolly. The leaf, generally somewhat longer than wide, is 2 to 6 inches long and entire or furnished with 2 short and sometimes indistinct lateral lobes or shoulders, which point away from the tip of the leaf. The sinuses between the lobes and the apex a

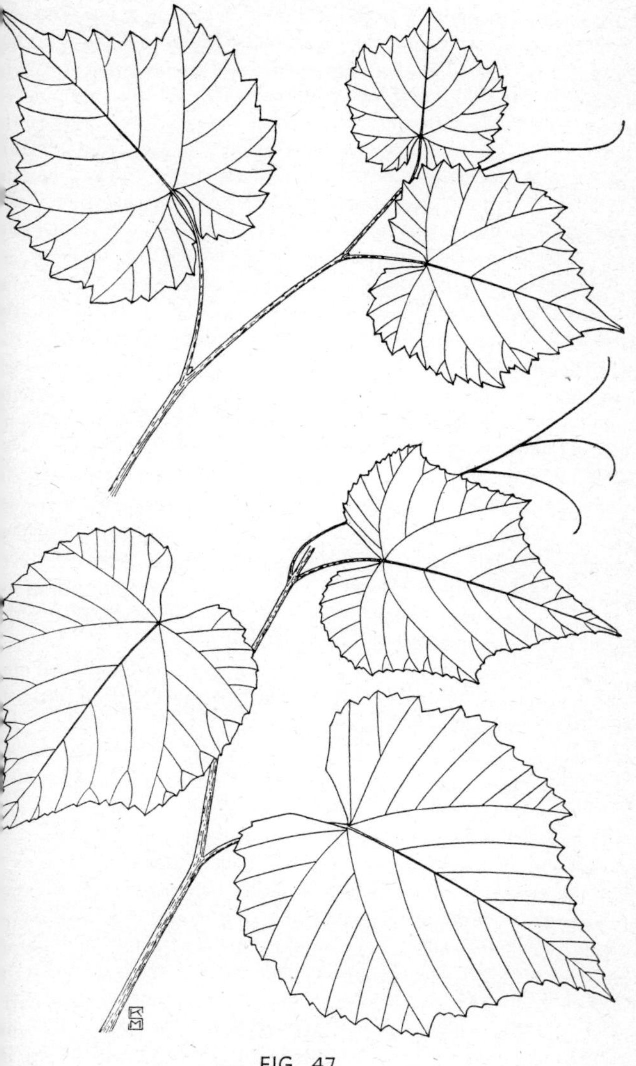

FIG. 47
Vitis vulpina
Vitis cinerea

broad and rounded. The leaf base is deeply and narrowly o
broadly V-shaped, and the basal lobes approach each othe
closely or overlap. The upper leaf surface is covered, whe
the leaf emerges, with whitish, cobwebby pubescence, whic
soon disappears, leaving the surface smooth, dull, and dar
green. The under surface is at first covered with white wooll
pubescence, but this disappears entirely at maturity, leavin
a short, abundant, gray pubescence at least on the veins. Th
petioles are one-third to two-thirds as long as the blade an
are densely covered with pubescence similar to that of th
branchlets.

The broad, loose inflorescence is 4 to 8 inches long an
stands on a peduncle ¾ to 2 inches long. The flowers ope
from the middle of June through the early part of July, an
the berries, which mature in clusters 2 to 6 inches long i
September and October, are slightly over ¼ inch in diamete
black, and as a rule without bloom, but sometimes somewh
frosty-powdered. Each contains 1 to 3 small seeds.

Distribution.—The Sweet Winter Grape ranges, in woo
and thickets, from southern Ohio to Nebraska and south
Louisiana and Texas. In Illinois, it ranges throughout t
southern third of the state, where it is a very common grap
and has been reported as far north as Champaign, Woodfo
and Henderson counties.

VITIS VULPINA Linnaeus

Frost Grape

The Frost Grape, fig. 47, is a high-climbing vine with chara
teristically heart-shaped, large, smooth leaves that are enti
or inconspicuously lobed. The branchlets are more or le
pubescent up to flowering time but smooth except on the nod
by the time the fruit is mature. The leaf blades are corda
ovate, just about as wide as long, commonly 3½ to 6 inch
long, acute or shortly acuminate at the apex, and mos
V-shaped at the cordate base. The leaf margin is more or le
ciliate and mostly without lobes but sometimes has 2 sho
lateral lobes which are acute and less than ½ inch long. T
teeth are irregular, tipped with a very distinct point, and rar
acute. The upper leaf surface is smooth, as is also the low
surface, except that all of the larger veins and sometimes t

smaller ones are covered with white hair, which sometimes s rusty in the axils of the main veins. The petiole is about wo-thirds as long as the leaf blade and pubescent to glabrous ıt maturity, except where it joins the blade.

The loose inflorescence is cylindrical or somewhat pyramid haped, drooping, and 3 to 8 inches long. The flowers blossom n late May and through most of June, and the fruit begins o ripen about the middle of September. The fruit clusters re commonly 3 to 8 inches long and stand on peduncles ¾ to ½ inches long. The black, bloom-covered berries are somevhat less than ½ inch in diameter and generally contain 2 or 3 roadly ovate, small seeds.

DISTRIBUTION.—The Frost Grape ranges, in woods and hickets, from New York to Nebraska and south to Florida nd Texas. It is found throughout Illinois, being especially ommon in fence-row thickets, and is perhaps the commonest nd most abundant wild grape in the state. It is, however, are, perhaps entirely absent, in the northeastern corner of ıe state in the counties bordering on Lake Michigan.

VITIS PALMATA Vahl

Catbird Grape

The Catbird Grape, fig. 48, is a climbing vine with bright d branchlets, shreddy bark, and distinctly triangular, 3-lobed, arp-pointed leaves. The branchlets become reddish brown maturity and are smooth by flowering time, except for warty ands on the lower internodes. The leaf blades, usually longer an wide, are 2 to 5 inches long, long-acuminate at the apex, d very broadly U-shaped at the base. The leaf margin is ooth or slightly ciliate and provided with 2 short but distinct teral lobes, or sometimes the leaf is 5-lobed, and the lobes e separated by deep or shallow, acute or obtuse sinuses. The eth terminating primary veins are distinctly longer and sharper an the other convex or acute teeth, but all are tipped with a nder, small spine. The leaf surface is bright green and ooth above, except on the veins, and smooth beneath except the veins and in the axils of the larger veins, which are mmonly bright red. The petioles are one-half to two-thirds long as the blade and usually glabrous.

The inflorescence is either branched or shouldered, and 2 to

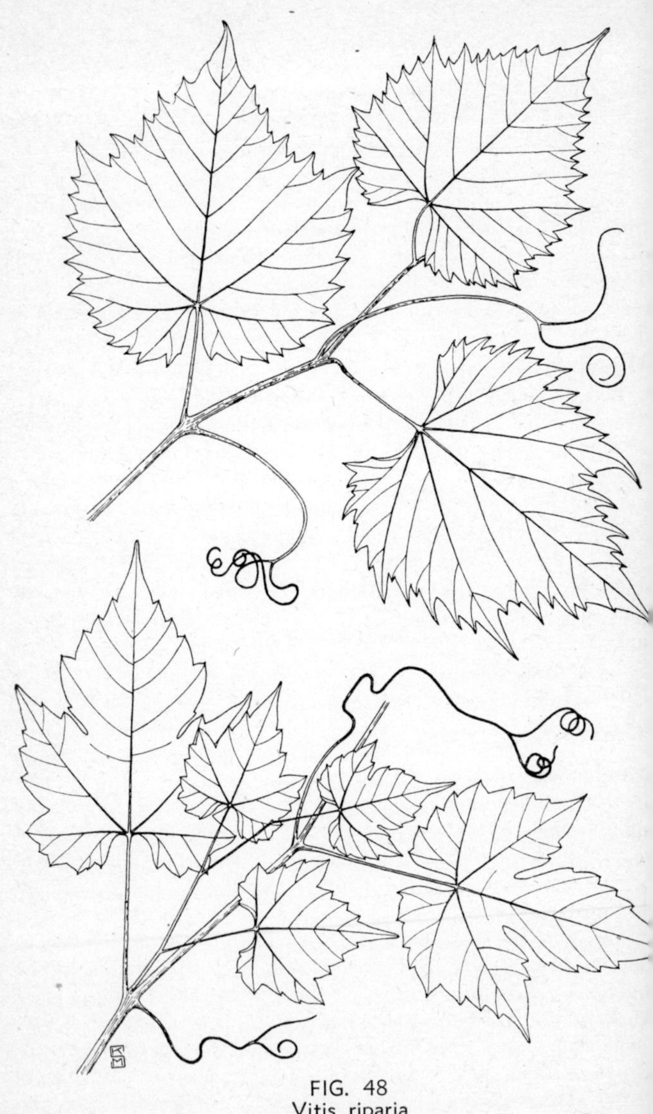

FIG. 48
Vitis riparia
Vitis palmata

5 inches long. Flowering occurs during the early part of July, and the fruit, which hangs in loose or compact clusters 2 to 6 inches long, ripens about the first of October. The berries are somewhat more than ¼ inch in diameter, black, and without bloom. Each contains 1 or 2 seeds, which may be globose or hemispherical.

Distribution.—The Catbird Grape grows in damp situations, such as the low ground bordering ponds and backwaters of rivers, from Illinois to Iowa and south to Louisiana and Texas. In Illinois, it follows the Wabash valley from Lawrence County south to the Ohio River, around the state in the Ohio and Cache River valleys, and northward along the Mississippi to St. Clair County.

VITIS RIPARIA Michaux

Riverbank Grape

The Riverbank Grape, fig. 48, is a high-climbing, large vine with shreddy bark and cordate, markedly acutely lobed, acute-toothed leaves. The branchlets are smooth or sometimes somewhat cobwebby, and the leaf blades, about as long as wide, are 2 to 6 inches long, acute or acuminate at the apex, and very broadly U-shaped at the base. Rarely the basal sinus s so narrow that the basal lobes overlap. The margin is densely ciliate and provided with 2 conspicuous lateral lobes up to ¾ inch long, which may point either forward or outward. Their sinuses are acute. The teeth on the margins are acute and each is tipped with a small short spine. The surface of the leaf is smooth above, except on the main veins, and more or less pubescent with whitish hair on all of the main veins below. The petioles are one-third to two-thirds as long s the leaf blade and more or less pubescent, especially on the upper side.

The inflorescence stands opposite a leaf and is 2 to 5 inches ong. The flowers open from the middle of May to about the middle of June, and the fruit ripens during the latter part of August. The fruit clusters are generally compact, rarely loose, omewhat larger than the original inflorescence, and characteristically provided with a large branch. The very sour, black, densely bloom-covered berries are nearly ½ inch in diameter, and each contains 1 to 4 seeds.

Distribution.—The Riverbank Grape, as its name infers, prefers low, alluvial soil along streams. It ranges from New Brunswick to Manitoba and south to Virginia and Texas. In Illinois, it is a very common and abundant grape, distributed through the length and breadth of the state. In prairie regions, however, small streams without floodplains do not support it.

AMPELOPSIS Michaux

Ampelopsis

The Ampelopsis genus consists of climbing vines with a few tendrils, alternate, simple or pinnately compound leaves and for the most part, perfect flowers arranged in cymes. There are 5 sepals, and the 5 petals are distinct and expand into a flower. The ovary is 2-celled and capped by a slender style The fruit is a berry which, at maturity, is nearly dry and contains 2 to 4 seeds.

There are about 15 species, all natives of temperate and warm regions. Two are known to occur in North America one is native in Illinois. The distinction between *Ampelopsi* and *Parthenocissus* is quite technical. For Illinois species, tendrils furnish the most reliable character, those of *Parthenocissus* having adhesion disks, those of *Ampelopsis* having none.

AMPELOPSIS CORDATA Michaux

Heartleaf Ampelopsis

The Heartleaf Ampelopsis, fig. 49, is a large climbing vin with tight, sometimes deeply furrowed bark and unbranche tendrils which often end in a disk. The leaves are ovate t broadly ovate, sometimes fully as wide as long, and commonl 2 to 5 inches long. They are acuminate at the apex and cordate less often truncate, at the base, and the margin is coarsely an irregularly toothed and often provided with 2 short latera lobes. The surface is smooth, both above and beneath, excep for a few hairs on the veins at the base of the leaf, and th under surface commonly is lighter green than the upper. Th petioles are about one-half as long as the blade, and the bas half is smooth, while the upper half is more or less pubescen

The small flowers occur in panicles of 25 to 70 opposite th leaves, or sometimes in smaller panicles on the branches

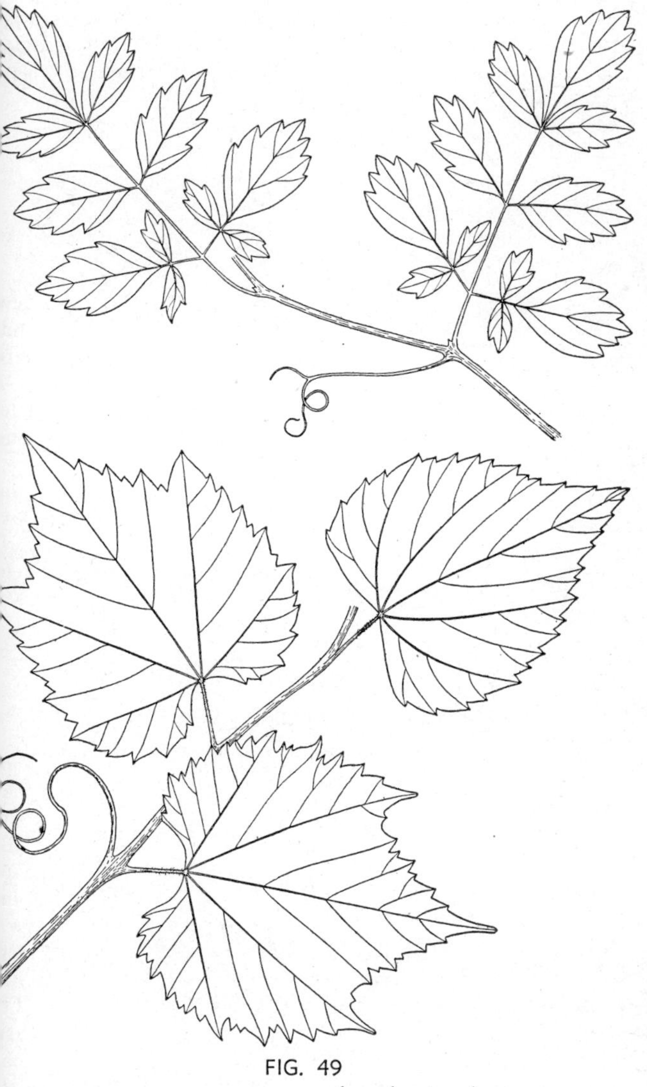

FIG. 49

Ampelopsis arborea

Ampelopsis cordata

tendrils, and the panicles are usually forked. The peduncle below the fork is ¾ to 2½ inches long. Blossoms open in June or early July, and the fruit matures in September and October as a flattened spherical berry about ¼ inch in diameter, which is bluish and provided with a thin, dry pulp. There are, as a rule, 2 broadly ovate seeds in each berry.

Distribution.—The Heartleaf Ampelopsis is a vine which prefers wooded floodplains along rivers. It ranges from Virginia to Nebraska and south to Florida and Texas. In Illinois, it is distinctly a southern vine, to be searched for in the valleys of the Wabash River from Wabash County south, around the state in the valleys of the Ohio and Cache rivers and up the Mississippi River as far as the southern tip of Jersey County. It also extends some distance up the Illinois from its union with the Mississippi.

A second species, *A. arborea* (Linnaeus) Koehne, fig. 49, sometimes called the Pinnate-Leaved Ampelopsis, may occur very sparingly in the extreme southern part of the state. It was recorded many years ago in Jackson County and has been reported in recent years in Union, Alexander and Pulaski counties. It is distinguished from the more abundant species by having pinnately or bi-pinnately compound leaves, which are definitely serrate on the margins.

PARTHENOCISSUS Planchon

Woodbine Five-Leaved Ivy

The woodbines are climbing or trailing vines with forking tendrils sometimes tipped with adhesive disks and with alternate, palmately 5- to 7-foliate leaves. The flowers are perfect or dioecious and borne in compound cymes. There are 5 sepals 5 petals and 5 stamens; and the 2-celled ovary ripens into a berry, which has but little flesh and is nearly inedible. The seeds are indefinitely 3-angled.

There are about 10 species in this genus, all of them natives of eastern North America or Asia. Two occur in Illinois.

Key to the Woodbine Species

Leaves dull above, inflorescence not dichotomously branched
.... **P. quinquefoli**

Leaves shiny above, inflorescence dichotomously branched
.... **P. insert**

PARTHENOCISSUS QUINQUEFOLIA (Linnaeus) Planchon

Virginia Creeper Woodbine

The Virginia Creeper, fig. 50, is a high-climbing vine with tight bark furrowed on large stems, palmately compound, 5-parted leaves and small, dry, grapelike fruit. Terminal branchlets are more or less pubescent, but fruiting and lateral branchlets are usually smooth. Tendrils are branched and have from 3 to 8 offshoots, of which 1 or more may be provided with disks. The leaves vary greatly in shape and size, but are composed normally of 5 ovate, oblong-ovate, or even obovate leaflets, of which the middle or terminal 1 is distinctly the largest and the 2 at the rear are distinctly smallest. The leaflets may be as much as 6 inches long and nearly 4 inches wide. The lateral leaflets of each group are asymmetrical, having one-half of the blade much larger than the other. These leaflets are acute or acuminate at the apex and narrowed at the base, and the margins are coarsely and irregularly serrate. The surface is often smooth above and beneath, or more or less densely pubescent, and the leaves on terminal branchlets are generally more hairy than those on other branchlets. The blade is dull green above and distinctly paler beneath. The leaflets may be nearly sessile or set on stalks up to ¼ inch long, and the entire leaf stands on a petiole which may be as much as 8 inches long.

The flowers, which are borne in panicles and open from late June through July, or sometimes even on into August, are clustered in groups of 10 to 20 at the ends of the branches of the panicle. The fruit, which matures in autumn, is a nearly globose, blue-black, dry berry covered with a whitish bloom. It varies considerably in size but is commonly about ¼ inch in diameter, and contains from 1 to 4 seeds.

Distribution.—The Virginia Creeper is a vine which commonly inhabits woody regions, without particular regard to other habitat characteristics. It ranges from New England to Missouri and south to Florida and Mexico. In Illinois, it grows throughout the state. It is no longer limited to woods but, because its fruit is attractive to birds, it has become a common fence-row straggler. Its berries have been suspected—probably erroneously—of being poisonous when eaten in quantity.

This is the vine so commonly cultivated as Virginia Creeper.

FIG. 50

Parthenocissus quinquefolia

Parthenocissus inserta

The variableness of its characteristics has given rise to the naming of several varieties, of which the following are authentically reported in Illinois. Variety *Saint-Paulii* (Graebner) Rehder, which is distinguished by branchlets sometimes producing aerial roots, by tendrils having 8 to 10 branches, and by oblong-obovate leaflets cuneate at the base, short stalked, pubescent above, doubly serrate with usually flaring teeth, and elongated panicles, occurs in St. Clair County and also near Mascoutah and Peoria. Variety *hirsuta* (Pursh) Planchon, which has branchlets, tendrils, petioles and leaves pubescent at least while young, has been reported in the southeast corner of the state, in Pope County.

PARTHENOCISSUS INSERTA (Kerner) K. Fritsch

Virginia Creeper Thicket Creeper

This Virginia Creeper, fig. 50, is usually a low and rambling vine with stems 15 to 60 feet long, which climbs over bushes and is rarely high climbing. The branchlets are smooth, and the tendrils, which are also smooth and lack disks, usually have 1 to 4 branches. There normally are 5 leaflets per leaf, which are ovate to obovate, acute or acuminate at the apex, and wedge shaped or narrowed at the base. The margin is coarsely toothed, except that the base usually is entire. The leaf blade is lustrous and smooth above and beneath, except that the veins are somewhat hairy near the base of the leaflet. The lower leaflets are small and asymmetrical, and the terminal is slightly the largest and symmetrical, measuring as much as 6 inches long by 2 to 2½ inches wide. The leaflets are nearly sessile or shortly stalked, and the smooth petioles on which they stand may be 6 to 7 inches long.

The flowers, which appear from about the middle of June to the middle of July, are arranged in panicles somewhat longer than the petiole of the leaf opposite which they stand. The panicles are dichotomously branched, and the divisions end in clusters of 10 to 20 flowers. The blue-black fruit, which matures about the last of August and later, is lightly covered with white bloom, nearly globose, and about ¼ inch in diameter. It contains 1 to 4 seeds.

Distribution.—This Virginia Creeper is an inhabitant of thickets in woody regions and ranges from eastern Canada to

Manitoba and south to New York and Texas. In Illinois, it seems to be generally uncommon; but it has been reported very frequently in the northeast corner of the state, and throughout the northern third. It has been reported occasionally as far south as Wabash County in the east and Macoupin County in the west.

HYPERICACEAE

The St. John's-Wort Family

The St. John's-worts are shrubs or herbs, which bear opposite or, rarely, whorled, entire, translucently dotted leaves, no stipules, and perfect, regular flowers in cymes. The flowers have 4 or 5 sepals and 4 or 5 yellowish to pink petals. The stamens may be few or many and are usually divided into 3 or 5 groups. The ovary, which consists of several united pistils, is 1-celled or 3- to 7-celled. The styles are distinct or united, and the stigmas often are capitate. The fruit is a capsule, which opens by splitting along the septums.

There are some 300 species in the St. John's-wort family. They are distributed among 10 genera, which range mostly in temperate and warm regions. In the northeastern United States, the family is represented by 4 genera, and in Illinois there are 3 species which may be considered as shrubs.

Key to the Genera

Low, diffuse shrubs with 4 sepals, 4 petals and 2 pistils .... **Ascyrum**

Erect shrubs with 5 sepals, 5 petals and more than 2 pistils .... **Hypericum**

ASCYRUM Linnaeus

St. Andrew's Cross   The St. Peter's-Worts

These plants are low, leafy shrubs with opposite, black-dotted leaves and perfect, solitary, terminal flowers borne on 2-bracted pedicels. The 4 sepals are very unequal, the outer 2 being much larger, and the 4 petals are yellow and somewhat oblique. The stamens are distinct, or the filaments may be united toward the base, and the anthers open lengthwise. The ovary is 1-celled, and develops into a tapering capsule.

There are about five species, all native in the western hemisphere. Of the two that occur in eastern North America, one is native in Illinois.

ASCYRUM HYPERICOIDES Linnaeus

St. Andrew's Cross

The St. Andrew's Cross, fig. 51, is a low, diffuse shrub with creeping stems from which flattened, 2-edged branchlets rise erectly to a height of 6 to 12 inches. The branchlets are many and reddish brown, and the bark is shreddy. The sessile, opposite leaves are oblanceolate or spatulate, about ½ to 1 inch long by ¼ inch wide, and nearly without petioles. They are obtuse or rounded at the apex, narrowed to the base, and very minutely black dotted both above and below.

The flowers, which appear in July and August, are solitary in the axils of upper leaves or grouped in twos or threes at the end of branchlets. They are about ½ inch in diameter and stand on very short pedicels bearing 2 bracts. The fruit matures in the autumn as a flat, ovoid capsule composed of 2 cells, which contain many tiny, oblong seeds, the surfaces of which are pitted in many lengthwise lines.

Distribution.—St. Andrew's Cross prefers poor soil on the slopes or tops of ridges, especially in open places in wooded regions. It ranges from Massachusetts to Nebraska and south to Florida and Texas. In Illinois, it is distinctly southern in occurrence, being limited to the southern tip of the state and apparently not extending north of the Ozarks.

HYPERICUM (Tournefort) Linnaeus

The St. John's-Worts

The St. John's-worts are herbs or shrubs with opposite, usually sessile leaves which are thick, entire or nearly so, and punctate. The flowers are borne in cymes and have 5 somewhat unequal sepals and 5 yellow petals. The stamens are numerous, and the 1-celled ovary develops into a 1- to 5-celled capsule containing numerous seeds.

The are more than 200 species of St. John's-worts, with wide geographic distribution. Between 30 and 35 species occur in North America, and the 2 following are more or less shrubby in Illinois.

Key to the Shrubby Species

Leaves completely sessile; flowers with 5 styles, capsules 5-celled .... H. Kalmianu
Leaves on very short but distinct petioles; styles 3, capsules 3-celled .... H. prolificu

HYPERICUM KALMIANUM Linnaeus

Kalm's St. John's-Wort

Kalm's St. John's-Wort, fig. 51, is a low shrub seldom mor than 12 to 30 inches high, with ascending branches and branch lets bearing entirely sessile, opposite leaves. The leaves ar oblanceolate to linear-oblong, 1 to 2 inches long by about ½ inch wide, obtuse or acute at the apex and rounded at the base The lower surface is glaucous, and the upper surface is covere with minute black dots.

The flowers, which appear in July and August, are arrange in small, compound cymes at the end of branchlets. The yellow flowers are ¾ to 1 inch wide and stand on short pedicels. Th fruit, which matures in the autumn, is a 4- to 6-celled, ovoi capsule about one-third inch long, which contains numerou oblong seeds pitted on the surface in lengthwise rows.

Distribution. — Kalm's St. John's-Wort is a shrub whic prefers sandy situations and it ranges, where habitats ar suitable, from Quebec to Wisconsin and south into New Yor and Illinois. Its Illinois distribution is remarkable, in that i is limited to the region directly adjacent to Lake Michigan in the northeast corner of the state, to a relatively small terri tory in the western part of the Ozarks, and to Pope County in the southern part of the state. There apparently are no inter vening situations in which this plant is found.

HYPERICUM PROLIFICUM Linnaeus

Shrubby St. John's-Wort

The Shrubby St. John's-Wort, fig. 51, is a low and usuall widely branching shrub, which reaches a height of 2 to 3½ feet. Its ascending or erect, 2-edged branches bear numerou opposite, very shortly petioled leaves, which are linear-oblon to oblanceolate and ¾ to 4 inches long by ¼ to ¾ inch wide They are obtuse at the apex, the main nerve running ou

FIG. 51
Ascyrum hypericoides
Hypericum prolificum Hypericum Kalmianum

through the apex to form a short point, and narrowed at th base to very short petioles.

The flowers, which appear from about the last of June o through most of August, are solitary or in 1 or more pair in the axils of the uppermost leaves, or they also may occur i small clusters that terminate the branchlets. The bright yellov flowers are generally about ¾ inch wide and stand on pedicel about ⅛ inch long. The fruit, which matures in autumn, is 3-celled capsule up to ½ inch long, containing many oblong o often curved seeds, the surfaces of which bear numerous pit arranged in lengthwise lines.

Distribution.—The Shrubby St. John's-Wort grows in lov places, especially about small lakes and marshes, and prefer shaded to open situations. It ranges from southern Ontari to Minnesota and south to Georgia and Mississippi. It range through most of Illinois as a widely distributed but infrequen and localized shrub, which tends to occur individually rathe than in groups. It has not been reported, however, in the regio north and west of the Rock River.

CISTACEAE

The Rock-Rose Family

Members of the rock-rose family are either shrubs or lov undershrubs with alternate or opposite leaves and nearly regu lar, usually perfect flowers borne either solitarily or in variou types of inflorescences. The flowers are made up of 3 to persistent sepals and of 3 or 5 petals, which are soon lost an may sometimes be wanting. The stamens are 8 in numbe and the ovary consists of several united pistils which develo into a capsule containing several or many seeds.

The more than 150 species in this family are divided int about 8 genera, 3 of which occur in northeastern North Americ In Illinois, the following is the single shrubby genus.

HUDSONIA Linnaeus

Beach Heather

The beach heathers are low, tufted, much-branched shrul with small, scalelike, persistent leaves and small, regular, pe fect flowers, which terminate branches. The flowers have sepals and 5 yellow, oblong petals. There are 8 stamens, and the ovary consists of 3 united carpels capped by a single filiform style. The fruit, a 3-valved but 1-celled capsule containing 3 to 5 seeds, is inclosed at maturity in the mature calyx.

There are three species of beach heathers, all native in eastern North America. Only the following is native in Illinois.

HUDSONIA TOMENTOSA Nuttall

Woolly Hudsonia False Heather

The Woolly Hudsonia, fig. 52, is a low, diffuse and very branchy shrub 4 to 8 inches tall, which forms dense tufts. The leaves are very numerous, small, narrow and awllike, the

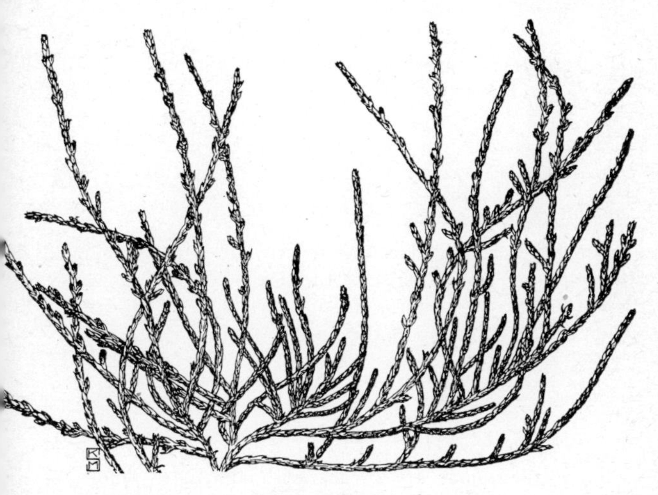

FIG. 52
Hudsonia tomentosa

longest being hardly 1/8 inch long. They overlap so that they cover the branches and branchlets, and they are hoary-pubescent all over.

The flowers, which appear during the last of May and continue until the middle of July, stand at the end of short branchlets. They are minute, yellow, and very short pediceled.

The sepals are densely long-hairy. The fruit, which matures very shortly after the petals wither, is an ovoid, 3-angled, smooth capsule, which bears 1 or 2 minute, oblong seeds.

DISTRIBUTION.—The Woolly Hudsonia is a shrub of sandy regions and in them is distributed from New Brunswick to Manitoba and south to North Carolina and North Dakota. It is widely distributed but nevertheless exceedingly rare and localized in northern Illinois. Records of its occurrence include three stations in Jo Daviess County and one in Lee County. Numerous individuals growing in one place form extensive mats.

THYMELAEACEAE

The Mezereum Family

The mezereum family consists of shrubs or trees having acrid juice and tough bark and bearing perfect or polygamous flowers and alternate or opposite, simple leaves without stipules. The calyx of the flower consists of 4 or 5 united sepals, which often bear 4 or 5 scales within. There is no corolla. There are as many, or twice as many, stamens as sepals, and a solitary pistil with a usually eccentric style, which develops into a berry-like drupe.

This family contains over 400 species, divided among 37 genera. It is very widely distributed but is most abundant in Australia and South Africa. In eastern North America it is represented by two genera, one of which is an escape from cultivation. The following is the native genus.

DIRCA Linnaeus

The Leatherwoods

The leatherwoods are shrubs with alternate, simple, entire leaves and with flowers, which appear before the leaves, that have a funnel-shaped, corolla-like, wavy, slightly 4-lobed calyx. There are 8 stamens, the filaments of which are longer than the calyx, though unequal in length. The 1-celled ovary develops into a 1-seeded drupe.

There are two known species in this genus, both natives of North America. One species occurs only in California; the other is native in Illinois and in other parts of eastern North America.

DIRCA PALUSTRIS Linnaeus

Leatherwood Moosewood

The Leatherwood, fig. 53, is a widely branching shrub that reaches a height of more than 6 feet and has smooth, gray-barked stems of large diameter. The exceedingly tough bark gives rise to the common name, Leatherwood. The branches

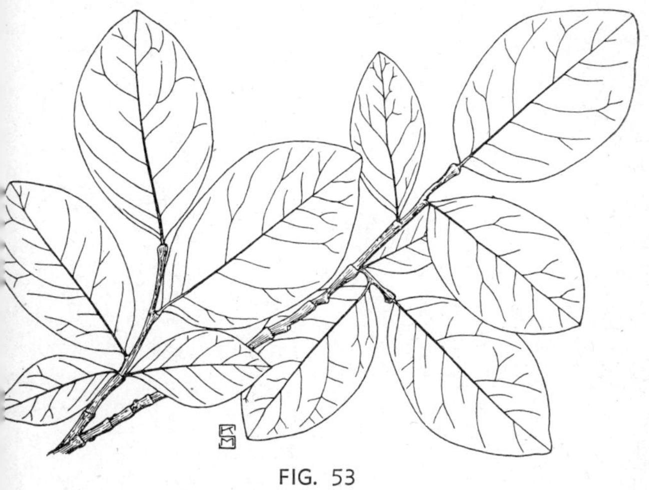

FIG. 53
Dirca palustris

and branchlets have peculiar nodes, readily recognized when once seen, that frequently are described as "socket joints." The simple, alternate leaves, which stand on very short petioles, are for the most part obovate or oval and 1½ to 4 inches long by 1 to 2½ inches wide. The margins are entire, and the blades are obtuse at the apex and rounded or narrowed at the base. The leaf is pubescent when young but soon becomes entirely glabrous.

The flowers, which appear in April before the leaves emerge from terminal and upper buds, stand in clusters of 3 on short peduncles. They are light yellow and less than ¼ inch long. The scales inclosing buds are densely brown-pubescent on the outside and are slow to fall. The fruit, a 1-seeded drupe which usually matures in May and drops early, is about ½ inch long spindle shaped, and light green, and when ripe sits on a pedice about ¼ inch long. The dark brown stone is characterized by a lengthwise white streak.

DISTRIBUTION. — The Leatherwood prefers moist, shade situations along the banks and bluffs of streams. It range from New Brunswick to Minnesota and south to Florid and Mississippi. In Illinois, it is widely distributed and range from the northeastern to the northwestern corner of the stat and southward at least as far as Pope County. Although widel collected, it is a relatively infrequent and localized shrub.

ELAEAGNACEAE

The Oleaster Family

The oleaster family consists of shrubs or trees recognize with especial ease because of the silvery, scaly or stellate pu bescence on the leaves and branchlets. The leaves are entir and may be either alternate or opposite. Perfect, polygamou or dioecious flowers are borne in clusters in the axils of leaves There are 4 sepals, which are deciduous, and the corolla i lacking. The stamens may be either 4 or 8, and the ovary i 1-celled and inferior. The fruit is a somewhat fleshy drup composed of the thickened perianth base.

The 20 or so widely distributed species that compose thi family are grouped in 3 genera, 2 of which occur in easter North America. These are distinctive in appearance, because o the silvery color given by the covering of scales. Only the fol lowing is native in Illinois.

SHEPHERDIA Nuttall

Buffaloberries Bullberries

The buffaloberries, shrubs with silvery or brown, scaly o stellate pubescence, bear opposite, petioled leaves and smal dioecious flowers that arise in clusters at the nodes on branche of the preceding season. The stamens are 8 in number, an the fruit is drupelike.

There are three species, one limited to Utah, one far norther and western, and the following, native in Illinois and easter North America.

SHEPHERDIA CANADENSIS (Linnaeus) Nuttall

Buffaloberry

The Buffaloberry, fig. 54, is an erect shrub commonly 3 to 5 feet high, with stems, branches and branchlets densely and conspicuously covered with fringed, silvery or brown scales. The simple leaves are opposite, ovate or elliptic, 1¼ to 3 inches

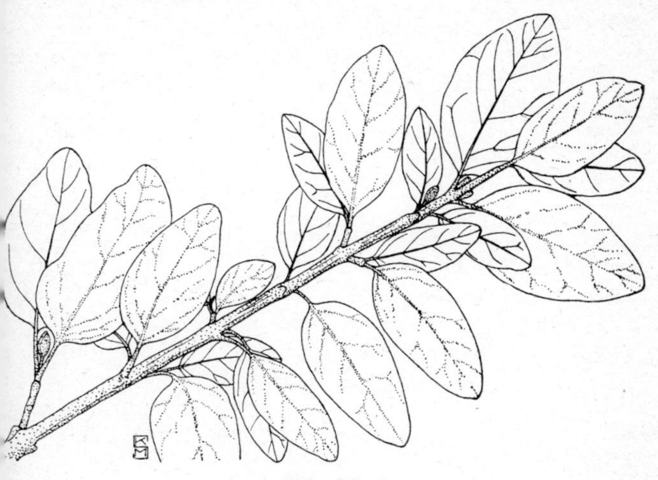

FIG. 54
Sheperdia canadensis

long and, at the most, 1¾ inches wide. They are thick, obtuse at the apex, rounded or sometimes narrowed at the base, and entire on the margins. The surface is dull green above and more or less densely covered with tufted pubescence; beneath it is densely and conspicuously covered with a mixture of silvery and reddish-brown fringed scales.

The dioecious flowers, which appear before the leaves, are borne in short, lateral racemes. They are yellowish green and nearly ¼ inch wide. The fruit is red to yellowish, drupelike, oval, less than ½ inch long, and contains 1 seed.

DISTRIBUTION. — The Buffaloberry, a shrub of woods and stream banks, ranges from Newfoundland to Alaska and south to New York and southwestern Wisconsin. In Illinois, it is confined entirely to the northeastern corner of the state, on dry bluffs of ravines near Lake Michigan at Lake Forest, at Glencoe and at Willow Springs. It is said to be common in that region. Its fruit, though sweetish, lacks the flavor possessed by the fruit of certain other species and is little if at all used as food.

ARALIACEAE

The Ginseng Family

The members of the ginseng family include herbs, shrubs and trees. They are aromatic and bear alternate or whorled, simple or compound leaves and inconspicuous, umbellate inflorescences made up of perfect or polygamous, regular flowers. There are 5 often very small sepals and 5 or 10 petals. The stamens number 5 or 10 and stand alternate with the petals. The ovary consists of 2 to 5 united carpels and is 2- to 5-celled, with the same number of styles. The fruit is either a berry or a drupe.

There are about 475 species in this family, widely distributed in both temperate and tropical regions. They are segregated into about 50 genera, 3 of which are native in northeastern North America. The single genus which follows is the only shrubby one native in Illinois. Many members of the family have been considered important as medicinal and dye-yielding plants.

ARALIA (Tournefort) Linnaeus

The Spikenards Sarsaparilla

The spikenards are either perennial herbs or shrubs, which bear alternate, petioled, pinnately or ternately compound leaves with serrate leaflets. The flowers are perfect or polygamous and are borne in raceme-like or panicle-like umbels, or in compound umbels. There are 5 sepals, 5 petals and 5 stamens, and the 5-celled ovary is capped by 5 spreading styles. The fruit is a 5-lobed and 5-celled drupe, which contains as a rule 5 seeds.

There are about 30 species of spikenards, all natives of North America and Asia. Six of these species occur in North America and 4 of them occur in the northern and eastern part of the United States. Only the following is shrubby.

ARALIA SPINOSA Linnaeus

Hercules' Club Devil's-Walkingstick

The Devil's-Walkingstick, fig. 55, is a large, erect shrub up to 20 feet high with stems covered with tight bark and many strong, straight, or curved spines, which are located mostly at the nodes. The leaves are alternate, bipinnate, and sometimes as much as 4 feet long and 3 feet wide. The petioles may be 10 to 20 inches long, and both they and the midribs are usually beset with prickles. The leaflets are variable in number, but always many, and stand on short stalks. The blades of the leaflets are thin or thick at maturity, ovate, and 1½ to 3½ inches long by ¾ to 2 inches wide. They are acute or acuminate at the apex and generally rounded to subcordate and asymmetrical at the base. The margin is sharply serrate to entire, and the surface is smooth above and slightly glaucous and more or less pubescent on the veins beneath.

The minute, white flowers, which open early in August, are arranged in large compound panicles, so that 10 to 30 flowers stand in umbels at the end of divisions of the panicle. The divisions of the panicle are densely pubescent and provided

FIG. 55
Aralia spinosa

with stalked glands. Fruit ripens in September and Octobe as a globular, black, berry-like drupe about 1/4 inch in diameter with often as many as 5 flat, oblong seeds inclosed in its juic pulp.

DISTRIBUTION.—The Devil's-Walkingstick prefers dry situa tions in open woods and clearings. It ranges from Pennsylvani to Iowa and south to Florida and Texas. In Illinois, it is relatively rare shrub with a limited distribution, which include only the southern tip of the state. The most northern record of occurrence include White County on the east and Unio County on the west. It apparently does not pass inland int the middle of the state north of the Ozarks.

CORNACEAE

The Dogwood Family

Members of the dogwood family include shrubs, trees an a few perennial herbs, which bear alternate or opposite, usuall entire, often firm leaves without stipules. The flowers are per fect or monoecious and occur in cymes or heads, or rarel staminate flowers may be borne in catkin-like spikes. Ther are 4 or 5 sepals, 4 or 5 petals, and 4 or 5 stamens in eac flower, and the ovary consists of 1 to 4 united carpels, whic develop into a drupelike fruit containing a 1- to 4-celled stone

The 80 to 90 species comprising the dogwood family rep resent about 15 genera widely distributed in the norther hemisphere. Four of the genera are native in northeaster North America, but only one shrubby genus is represente in Illinois.

CORNUS (Tournefort) Linnaeus

The Dogwoods

The dogwoods are shrubs, or less often trees, mostly wit opposite branches and opposite or, rarely, alternate, entir leaves. The flowers are perfect and arranged in open, dichot omously branched cymes. The 4 sepals usually are small and the 4 petals are white. The 4 stamens have filiform o awl-shaped filaments. The fruit is a thinly fleshy drupe which contains a usually 2-celled, bony stone, and the seeds are flattened.

There are about 20 poorly understood species of dogwoods, nost of them natives of the north temperate zone. The fol- owing occur in Illinois.

Key to the Dogwood Species

'ubescence on young twigs, inflorescence and leaves woolly and more or less spreading.
- Leaves rough on upper surface, branchlets brown, fruit white .... **C. asperifolia**, p. 214
- Leaves not rough to the touch on the upper surface.
  - Leaves roundly ovate, with 7 to 9 pairs of veins, branchlets greenish, fruit blue .... **C. rugosa**, p. 213
  - Leaves ovate or elliptic, with 4 to 6 pairs of veins.
    - Branchlets purplish, fruit blue .... **C. Amomum**, p. 214
    - Branchlets brown, fruit white .... **C. Baileyi**, p. 216

'ubescence either none or, if present, entirely appressed on the leaves, inflorescence and young twigs.
- Leaves opposite, fruit white.
  - Leaves broadly ovate, branches red ...... **C. stolonifera**, p. 217
  - Leaves lanceolate, branches gray .... **C. foemina**, p. 219
- Leaves alternate, fruit blue .... **C. alternifolia**, p. 219

CORNUS RUGOSA Lamarck

Roundleaf Dogwood

The Roundleaf Dogwood, fig. 56, is an erect shrub 6 to 10 eet high, with gray or brownish-green branches and green ranchlets which may be nearly smooth, partly pubescent, or ven woolly pubescent. The opposite leaves are nearly circular o broadly ovate, and variable in size, being at times 6 inches ong. The blade is abruptly narrowed at the tip to a short oint and rounded or, rarely, narrowed at the base. It is hort-pubescent with appressed hairs above and pale and voolly beneath. The veins are arranged in 7 to 9 pairs, and he petioles are short, commonly about ¼ inch in length.

The flowers appear from late in May until about the middle f June, and the fruit, which matures in autumn, is globose, lue, and contains a globose stone which is rounded at each nd, somewhat oblique, and marked with 8 shallow, length- vise furrows.

Distribution.—The Roundleaf Dogwood, which prefers andy habitats, ranges from Nova Scotia to Manitoba and south o Virginia and Iowa. In Illinois, it is abundant chiefly on he sands near Lake Michigan, but it has been reliably reported also from sandy areas in Will, Kane and Jo Davie counties in the extreme northern part of the state. Possib the southern records for Pope and Hardin counties apply C. *asperifolia* through mistaken identification.

CORNUS AMOMUM Miller

Silky Dogwood

The Silky Dogwood, fig. 56, is an erect shrub 4 to 10 fe high, with brown, pubescent branchlets and ovate to oblor leaves. The leaf blades usually are 2 to 5 inches long by to 1¼ inches wide, abruptly acute to short-acuminate at tl apex, and usually narrowed, though sometimes rounded, the base. The surface is glabrous or somewhat sparingly p bescent above with appressed hairs, but the underside is covere with long, appressed, reddish hairs. This reddish coverin which usually is dense, is one of the most striking chara teristics of the species. The petioles are short, somewhat mo than ¼ inch long as a rule, and are pubescent at least on tl upper side.

The flowers, which appear in June, are borne in pubescen cymose inflorescences, which are covered by both colorless an reddish hairs. The fruit, which matures in autumn, is globo and bluish.

Distribution.—The Silky Dogwood, which prefers lo woods about ponds and lakes and along streams, ranges fro Newfoundland to Florida and Kentucky. In Illinois, in i typical form and in the variation sometimes called *C. obliqu* Rafinesque, it ranges throughout the state and is the mo widely collected and frequently reported of the dogwoods.

CORNUS ASPERIFOLIA Michaux

Roughleaf Dogwood

The Roughleaf Dogwood, fig. 56, is an erect shrub, or times a small tree with a spreading top, which stands as hig as 18 feet and has trunks or stems 3 to 4 inches in diamete The branches are reddish brown at first but become gra while the branchlets, at first greenish, soon become reddis brown. They are woolly or closely pubescent with colorles long hairs, among which some reddish ones occur. The oppc

FIG. 56

Cornus rugosa
:ornus asperifolia

Cornus Baileyi
Cornus Amomum

site leaves are broadly to narrowly ovate and have mostly or 5 pairs of veins. They measure at most about 5 inche long by 2½ inches wide. They are usually abruptly narrowe to a short or longish point at the apex and rounded or nar rowed, rarely subcordate, at the base, and large leaves ofte are conspicuously asymmetrical at the base. The surface i pubescent above and distinctly rough to the touch. Beneatl it is woolly and mealy, and the hairs beneath are usually color less but may be reddish on the veins. The petioles are shor commonly about ¼ inch long.

The inflorescence, a convex cyme, is likewise covered wit pubescence which frequently contains reddish hairs. The flow ers, which are open from late May through most of June mature fruit on bright red pedicels in August and Septembe The fruit is white, nearly globose, and pulpy, and contain stones that are conspicuously flattened laterally, but broade than high, and smooth on the surface.

DISTRIBUTION.—The Roughleaf Dogwood prefers moist so along streams and rivers and ranges from Ontario to Sout Dakota and south to Florida and Texas. In Illinois, it ma be found throughout the state, along streams and rivers bor dered by woods or shrub thickets. A hybrid between this specie and *C. Amomum* is in cultivation as an ornamental and is know as × *C. Horseyi* Rehder.

CORNUS BAILEYI Coulter & Evans

This dogwood, fig. 56, is an erect shrub 3 to 6 feet high wit purplish or bright red, smooth branches and green or reddis branchlets, which are at first pubescent but eventually becom smooth and purplish. The ovate leaves are 1¼ to 4 inche long by ¾ to 2½ inches wide, short or long pointed at th apex because of the narrowing of the leaf blade, and rounde or narrowed to the petiole below. There are as a rule 4 to pairs of veins per leaf. The upper surface is more or les pubescent with appressed hairs, and the lower surface is wool and densely white-mealy. The veins are frequently reddish o the underside of the leaf.

The inflorescence, a pubescent and generally also wool cyme 1 to 2 inches wide, blooms from about the middle c May through the first week in June, and rarely also late i he fall. The fruit, which matures from early in July until)ctober, is a white, flattened globe about one-third inch in iameter with more or less pulpy flesh and a dark stone, which s variable in size and shape, nearly smooth, and only faintly narked on the surface with a longitudinal groove around its videst diameter.

Distribution. — This dogwood, which prefers wet, sandy oils, ranges from Ontario to Manitoba and south to Pennsyl-ania, Indiana and Illinois. In our state, it has been reported vith authority only from the vicinity of Lake Michigan in ook County. It is very closely allied to *C. stolonifera* and nay be found more widely distributed, if collectors will care-ully observe the woolly under surfaces of leaves.

CORNUS STOLONIFERA Michaux

Red-Osier Red-Dogwood

The Red-Osier, fig. 57, is an erect or spreading shrub, the tems of which arise from underground stolons and grow to height of 4 to 10 feet. Its smooth branches are purplish o bright red, and the branchlets, at first greenish and pu-escent, become smooth and purplish or bright red. The oppo-ite leaves are ovate to oval, 1¾ to 3 inches long by ¾ to ¾ inches wide, acute or acuminate at the apex, narrowed r rounded at the base, short-pubescent above with appressed airs, and densely mealy and closely pubescent beneath, so nat the lower surface appears grayish.

The inflorescence is a flat-topped cyme commonly ¾ to 1½ nches wide. The flowers blossom in the latter part of May nd the early part of June, and fruit matures in July and ugust as a white, pulpy, flattened-globose drupe about ¼ nch in diameter, which contains a dark stone sometimes narked with a faint longitudinal groove.

Distribution.—The Red-Osier prefers wet, swampy situa-ons and sandy soils and it ranges from Newfoundland to ukon and south to Virginia, Tennessee and California. In linois, it is statewide in distribution but most abundant in ne sandy regions of Cook and Lake counties. It also occurs requently in sands in Will, Kankakee and Tazewell counties nd has been sparingly reported in many other places, some f them in the southernmost tip of the state.

FIG. 57

Cornus foemina

Cornus stolonifera

Cornus alternifolia

CORNUS FOEMINA Miller

Gray Dogwood

The Gray Dogwood, fig. 57, is an erect, quite leafy shrub
to 7 feet high, with smooth gray branches and light reddish-
rown to gray, more or less angled branchlets. The ovate
o lanceolate leaves have, as a rule, 3 or 4 pairs of veins, are
ariable in size, reaching 3 inches long by 1½ inches wide,
nd are generally long-acuminate at the apex and wedge shaped
r rounded at the base. The surface is short-pubescent with
ppressed, colorless hairs above and below and also mealy beeath. The inflorescence is a convex cyme, 1 to 2 inches wide,
hich is sparsely pubescent with appressed colorless hairs.

The flowers, which appear during June, mature in August
nd September as moist, pulpy, flattened-globose drupes less
han ¼ inch wide, containing stones somewhat compressed
aterally, longer than wide, and marked with shallow furrows
hich reach from the apex to the middle or below.

Distribution.—The Gray Dogwood grows in moist or dry,
andy or gravelly soils along the shores of lakes and streams,
long roadsides and fences, and in clearings in woods. It ranges
om Maine to Minnesota and south to the Carolinas and
rkansas. In Illinois, it ranges throughout the state and is one
f the most abundant dogwoods.

CORNUS ALTERNIFOLIA Linnaeus *filius*

Alternate-Leaved Dogwood   Pagoda Dogwood

The Alternate-Leaved Dogwood, fig. 57, is an erect shrub
ith a spreading top, which grows to a height of 15 feet and
as coarse stems up to 2 inches in diameter. The branches
nd branchlets are smooth, usually greenish, and bear alter-
ate or, rarely, a few opposite leaves, which are as a rule
ustered at the end of the branches on petioles ½ to 2 inches
ng. The leaf blades are mostly oval but vary to ovoid or
ovate and are 1½ to 4 inches long by ¾ to 2½ inches wide,
ort pointed at the apex, narrowed or, less often, rounded at
e base, and yellowish green. The leaf surface soon becomes
nooth above but remains woolly and mealy beneath.

The flowers, which bloom from early in May until early in
une, are borne in flat, small cymes. The thinly pulpy, globose

fruit, which matures in July and August on red pedicels, i bluish black and contains a small stone shallowly groove between 8 lines, which run from the base to the middle o nearly to the tip.

Distribution.—The Alternate-Leaved Dogwood grows o low land along streams and lakes and at the base of wood slopes. It ranges from New Brunswick to Minnesota an south to Missouri and Florida. In Illinois, it ranges acros the entire northern part of the state and extends southwar in the east to Clark County and in the west to Calhoun County

The very beautiful Flowering Dogwood, *C. florida* Linnaeus is abundant in many parts of the state, especially on the border of woods, and is familiar to many people. It is in realit a small tree, which may be recognized during flowering seaso by the brilliant white leaves that surround the inconspicuou flowers.

ERICACEAE

The Heath Family

The heath family includes herbs, shrubs and trees that bea opposite, alternate or whorled leaves, which usually a leathery and persistent and lack stipules. The perfect flowe have 4 or 5 distinct or partially united sepals, a regular coroll of 4 or 5 more or less united petals, and stamens of the sam number or twice as many as the petals. The ovary is mad up of 2 to 5 united carpels, the styles of which are unite and provided with a capitate or peltate stigma. The fru usually is a capsule but sometimes may be a berry or drup

There are over 1,000 species in this large family, which distributed throughout the world. Among about 60 gener more than 20 are native in the northeastern United State and 5 are represented in Illinois by native shrubby species.

Key to the Shrubby Genera

Leaves in close clusters of 3 to 5 at the end of upright branches .... **Gaultheria**, p. 2

Leaves definitely arranged along the length of branchlets.

  Leaves linear to narrowly lanceolate and nearly sessile .... **Andromeda**, p. 2

  Leaves broader and distinctly, if shortly, petioled.

    Margins of the leaves entire .... **Arctostaphylos**, p. 2

Leaf margins at least ciliate-toothed.
  Leaves densely covered on both sides with minute, round, scurfy scales.................... **Chamaedaphne**, p. 224
  Leaves hairy only on the midrib and lateral veins beneath.............................. **Azalea**, p. 221

AZALEA Linnaeus

The Azaleas

The azaleas are for the most part tall, erect, branching hrubs with alternate, thin, deciduous leaves and large, colred flowers arranged in terminal umbels. The calyx is small nd 5-parted, and the somewhat 2-lipped corolla consists of petals, which are united below into a narrow tube. There re 5 or, rarely, 10 stamens, which extend beyond the tube of he corolla, and the 5-celled ovary develops into a 5-celled apsule, which contains many seeds and opens along the septa rom the top downward.

There are about 40 species of azaleas native in North merica and Asia. Some 10 of these are native in the eastern Jnited States, but only 1 occurs in Illinois. The azaleas usually re included in the genus *Rhododendron,* and the Pink Azalea ien is known as *R. nudiflorum* (Linnaeus) Torrey.

AZALEA NUDIFLORA Linnaeus

Pink Azalea — Wild Honeysuckle

The Pink Azalea, fig. 58, is a shrub which grows to a height f 2 to 6 feet, producing stems that are unbranched below but ranched above into glabrous or stiffly hairy twigs. The oblong ovate leaves are 2 to 4 inches long, acute at both ends, short etioled, hairy on the midrib and sometimes on the veins beeath, glabrous above when old, and ciliolate on the serrate argins.

The pink to nearly white, slightly odorous flowers, which pen before or at the time the leaves appear, are 1½ to 2 inches road and are grouped in umbels at the tip of the branches. he corolla is somewhat 2-lipped and shorter than the narrow be. The stamens extend much beyond the corolla. The fruit a linear to oblong, strigose-hairy capsule about ¾ inch long, hich stands erect on a hairy pedicel.

Distribution.—The Pink Azalea grows in dry, sandy or

FIG. 58
Azalea nudiflora
Andromeda glaucophylla

rocky woods and thickets from Massachusetts west to Illinois and south to Florida and Texas. In Illinois, it is very limited n distribution and grows only on rocky bluffs and hillsides of the Ozarks in Union County, from Wolf Lake northward to the Big Muddy River in the vicinity of Aldridge.

ANDROMEDA Linnaeus

The Bog-Rosemaries

The bog-rosemaries are glabrous, evergreen shrubs with eathery, entire-margined, revolute leaves and with perfect lowers borne in terminal umbels. The 5 sepals are persistent, and the 5-toothed, globular corolla incloses the 10 stamens, he filaments of which are bearded. The ovary is 5-celled and s capped by a column-like style. The capsule is subglobose to -angled and opens by means of 5 valves to free the many eathery, shining seeds.

Two species of bog-rosemaries are recognized. One of them rows naturally in the far northwest and the other occurs in ortheastern North America.

ANDROMEDA GLAUCOPHYLLA Link

Downy Bog-Rosemary

The Downy Bog-Rosemary, fig. 58, is a low shrub that sends p ascending branches 4 to 10 inches long from a smooth, creep- g stem. The thick leaves are linear to lanceolate-oblong, ¾ o 2½ inches long by less than ½ inch wide, sessile or with a ery short petiole, abruptly acute and tipped at the apex, and ong-tapered to the base. The margins are entire and revolute, nd the blades are smooth and dark green above, and whitened ith fine hair beneath.

The white or pink, 5-petaled flowers, which appear from arly in May on through June, are borne, usually 5 to 10 ogether, in clusters at the end of branchlets, each on a re- urving pedicel, which is as a rule about twice as long as the ower or fruit. The fruit is a 5-celled capsule, which is much attened at the apex and opens by 5 valves to set loose the any shining, light brown seeds.

Distribution.—The Downy Bog-Rosemary is a shrub which rows in the peat and sphagnum of tamarack bogs, in which it ranges from Labrador to Manitoba and south to New Jersey Illinois and Minnesota. In Illinois, it is rare and has been reported only in the northeastern corner, in Lake and McHenry counties. It has not been reported since 1909, however, and now may be extinct.

CHAMAEDAPHNE Moench

The Leatherleafs

The leatherleafs are shrubs with branching stems, which bear alternate, leathery, slightly toothed leaves and perfec flowers in 1-sided, leafy racemes. The 5-lobed, star-shape calyx is subtended by 2 bracts, and there are 10 stamens, whic are included within the 5-lobed corolla. The ovary is 5-cellec with an elongate style, and the capsule is flattened, 5-valvec and many seeded.

This genus has one species, which is widely distribute through the north temperate zone.

CHAMAEDAPHNE CALYCULATA (Linnaeus) Moench

Leatherleaf — Dwarf Cassandra

The Leatherleaf, fig. 59, is a low but erect or ascendin much-branched shrub, 1½ to 3 feet high, with branchlets a first woolly pubescent and more or less densely covered wit scurfy scales. The leaves tend to be evergreen and are thic and leathery, oblong, elliptic, or oblanceolate, ½ to 1½ inche long, and up to ½ inch wide. The leaves in the inflorescen are smaller, tipped with a small point, rounded or acute the apex, and narrowed at the base. The margin is obscure toothed or erose, and the petioles are very short but defini and pubescent.

The inflorescense is a terminal, leafy-bracted raceme usual ¾ to 5 inches long, the flowers of which, arranged singly the axils of the bracts, begin to bloom during the early pa of May. The sepals are triangular to ovate, ciliate, thick, an scurfy on the back. The white corolla is oblong to cylindric and small. Fruit matures in September as a much-flattene 5-celled capsule containing many tiny, irregularly shaped seec

Distribution.—The Leatherleaf, found only in peaty bog

FIG. 59
Arctostaphylos Uva-ursi Chamaedaphne calyculata
Gaultheria procumbens

ranges from Newfoundland to Alaska and south to Georgia and Illinois. In Illinois, it is recorded only from Lake and Cook counties and is at the present time possibly extinct except in a bog near Volo in Lake County.

GAULTHERIA (Kalm) Linnaeus

Creeping Wintergreen

Creeping wintergreens are shrubs or undershrubs with alternate, long-persistent leaves and perfect flowers borne singl in axils or in axillary racemes. There are 5 sepals and a urn-shaped corolla inclosing the 10 stamens. The ovary an the capsule are 5-celled and 5-lobed. The calyx and othe flower structures enlarge and become fleshy, inclose the cap sule, and form a berry-like fruit.

There are about 100 species in this genus, most of whic occur in the Andes Mountains in South America. A few however, are North American and Asiatic, and the followin is native in Illinois.

GAULTHERIA PROCUMBENS Linnaeus

Creeping Wintergreen Checkerberry

The Creeping Wintergreen, fig. 59, is a prostrate shrub wit creeping, underground stems, from which rise branches 2 to inches long that rarely are branched and usually are wooll pubescent among the leaves at the top. The leaves occur 3 to together toward the end of the branches, and are persisten aromatic when bruised, thick and leathery, and oval to near round. The blades are ¾ to 2 inches long by about ½ to 1½ inches wide, crenate on the margins with bristle-tipped, lo teeth, apiculate and rounded or, rarely, acute at the apex, an narrowed or, rarely, rounded at the base. The surface smooth above or pubescent on the midrib and glabrous b neath. The petioles are short, about ⅛ inch long, and mo or less woolly.

White flowers, borne singly in the axils of leaves, appe from about the first of July on to the middle of August. Fru matures late in October and in November as bright red, fla tened, globose, fleshy structures, which persist on the plants un late the following spring, increasing in size during that time.

DISTRIBUTION.—The Creeping Wintergreen, a shrub of moist, sandy woods, ranges from Manitoba to Minnesota and south to Georgia and Tennessee. Its presence in Illinois is known only from one reported occurrence along the shore of Lake Michigan north of Chicago. It probably has been exterminated.

ARCTOSTAPHYLOS Adanson

The Bearberries Kinnikinnick

The bearberries are shrubs or small trees with alternate, thick, evergreen leaves and perfect flowers, which are borne in terminal racemes provided with small bracts. The flowers have 5 persistent sepals and an urn-shaped corolla with 4 or 5 recurved lobes. The 8 to 10 stamens have filaments which are wollen and hairy at the base. The ovary is 4- to 10-celled and develops into a drupelike fruit with a 1- to 8-seeded stone, r with seeds more or less separate.

Some 40 species of bearberries are known, almost all of them nhabitants of western North America. The following, native n Illinois, is widely distributed in the northern hemisphere.

RCTOSTAPHYLOS UVA-URSI (Linnaeus) Sprengel

Bearberry Kinnikinnick

The Bearberry, fig. 59, is a trailing shrub with more or less preading or upright branches 4 to 16 inches long which, when railing, often root at the nodes. They are covered by reddish-rown, exfoliating bark, and the branchlets are white-tomentose r, often, smooth by the end of the season. The leaves are vergreen, leathery, spatulate to broadly ovate, and $\frac{1}{2}$ to $1\frac{1}{4}$ nches long by $\frac{1}{8}$ to a little more than $\frac{1}{2}$ inch wide. The blade s rounded at the apex and narrowed at the base, and the leaf argin is entire, though sometimes ciliate. The surface is mooth above, or sometimes pubescent on the midrib toward he base, and smooth beneath except on the midrib. The petioles re short and often pubescent.

The inflorescence consists of axillary and terminal clusters f 1 to 6 flowers, which stand on short, reflexed peduncles. he white flowers with purplish-pink corolla lobes bloom in ay and early June and develop in July and August into bright, cherry-red, somewhat flattened-spherical fruits about 1/4 inch wide with thin, astringent pulp. Each fruit contains 5 nutlets more or less grown together into a stone.

DISTRIBUTION.—The Bearberry is a sand-loving shrub, which ranges from Newfoundland to Yukon and south to Virginia and Illinois, Colorado and California. In Illinois, it now is found only on the sand areas bordering Lake Michigan in Cook and Lake counties, but formerly it grew, according to records, as far south as Peoria.

VACCINIACEAE

The Huckleberry Family

The huckleberry family includes shrubs, small trees and a few delicate vines, which bear alternate, simple, sometime evergreen leaves and perfect flowers, which are either clustered or solitary. There are 4 or 5 sepals, 4 or 5 united petals, and twice as many stamens as there are lobes on th corolla. The ovary consists of 4 or 5 united carpels, is inferior, 4- to 10-celled, and develops into a pulpy berry o drupe.

The huckleberry family contains some 300 species, assigne to about 20 genera, and is of very wide geographic distribution. About 7 genera occur in northeastern North America and 2 are native in Illinois.

Key to the Shrubby Genera

Calyx and under surface of the leaves covered with resinous scales................................**Gaylussacia**, p. 22
Calyx and leaves without resinous scales.......**Vaccinium**, p. 22

GAYLUSSACIA Humboldt, Bonpland & Kunth

The Huckleberries

The huckleberries are shrubs with deciduous or evergree alternate leaves, the blades of which are entire and resinou dotted, and with flowers grouped in axillary, drooping raceme The sepals are 5, and the corolla is tubular and 5-lobed ar incloses 10 stamens. The ovary is 10-celled and develops in a drupe with a 10-celled stone or with 10 bony nutlets.

There are about 40 species in this genus, all of them Amer can. Only the following is native in Illinois.

GAYLUSSACIA BACCATA (Wangenheim) K. Koch

Black Huckleberry Highbush Huckleberry

The Black Huckleberry, fig. 60, is an erect or ascending shrub up to 4 feet tall but commonly 1½ to 2½ feet high, with branchlets that are more or less pubescent toward the end. The oval, oblong or oblanceolate leaves are 1 to 3 inches long by ¼ to 1¼ inches wide, acute, obtuse, or rounded at the apex, and narrowed at the base. The leaf margin is entire and ciliate, and the surface is green on both sides, but more or less pubescent and covered with scales beneath, the scales persisting until maturity of the leaves. The petioles are very short and pubescent.

The inflorescence consists of short racemes bearing up to 7 flowers, which arise from old axils on the former year's branchlets or sometimes on the present year's growth. The reddish or pink flowers bloom from early in May until early in June. The calyx, which is soon deciduous, is covered with resinous scales. The black or bluish fruit ripens from the last of July until September as a globose, sweet-fleshed drupe with at most only a slight bloom and contains 10 almond-shaped, small seeds.

Distribution.—The Black Huckleberry ranges, in acid, sandy soils, from Newfoundland to Manitoba and south to Georgia, Tennessee and Minnesota. In Illinois, it ranges through much of the northern third of the state and, without intervening occurrences, in Alexander County in the south. The region of greatest abundance is in the northeast corner of the state, but there are also records from the vicinity of La Salle, Castle Rock, Kankakee, Starved Rock and Peru.

VACCINIUM Linnaeus

Blueberry Bilberry Whortleberry

The blueberries are low shrubs with alternate, thin, deciduous leaves and with flowers borne singly, in racemes or in fascicles. The calyx lobes are 4 or 5, and the white, pink or purplish corolla is made up of 4 or 5 more or less united petals. The stamens are 8 or 10, and the fruit is a sweet and edible, blue-black or red berry sometimes covered with bloom.

FIG. 60

Vaccinium angustifolium
Gaylussacia baccata

Vaccinium vacillans
Vaccinium arboreum

There are more than 150 species in this genus, which has a very wide geographic distribution. Between 15 and 20 of them occur in North America. The following are the shrubby species occurring in Illinois.

Key to the Blueberry Species

Stems more or less upright, at least not creeping or trailing; fruit blue or black.
  Shrubs usually 3 feet or more tall; leaves glossy above; fruit black........**V. arboreum**, p. 231
  Shrubs commonly less than 3 feet high; leaves not conspicuously glossy; fruit blue or blue black.
    Leaves glabrous beneath at maturity.
      Lower surface of leaves green, margin serrulate ....**V. angustifolium**, p. 232
      Leaves glaucous beneath, the margin entire........**V. vacillans**, p. 232
    Leaves pubescent beneath at maturity.....**V. canadense**, p. 233
Stems trailing or creeping; fruit reddish.
  Bracts placed above the middle of the pedicel, green ....**V. macrocarpum**, p. 235
  Bracts generally placed below the middle of the pedicel, mostly colored........**V. Oxycoccus**, p. 236

VACCINIUM ARBOREUM Marshall

Farkleberry

The Farkleberry, fig. 60, is a shrub up to 10 feet high with straggling stems as much as 2 inches in diameter, which are covered with scaly, gray bark and bear green branchlets, which become gray or brown but remain more or less pubescent. The leaves stand on very short petioles and are obovate to nearly circular and up to 2½ inches long by 1½ inches wide. The margins are revolute and entire and usually bear large, sessile glands. The blade is acute or rounded, mucronate tipped at the apex and narrowed at the base, glabrous and shiny above and pale and more or less pubescent beneath. There often are sessile glands on the midrib and veins beneath.

The white flowers, which appear from late in May until mid June, are borne in axillary or, frequently, in terminal racemes composed of many flowers. Fruit matures in October or later as a black, globose, shiny, dry and inedible berry, which contains many seeds covered on the surface with shallow pits.

DISTRIBUTION.—The Farkleberry ranges in dry sandy soils in open woods from Virginia to Florida and westward into Texas. In Illinois, it grows only in the southern third of the state and is limited in its occurrence to the Ozarks. An exceptionally large shrub in Giant City State Park is recorded as being 20 feet high and having stems 3 inches in diameter. Glaucous-leaved shrubs with leaflike bracts in the inflorescence, taken near Tunnel Hill, Johnson County, have been referred to the variety *glaucescens* (Greene) Sargent.

VACCINIUM ANGUSTIFOLIUM Aiton

Lowbush Blueberry

The Lowbush Blueberry, fig. 60, is an ascending or erect shrub 1 to 2 feet high with yellow-green, wrinkled branches and branchlets, and with crowded leaves. The leaves are lanceolate to spatulate, ¼ to 1½ inches long by about ¼ to ¾ inch wide, acute or sometimes blunt at the apex, and narrowed at the base. The margins are sharply toothed and the teeth end in gland-tipped bristles. The surface is smooth or nearly so above and below at maturity, but the very short petioles are ciliate.

The white or pinkish flowers, which appear during the early part of May, are borne in short racemes of about 5 flowers. Fruit begins to ripen early in July and matures as a flattened globular, sweet and edible berry, about ½ inch in diameter covered with bluish bloom.

DISTRIBUTION.—The Lowbush Blueberry, a shrub of dry sandy soil, ranges from Newfoundland to Saskatchewan and south to Virginia, Illinois and Minnesota. In Illinois, it is limited to the northeastern part of the state, and has been reported frequently in sandy regions adjacent to Lake Michigan and in isolated cases in Kankakee County and at Starved Rock in La Salle County.

VACCINIUM VACILLANS Kalm

Dryland Blueberry

The Dryland Blueberry, fig. 60, is an erect shrub 1 to 2 or even 4 feet high with yellow-green branches and branchlets which are pubescent in lines and wrinkled on the surface. Th leaves are mostly oval but also lanceolate or nearly circular, up to 2½ inches long by 1¼ inches wide, acute or obtuse at the apex, and narrowed or, rarely, rounded at the base. The margin is finely toothed, and the surface is glabrous above and beneath at maturity. The midrib may be slightly pubescent toward the base, and the petiole is very short.

The greenish-yellow flowers are borne in short racemes consisting of 5 to 7 or sometimes a dozen flowers, which begin to open in late April and continue in blossom until early in June. Fruit ripens from early in July until well into September as blue-black, flattened, globose berries, usually densely bloom covered, which are sweet and edible and considerably less than ½ inch in diameter.

DISTRIBUTION.—The Dryland Blueberry grows in dry, sandy soil in woods from New Hampshire to Ontario and Michigan and south to Georgia and Kansas. In Illinois, it has a remarkable distribution. It is relatively abundant in the sandy regions in the northeast corner of the state and ranges, in isolated occurrences, to Castle Rock on the Rock River and, at least it formerly ranged, to Peoria on the Illinois River. It is, however, most abundant in the Ozarks in southern Illinois, where it has been collected in Pope and Union counties, in Giant City State Park, and in southeastern Jackson County. Specimens taken in Union County have been referred to the variety *crinitum* Fernald, which is distinguished by the branches being generally pubescent instead of pubescent in lines. The Illinois material of this species is by no means uniform, and critical examination of collections gathered in various sections of the state will suggest assignment of some specimens to *V. pallidum* Aiton, of some to, perhaps, *V. Torreyanum* Camp, and of some, even, to varieties of *V. corymbosum* Linnaeus, at least as these species are treated in various manuals.

VACCINIUM CANADENSE Kalm

Canada Blueberry

The Canada Blueberry, fig. 61, is an ascending or erect shrub 8 inches to 2 feet high with wrinkled, pubescent branches and branchlets bearing oval to lanceolate leaves usually 1 inch long by ⅜ inch wide. The leaf blades are acute at the apex, narrowed to the very short but distinct petiole, and entire on the

FIG. 61
Vaccinium canadense
Vaccinium macrocarpum Vaccinium Oxycoccus

margins. The upper leaf surface, though pubescent when young, is glabrous except on the midvein at maturity, and the lower surface is densely spreading-pubescent at maturity.

The greenish-white, red-tinted flowers, which appear early in May, occur 5 to 6 together in small racemes. The fruit, which matures early in July, is a somewhat flattened, globular, blue-black berry covered with bloom, which is sweet, edible, and about ¼ inch in diameter.

DISTRIBUTION. — The Canada Blueberry, a shrub of moist, often swampy, open or wooded situations, ranges from Labrador and Manitoba south to Virginia and Illinois. In Illinois, its occurrence is confined to the northern part of the state, where it has been a common inhabitant of drained tamarack swamps in Lake County and a persistent but not abundant shrub at Starved Rock in La Salle County and at Castle Rock on the Rock River.

VACCINIUM MACROCARPUM Aiton

Cranberry

The Cranberry, fig. 61, is a low, trailing shrub with slender stems 12 to 30 inches long, which root at the nodes and send up erect or ascending branches to a height of 4 to 8 inches. The branchlets, which vary considerably in length, are more or less pubescent, light to reddish brown, and bear oblong-elliptic leaves about ¼ to ½ inch long, which are obtuse or rounded at the apex and base, and entire and slightly revolute on the margin. The leaf surface is dark green and smooth above but glaucous and smooth beneath.

The pinkish flowers are borne in terminal racemes of as many as 8 flowers, and each raceme ends in a leafy shoot. Each flower pedicel bears 2 bracts, situated above the middle of the pedicel, which are smooth on both surfaces and ciliate along the margins. Blossoming occurs in late June and early July, and fruit matures from about the middle of August through the autumn. The reddish, globular to pear-shaped berries, which are about ½ inch in diameter, are sour but edible when cooked.

DISTRIBUTION.—The Cranberry, a shrub of sphagnum bogs, ranges from Newfoundland to Minnesota and south to West Virginia and Arkansas. In Illinois, it is very rare, if indeed it now exists in the state, and is limited to the extreme north east corner. It has been reported only in Lake and McHenr counties.

VACCINIUM OXYCOCCUS Linnaeus

Small Cranberry

The Small Cranberry, fig. 61, is a low, trailing shrub, wit slender, creeping stems that root at the nodes and send up ligh to dark brown branchlets, which slough off their bark but ar at first completely pubescent. The leaves are evergreen, oblon to ovate, about ¼ inch long and about ⅛ inch wide. The blad is acute or obtuse at the apex, rounded at the base, and pro vided with an entire, revolute margin, which is ciliate. Th leaf surface is dark green and smooth on the upperside an smooth but glaucous on the underside, and the petioles ar very short.

The pinkish flowers are borne up to 4 together in termina racemes, which often end in a leafy shoot, and the flower pedi cels, which may be ½ to 2 inches long, bear 2 usually colore bracts set, as a rule, below the middle of the pedicel. Blossom ing occurs about the middle of June, and fruit matures i autumn as a reddish, globose, sour but edible berry somewha more than ¼ inch in diameter.

DISTRIBUTION.—The Small Cranberry is a bog shrub tha ranges from Maine to Saskatchewan and southward to Nort Carolina and Minnesota. In Illinois, it is exceedingly rar There is but a single report of its presence, that of its occur rence in Cedar Lake bog in Lake County. Perhaps it might b found in other tamarack bogs in the same region.

SAPOTACEAE

The Sapodilla Family

The sapodilla family consists of shrubs and trees, whic sometimes are thorny and bear alternate, entire, estipulat leaves, and perfect or, rarely, polygamous, clustered flower The sepals, 4 to 12 in number, are arranged in 1 or 2 serie and the corolla ends in 4 lobes, which are deciduous. Th stamens correspond in number to the corolla lobes and ar adnate to the corolla tube opposite the lobes. The ovary co sists of several united carpels, is 4- to 12-celled, and develops into a berry containing as a rule 1 nutlike seed.

The more than 400 species in this family are for the most part inhabitants of tropical regions. They represent about 35 genera, 5 of which occur in North America and 1 in Illinois.

BUMELIA Swartz

The Bumelias Buckthorns

The bumelias are small trees or, with us, shrubs, which bear conspicuously nerved, simple, alternate leaves and, sometimes, spines in the axils of the leaves. The small, perfect flowers, borne in axillary clusters, are white, and the corolla lobes are longer than the tube and appended on each side. There are 5 stamens, and the ovary is 5-celled; but the berry is drupelike and usually contains a solitary seed.

There are about 35 species of bumelias, all of them native in America. The following two are shrubby and occur in Illinois.

Key to the Shrubby Species

Leaves glabrous or nearly so........................**B. lycioides**
Leaves rusty-woolly beneath.......................**B. lanuginosa**

BUMELIA LYCIOIDES (Linnaeus) Persoon

Southern Buckthorn Carolina Buckthorn

The Southern Buckthorn, fig. 62, is an erect, gray-barked shrub or sometimes a small tree up to 25 feet high with short, divergent branches which resemble spines and, on the branchlets, bark roughened by many lenticels. On terminal branchlets of the current season, the leaves are alternate, but on lateral branchlets from old wood they stand in clusters of 2 to 6. The leaf blades are elliptic to oblanceolate, commonly 2½ to 5 inches long and ½ to 1½ inches wide, with entire and slightly revolute margins. They are acute at the apex, wedge shaped at the base, and at maturity smooth both above and beneath and definitely reticulated. The petioles are short, commonly about ¼ inch long.

The white flowers, which appear at about the time the leaves are full grown, are borne on old wood in clusters ranging from 5 to 75 flowers, each on a short, glabrous petiole. The fruit,

FIG. 62
Bumelia lycioides
Bumelia lanuginosa

which matures in autumn, is a nearly black, ovoid, pulpy drupe usually about ½ inch long.

DISTRIBUTION.—The Southern Buckthorn, a shrub of moist situations and thickets, ranges from Virginia to southern Illinois and south to Florida and Texas. In Illinois, it is to be found in the valleys of the Ohio and Cache rivers, south of the Ozarks, where it may be sought in cypress swamps and in thickets along dry sloughs. It has been recorded in Hardin, Pulaski, Union, Johnson and Alexander counties.

BUMELIA LANUGINOSA (Michaux) Persoon

Woolly Buckthorn Gum Elastic

The Woolly Buckthorn, fig. 62, is a shrub up to 20 feet tall or sometimes, in the far south, a tree reaching a height of 60 feet, with usually spiny twigs and persistent, rather leathery leaves, which are glabrous above and densely pubescent beneath. The leaves are oblanceolate or oblong, usually obtuse at the apex and wedge shaped at the base, 1½ to 3 inches long by about ½ to 1 inch wide, and they stand on petioles up to ¼ inch in length. The flowers occur 3 to 18 together in fascicles developed on old wood, and the fruit, which is an oval, or globose, black berry, is ¼ to ½ inch in diameter.

DISTRIBUTION.—The Woolly Buckthorn is a shrub of thickets and woods, which ranges from Illinois to Kansas and south to Florida and Texas. It is exceedingly rare in Illinois and has been reported with authority only from the vicinity of Mound City in Pulaski County.

STYRACACEAE

The Storax Family

The storax family consists of trees or shrubs with alternate leaves more or less covered with stellate pubescence, without stipules and with regular, perfect flowers borne in clusters. The calyx is adherent to the ovary to some extent and consists of 4 to 8 parts, and the corolla has 4 to 8 lobes. The stamens are generally twice as many as the petals and inserted on the tube. The ovary consists of 2 to 5 cells and develops into a berry-like fruit or drupe, which is nearly dry, is 1-seeded and in some cases is winged.

There are some 75 species in this family, representing genera, which are mostly tropical and most abundant in South America. In the northeastern United States, and in Illinois the 2 following genera occur.

Key to the Shrubby Genera

Leaf margins finely serrate; fruit oblong and with 2 or 4 lengthwise wings............................... **Halesia,** p. 24
Leaf margins entire or very coarsely toothed; fruit globose or oblong and without wings..................... **Styrax,** p. 24

HALESIA Ellis

The Silverbells

The silverbells are small, more or less pubescent trees or shrubs, which bear thin, deciduous, finely dentate leaves and large, white, drooping, bell-shaped flowers in lateral clusters or in short racemes. The flowers appear before or with the leaves. The calyx is 4- to 5-ribbed, adnate to the ovary, and 4-toothed, and the bell-shaped corolla consists of 4 or 5 nearly separate petals. There are 8 to 16 stamens, and the 2- to 4-celled ovary develops into a dry, oblong, 2- to 4-winged, 1- to 4-celled fruit.

There are three species of silverbells, all of them native in southeastern North America. Only the following occurs in Illinois.

HALESIA CAROLINA Linnaeus

Silverbell — Snowdrop Tree

The Silverbell, fig. 63, is a tall shrub, 20 to 30 feet high or a small tree, reaching a maximum height in the south of about 45 feet and a trunk diameter of 12 to 18 inches. It bears oval to oblong, thin leaves, which are denticulate on the margin, acuminate at the tip, and narrowed at the base. The leaf surface is dark green and glabrous above at maturity but pale green and covered with stellate pubescence beneath. The leaves are 2 to 6 inches long by 1 to 3 inches wide and stand on short petioles.

The flowers are borne, up to 5 together, in clusters which appear at about the same time as the leaves. Each flower is borne on a slender pedicel 1 to 1½ inches long and consists

FIG. 63
Halesia carolina
Styrax americana
Styrax pulverulenta

of a minute calyx and a white corolla ½ to ¾ inch long. The 4-celled ovary develops into an oblong, 4-winged fruit 1 to 1½ inches long and usually somewhat longer than the pedicel on which it stands. It is capped by the persistent style.

Distribution.—The Silverbell inhabits wooded slopes and banks along streams from West Virginia to Illinois and south to Florida and Alabama. In Illinois, it is a rare shrub, with known occurrence that includes only the Wabash River valley in Wabash County, and the Ohio River valley, in the vicinity of Metropolis.

STYRAX (Tournefort) Linnaeus

The Snowbells

The snowbells are shrubs or small trees with alternate deciduous leaves and large, drooping flowers borne in latera or terminal racemes before the leaves appear. The calyx i persistent, adnate to the ovary, and 5-toothed, and the coroll is 5-parted and incloses 10 stamens. The ovary, which i 3-celled, develops into a globose to oblong, nearly dry, leather fruit, which commonly is only 1-seeded.

There are between 70 and 80 species of snowbells, widel distributed in America, Europe and Asia. Of the 5 that grow in southern and western parts of the United States, the follow ing 2 are native in Illinois.

Key to the Shrubby Species

Foliage and inflorescence glabrous.................. **S. american**
Lower surface of leaves and inflorescence stellate-pubescent .... **S. pulverulent**

STYRAX AMERICANA Lamarck

American Snowbell Smooth Storax

The American Snowbell, fig. 63, is a slender, erect shru 4 to 8 feet high with grayish or reddish-brown stems clothe in very thin bark and covered by stellate pubescence, the branch lets being more or less densely pubescent. The leaves are al ternate, without stipules, oval to obovate, and 1 to 3 inche long by ½ to 1 inch wide. They are pinnately veined, wit the principal veins prolonged beyond the margin into shor incurved hooks, so that the margin appears obscurely an oarsely crenate-dentate. The blade is acute and short-pointed, arely obtuse, at the apex, and narrowed at the base to a ery short petiole. It is smooth above and either smooth or early so beneath, but the petioles commonly are somewhat ubescent.

The white flowers, which are regularly 5-parted, are borne n groups of 2 to 7 in short, leafy racemes. They appear from he last of May until about the middle of June. The fruit, vhich matures from the last of September on into October, s a nearly globose, densely white-pubescent, dry drupe about ¼ inch in diameter, which breaks at the tip into 3 thin valves o expose the brown stone it contains.

Distribution.—The American Snowbell is an inhabitant of noist thickets and swamps from Virginia west to Missouri and outh to Florida and Louisiana. In Illinois, it occurs infrequent- y in the Wabash and Ohio river valleys; it is reported from awrence, Massac and Pulaski counties.

STYRAX PULVERULENTA Michaux

Downy Storax

The Downy Storax, fig. 63, is a shrub 4 to 10 feet high with lender stems and branchlets covered by stellate-pubescent, thin, eddish-brown bark, which eventually becomes gray. The oval o oblong leaves are alternate, without stipules, acute at each nd, denticulate or nearly entire on the margins, and short etioled. The blades are 1 to 2½ inches long by 1 to 1¼ nches wide, green and smooth above but pale and densely overed on the lower surface with stellate hairs.

The white flowers are borne in short, 2-flowered, terminal acemes or, often, in pairs in axils of leaves on the current eason's growth. The petals are oblong-lanceolate and acute, nd the calyx is small. The flowering period ranges from late n May until about the middle of June, and fruit matures in ate September and October as a globose, whitely hairy, dry nd leathery, 1-seeded drupe, ¼ inch in diameter, which breaks pen in 3 parts at the top, revealing a single globular seed.

Distribution.—The Downy Storax ranges in moist woods nd thickets from Virginia to Arkansas and south to Florida nd Texas. In Illinois, it has been recorded only once, in a ypress swamp near Rago in Johnson County.

OLEACEAE

The Olive Family

The olive family consists of trees, shrubs and a few almos herbaceous plants with opposite or, rarely, alternate, simpl or pinnately compound leaves without stipules. The regula flowers are perfect, polygamous or dioecious, and usuall have 2 to 4 sepals and 2 to 4 petals. There usually are stamens inserted on the corolla tube, and the superior 2-celled ovary develops into a fruit, which may be a capsule a samara, a berry or a drupe.

The more than 500 species in this family, representing 2 or more genera, are widely distributed in temperate an tropical regions. Of the shrubby forms only one is native i Illinois, but both the common Lilac, *Syringa vulgaris* Linnaeus and the common Privet, *Ligustrum vulgare* Linnaeus, occur i the state as occasional escapes from cultivation.

FORESTIERA Poiret

The Swamp Privets

The swamp privets are shrubs with opposite, simple, toothe or entire leaves, which may be deciduous or persistent, an with small, yellow or greenish flowers borne before the leave open in short racemes or panicles in the axils of leaves of th preceding season. There is either no calyx or a minute, 4-toothe calyx, and no corolla or at most 1 or 2 small, soon deciduou petals. There are 2 to 4 stamens, and the 2-celled ovary de velops into an oblong to nearly globose drupe, which contain 1 seed, or less often 2 seeds.

There are about 15 species of swamp privet, which rang through the southern United States to Mexico, Central Americ and Brazil. Only the following occurs in Illinois.

FORESTIERA ACUMINATA (Michaux) Poiret

Swamp Privet

The Swamp Privet, fig. 64, is a tall, spreading shrub 12 t 15 feet high, or rarely a tree of much greater height, with smal spreading branches and slender, light brown branchlets marke by numerous lenticels. Lateral twigs in the angles of the leave ecome spinelike. The leaves are ovate to oblong, acuminate r acute at both ends, finely toothed on the margins, 1 to 4 ıches long by ½ to 2 inches wide, and stand on slender petioles ne-third to two-thirds inch long.

The flowers are of two kinds, the staminate occurring in ascicles and the pistillate in short panicles. There usually is

FIG. 64
Forestiera acuminata

ɔ calyx and no corolla, but in the staminate flowers there are stamens with bright yellow anthers, which are seldom present the fertile flowers. The flowering period is from late April to May, and the dark blue to purple fruit ripens in June and ıly and falls as soon as it is mature. It is oblong to ovoid, cute at the tip, crowned with the remnants of the style, and to 1¼ inches long by about ¼ inch thick, with thin dry flesh vering a single striated seed.

Distribution.—The Swamp Privet inhabits the borders of reams and swamps in low, moist soil from southern Indiana Arkansas and south to Georgia and Texas. In Illinois, its stribution follows the tributary and large river valleys around e southern part of the state from Lawrence County in the st to Pike County in the west and up the Illinois River at

least as far as Tazewell County. The most northerly poin
recorded for this shrub in Illinois is an island in the Illinoi
River lying just north of the Mason-Tazewell county line.

BIGNONIACEAE

The Trumpetcreeper Family

The members of the trumpetcreeper family include tree
shrubs, woody vines and some herbs with mostly opposit
leaves, which are simple or pinnately compound and lack stip
ules. The large, showy flowers are perfect and irregular, th
calyx having 5 lobes arranged in 2 lips and the corolla bein
likewise 5-lobed and more or less 2-lipped at the top of it
funnel-shaped tube. There are 5 stamens, 1 or 3 of whic
usually are rudimentary or sterile, and the ovary is a 1-celle
compound pistil, which develops into a leathery or woody cap
sule containing numerous winged seeds.

The more than 500 species in this family, representing abo
100 genera, are widely distributed in tropical regions, but
few species grow in both the north and south temperate zone
In Illinois, the common Catalpa tree is perhaps the family
best known member. The following woody vines also occur i
the state.

Key to the Shrubby Genera

Leaf margins entire; vines with tendrils .... **Bignonia**, p. 2
Leaf margins toothed; vines without tendrils ...... **Campsis**, p. 2

BIGNONIA (Tournefort) Linnaeus

The Trumpet-Flowers

The trumpet-flowers are high-climbing, often evergreen vine
which climb by means of tendrils and bear opposite, compour
leaves consisting of 2 leaflets, the rachis of which ends in
branched tendril that clings by small disks. The flowers a
borne in axillary cymes. The calyx is 5-lobed, and the corol
is bell shaped, with a 5-parted, slightly 2-lipped, spreading fac
There are 4 stamens, which are included within the coroll
and the fruit is an elongated capsule flattened parallel with i
thin internal partition, which contains many small, winged see
arranged in 2 rows in each part of the capsule.

There is but a single species in this genus.

FIG. 65

Campsis radicans Bignonia capreolata

BIGNONIA CAPREOLATA Linnaeus

Crossvine

The Crossvine, fig. 65, is a long, slender vine, which climb
over trees of great height and is provided with an extensiv
underground root system. The rough bark on old stems
scaly and exfoliates lengthwise. The branchlets are smoot
and bear opposite, compound leaves, each usually with 2 smal
stipule-like leaves in its axil. The short petiole is pubescen
above and usually is prolonged between the 2 leaflets into
tendril, which subdivides by threes and ends in disks. The lea
lets are oblong to ovate, 3 to 8 inches long, and 1½ to 6 inche
wide, entire, often somewhat wavy margined, short or long poin
ed at the apex, and generally cordate or obtuse at the base. Th
surface is dark green and smooth above and smooth beneath.

The flowers, which appear through May, are borne on gl
brous pedicels in clusters of 3 to 5 in the axils of leaves. Th
showy mahogany-red or deep orange, trumpet-shaped flowe
are often 2 or more inches long. The fruit is a large, fla
2-celled capsule frequently 5 to 7 inches long and ¾ to 1 in
wide, which contains many flat, winged seeds measuring, i
cluding the wings, as much as 1½ inches long.

Distribution.—The Crossvine, a vine of low, moist wood
ranges from southern Virginia to southern Illinois and sou
to Florida and Louisiana. In Illinois, its distribution is entire
southern and follows the valleys of the Wabash, Ohio and Mi
sissippi rivers from Wabash County southward around t
lower end of the state, south of the Ozarks, and north aga
at least as far as St. Clair County.

CAMPSIS Loureiro

The Trumpetcreepers

The trumpetcreepers are woody vines, which twine or cli
by aerial rootlets and bear opposite, pinnately compound leav
with toothed leaflets and clustered, often paniculate, perf
flowers. The calyx is short, tubular and 5-lobed, and the coro
is long, funnel-shaped, 5-lobed and somewhat 2-lipped. The
are 4 stamens included within the corolla, and the fruit is
firm, leathery capsule flattened crosswise to the partition, wh
contains numerous winged seeds.

TRUMPETCREEPER *Campsis radicans* (Linnaeus) Seemann

There are two species in this genus, one native in Japan, the ɔther in eastern North America.

CAMPSIS RADICANS (Linnaeus) Seemann

Trumpetcreeper Trumpet-Flower

The Trumpetcreeper, fig. 65, is a large, long, twining vine vith stems often as much as 3 and 4 inches in diameter and with ;labrous branches, which bear pinnately compound leaves oppoitely arranged and on petioles 1 to 2 inches long. There comnonly are aerial rootlets opposite or just below each leaf on he stem. There are 7 to 13 ovate to lanceolate leaflets per eaf, the individual leaflet measuring 3 to 7 inches long and 2 o 3 inches wide. The terminal one usually is long stalked and he lateral ones are shorter stalked or nearly sessile. The eaflet margins are very coarsely serrate, and the blades are cuminate at the apex and mostly narrowed or sometimes squarsh but definitely asymmetrical at the base. The surface is mooth above but usually more or less pubescent beneath, espeially on the midrib.

The trumpet-shaped flowers, which appear early in June and ll through the summer, are reddish orange, showy, and as much s 2 inches long. The fruit, which begins to mature in late ugust, is a 2-celled capsule flattened at right angles to its partion, which measures from 4 to 10 inches in length by ¾ to 1 ıch in diameter. It contains numerous flat seeds with tissueke wings, which are eroded on the edges.

Distribution. — The Trumpetcreeper, normally a vine of oist woods and thickets, ranges from New Jersey to Iowa nd south to Florida and Texas. It is impossible to say what s original range in Illinois may have been, since it has been read widely into cultivated grounds and in many parts of e state is now a troublesome weed. It grows abundantly as hardy and well-naturalized vine as far north as Peoria and Ienderson counties.

RUBIACEAE

The Madder Family

The madder family consists mostly of herbs but contains few shrubby plants with opposite or verticillate leaves and perfect, regular, symmetrical flowers. The calyx is small, with its 4 or 5 sepals more or less united and adnate to the ovary, and the corolla consists of a long or short tube of 4 or 5 petals, which are separated to varying degrees. Alternate with the petals are 4 or 5 stamens. The ovary is 1- to 10-celled and develops into a capsule, a berry or a drupe containing 1 to many seeds.

There are more than 6,000 species in this family, which represent nearly 350 genera and have a very wide distribution especially in the tropics. The following is the only shrubby form in Illinois.

CEPHALANTHUS Linnaeus

The Buttonbushes

The buttonbushes are shrubs or small trees with 4-angle branches and opposite or, rarely, whorled, entire leaves. Th perfect flowers are axillary or terminal and are borne singl or in densely panicled heads. There are 4 sepals, and the whit or yellowish, funnel-shaped corolla is tipped by 4 lobes. Th 4 stamens are adnate to the throat of the corolla, and th 2-celled ovary develops into a dry fruit, which broadens fror the base upward and contains 2 to 4 nutlets.

The seven species of buttonbush are natives chiefly of Asi Only one occurs in North America.

CEPHALANTHUS OCCIDENTALIS Linnaeus

Buttonbush Honeyballs Globeflower

The Buttonbush, fig. 66, is a large, spreading shrub, i southern Illinois almost of tree size but commonly 4 to 1 feet high, with usually furrowed bark and smooth branchle on which the leaves are opposite or whorled. The ovate t lanceolate leaves stand on petioles ¼ to ¾ inch long an usually point forward along the branches. The leaf blad are entire on the margins, acute or acuminate at the ape rounded or narrowed at the base, 3 to 6 inches long by 1½ to 3 inches wide, smooth and dark green above, and lig green and more or less hairy on the midrib and veins b neath.

The flowers are borne in globular heads of as many as 2

flowers each; and the heads may be either terminal or lateral but in any case situated toward the end of the twigs and frequently beyond the last leaves. The small, creamy white, mostly 4-parted flowers blossom from early in July until early in

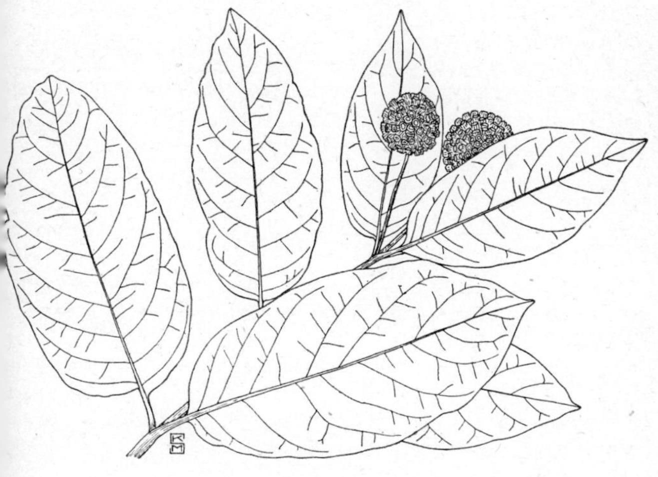

FIG. 66
Cephalanthus occidentalis

September. Fruit matures in the autumn, forming globose heads composed of numerous pyramid-shaped capsules generally about 1/4 inch long.

DISTRIBUTION.—The Buttonbush inhabits margins of swamps, ponds and sloughs from New Brunswick to southern Minnesota and south to Florida and Texas. In Illinois, it is statewide in distribution and increases both in abundance and size from north to south, being rarely abundant in running water but extremely common wherever water is still. In many situations it invades the margins of ponds, and in southern Illinois often is the principal shrub on the edges of the backwaters of the large rivers.

A variety, *pubescens* Rafinesque, is distinguished on the basis that branchlets, peduncles, petioles and the entire under surface of the leaf are pubescent. This form is probably coextensive with the rest of this species in Illinois.

CAPRIFOLIACEAE

The Honeysuckle Family

The honeysuckle family includes shrubs, vines, and a few small trees with opposite, simple, or pinnately compound leaves without stipules. The perfect flowers may be regular or irregular. The calyx is 3- to 5-lobed or, if tubular, ends in 3 to 5 teeth, and the corolla has 5 petals that are more or less united and it is sometimes 2-lipped at the apex. There are 5 stamens, and the inferior ovary, which is 1- to 6-celled develops into a berry, drupe or capsule.

There are some 400 species in this family, divided into about 10 genera, which are for the most part native in the northern hemisphere, with a few in South America and Australia. Many species are in cultivation as ornamentals, a few species are important as sources of drugs, and some species furnish frui used as food. The following shrubs and vines occur as native in Illinois.

Key to the Shrubby Genera

Leaves compound .... **Sambucus**, p. 25
Leaves simple.
  Leaf margins definitely toothed.
    Branchlets with finely hairy lines running downward from the leaf bases or leaf-scars .... **Diervilla**, p. 27
    Branchlets smooth or, if pubescent, the pubescence not arranged in lines .... **Viburnum**, p. 25
  Leaves with entire or nearly entire margins.
    Vines or at most semierect shrubs .... **Lonicera**, p. 26
    Low, spreading shrubs .... **Symphoricarpos**, p. 26

SAMBUCUS (Tournefort) Linnaeus

The Elders

The elders are shrubs or trees with opposite, odd-pinnate compound leaves and small, whitish flowers borne in compoun cymes. The 5 calyx lobes are minute and the 5-lobed coroll is wheel or saucer shaped. Five stamens are inserted at th base of the corolla, and the 3- to 5-celled ovary develops in a berry-like drupe, each cell of which contains one seed.

The elders are widely distributed and number some 25 specie of which about 12 occur in North America. Two are native Illinois.

Key to the Elder Species

Uppermost pair of leaflets definitely, if only shortly, stalked; mature fruit black.............................**S. canadensis**
Uppermost pair of leaflets sessile; mature fruit bright red ....**S. pubens**

SAMBUCUS CANADENSIS Linnaeus

Elderberry American Elder

The Elderberry, fig. 67, is an erect, only somewhat woody shrub 4 to 12 feet high with gray bark, large pith, and smooth branches and branchlets. The odd-pinnately compound leaves, 6 to 10 inches long, consist of 5 to 11 but commonly 5 or 7 toothed leaflets set oppositely in pairs along the rachis. Each leaflet is ovate to lanceolate, up to 6 inches long by 2½ inches wide, closely and finely serrate on the margin, abruptly narrowed at the apex to a short or long point, and narrowed or rounded asymmetrically at the base. The surface is smooth above but more or less pubescent on the midrib or veins beneath. Lateral leaflets usually stand on short stalks, the terminal one on a definitely longer stalk.

The inflorescence is usually a 5-branched, compound cyme bearing numerous small, white flowers, which blossom from early in June through most of August. The fruit, which begins to mature in late August, is a small, spherical, black berry less than ¼ inch in diameter with crimson juice. It contains 3 to 5 small seeds.

Distribution.—The Elderberry grows in moist soil along streams, about lakes, and in open woodlands from Nova Scotia to Manitoba and south to Florida and Texas. In Illinois, it ranges through the entire state and may be expected in any place where there is suitable soil and an abundance of light. Frequently it becomes a nuisance as a weed, since, if cut off above the ground, it will sprout from the roots. Shrubs with leaflets grayish green and soft-pubescent beneath are distinguished as var. *submollis* Rehder.

SAMBUCUS PUBENS Michaux

Scarlet Elder

The Scarlet Elder, fig. 67, is an erect shrub 4 to 10 feet high with stems covered by warty bark and with smooth, gray

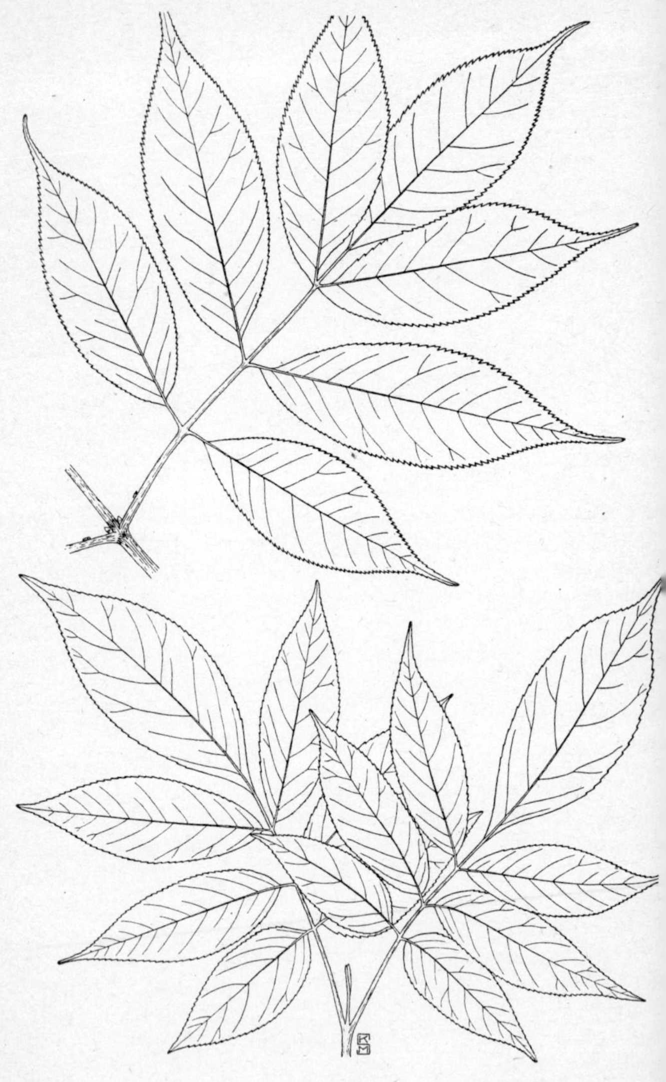

FIG. 67
Sambucus pubens Sambucus canadensis

branches and pubescent, partly pubescent, or smooth branchlets. The pinnately compound leaves are made up of 5 or 7 leaflets, and there generally are 2 large glands in place of stipules at the base of the petiole. The leaflets are ovate-lanceolate to oval, 2½ to 6 inches long, and up to 2 inches wide, with finely serrate margins and with blades gradually narrowed to a long point or acuminate at the apex and narrowed or rounded and asymmetrical at the base. At maturity, the surface is smooth above and lighter green and pubescent beneath. The uppermost 2 leaflets are sessile; the others stand on short stalks; and the terminal leaflet stands on a stalk a little more than ¼ to 1 inch long.

The inflorescence is a pyramid-shaped, crowded and congested cyme, which bears a large number of small, white flowers that blossom in the early part of May. The fruit matures in late June as a scarlet to red, broadly ovate, flat-topped berry with yellowish juice and it contains 3 small seeds.

Distribution.—The Scarlet Elder, a shrub of bogs and wet woods, ranges from Newfoundland to Alaska and southward as far as Georgia and California. In Illinois, it is limited in occurrence to the northeastern part of the state. There it is especially abundant in Cook County, less frequent in Kankakee, Will and La Salle counties. There is an isolated report, possibly to be doubted, of its occurrence in Cass County.

VIBURNUM (Tournefort) Linnaeus

Arrowwood Cranberry Tree Snowballs

The arrowwoods are shrubs or small trees with simple, though sometimes lobed, opposite leaves with or without stipules, which bear flowers in compound cymes. There are 5 calyx teeth, and the regular corolla, which is wheel shaped or shortly bell shaped, has 5 lobes. There are 5 stamens and a 1- to 3-celled ovary which develops into a 1-seeded drupe.

The viburnums are widely distributed and comprise more than 100 species. Between 15 and 20 of them occur in North America, and the 9 species given below are native in Illinois. They constitute a very difficult group, upon which the best authorities are not at the present time in agreement. Besides those given below, there probably are others native in the state.

Key to the Shrubby Species

Leaves not lobed, veins pinnately arranged.
  Margins round-toothed or entire..........**V. cassinoides**, p. 256
  Margins definitely, even when finely, sharp toothed.
    Leaves conspicuously long pointed, lower surface bearing red-tinted scales.......................**V. Lentago**, p. 258
    Leaves at most acuminate; no reddish scales present.
      Pubescence on leaves or twigs consisting of simple hairs.
        Petioles winged, pubescence on petioles and veins red...........................**V. rufidulum**, p. 258
        Petioles without wings, pubescence white.
          Petioles up to ¾ inch long.
            Margins finely toothed.........**V. prunifolium**, p. 259
            Margins coarsely toothed.........**V. dentatum**, p. 261
          Petioles mostly ¼ inch long or less.....**V. affine**, p. 261
      Pubescence on leaves and young twigs stellate...**V. molle**, p. 262
Leaves 3-lobed; main veins 3 or 5, palmately arranged.
  Leaves densely pubescent beneath; petioles without glands....................................**V. acerifolium**, p. 264
  Leaves pubescent only on the veins beneath; petioles bearing glands near the base of the leaf blade....**V. trilobum**, p. 265

VIBURNUM CASSINOIDES Linnaeus

Withe-Rod

The Withe-Rod, fig. 68, is an erect shrub with a wide-spreading top, which grows to a height of 4 to 8 feet and is more or less scurfy on the branchlets. The leaves are elliptic to oval or oblong but variable in size as well as shape, measuring 1½ to nearly 4 inches long by ¾ to 2½ inches wide, and they lack stipules. The blades are acute to short-acute at the tip, narrowed or rounded at the base, and irregularly round-toothed to entire on the margins. The leaf surface is scurfy spotted above and below when young but soon becomes smooth or nearly so above. The petioles are usually less than ½ inch long, flat and channeled above, and scurfy.

The white flowers, which appear in June, are produced in gland-bearing cymes up to 3 inches wide. There are usually about 5 sterile flowers in each cyme. The fruit, which matures in September and October, is black, bloom covered, globose to slightly oblong, and more than ¼ inch long. This fruit contains a broadly oval, lens-shaped stone, 1 surface of which is marked with a faint rib, and the other surface with a wide groove.

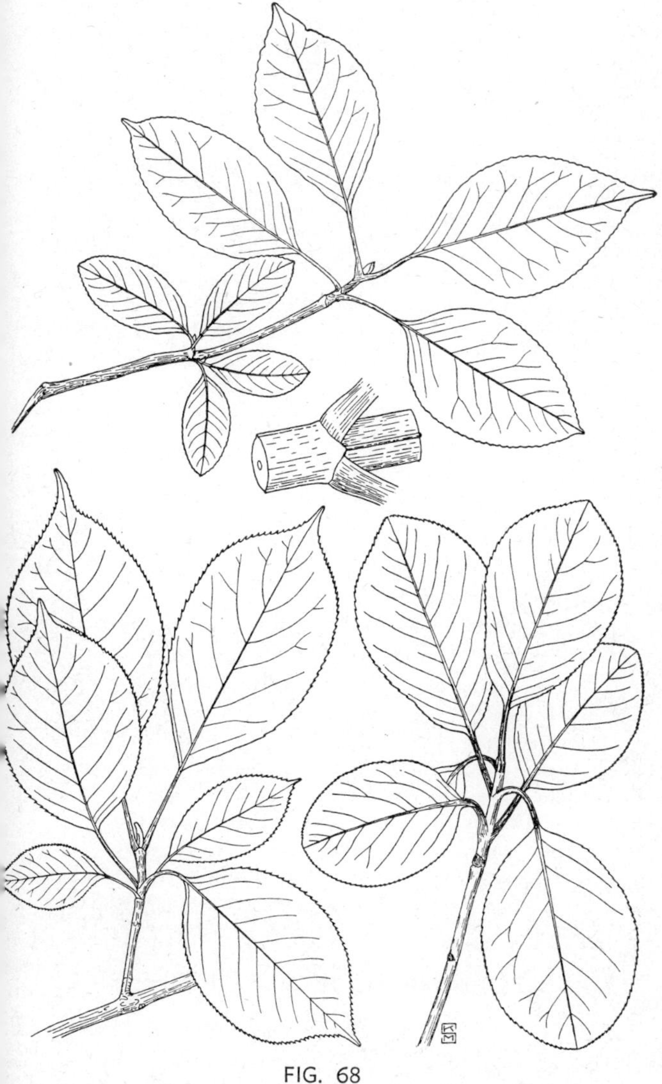

FIG. 68

Viburnum Lentago Viburnum cassinoides Viburnum rufidulum

Distribution. — The Withe-Rod is a shrub of low, sandy ground and swamps, which ranges from Newfoundland to Manitoba and south to Alabama and Georgia. Its known occurrence in Illinois is limited to two stations in the southern part of the state, one near Ware in Union County, the other near Dixon Springs in Pope County.

VIBURNUM LENTAGO Linnaeus

Nannyberry

The Nannyberry, fig. 68, is an erect shrub 3 to 18 feet high with a bushy top composed of smooth branches and branchlets which bear ovate to orbicular, serrate leaves, the tips of which commonly are drawn out into conspicuously long, entire points. The leaf blades are rounded or narrowed at the base, sharply and finely serrate on the margin, and smooth above and beneath, except that the lower surface is covered more or less densely with reddish scales. The petioles are ¼ to ¾ inch long. The white, sweet-smelling flowers, which open late in May and continue through much of the month of June, are produced in nearly sessile cymes which include 3 to 4 or, rarely, 5 sterile flowers. The fruit, which matures in September and October, is black, bloom covered, edible, oblong, and about ½ inch in length. It contains an oval to oblong stone, one surface of which is flat, the other convex, but neither marked with grooves or ridges.

Distribution.—The Nannyberry is a shrub which prefers low ground and bogs near lakes and ponds. It ranges from Quebec to Manitoba southward to West Virginia and Colorado. In Illinois, it ranges throughout a great part of the state, from the northern boundary south at least as far as Franklin County, Giant City State Park in Jackson County, and St. Clair County. It apparently does not range south of the Ozarks.

VIBURNUM RUFIDULUM Rafinesque

Southern Blackhaw

The Southern Blackhaw, fig. 68, is an erect shrub or sometimes a bushy tree 15 to 30 feet tall with thick, deeply furrowed bark broken into short lengths and with branchlets covered more or less densely with rusty red tomentum. The leaves are very thick, elliptic to obovate, and often carry a pair of stipular leaves about 1/4 inch in diameter. The blades are generally about 2 inches wide by 3 inches long, acute or rounded at the apex, and have the margins finely serrate to very near the base, which extends downward along the petiole to form a narrow but distinct wing on each side of the petiole. The surface is smooth and glossy above and smooth beneath or covered more or less densely, especially on the veins, with rusty tomentum.

The white flowers, which appear in June, are borne in terminal, nearly sessile cymes. There commonly are 4 neutral flowers in each cyme. The fruit, which matures in October, is black, bloom covered, edible, usually oblong, and about 1/2 inch long. It contains a broadly oval, flat stone with a low ridge in the center of one surface and a groove on the opposite face.

Distribution.—The Southern Blackhaw is a shrub which grows on wooded and often rocky slopes from Virginia and southern Illinois south to Florida and Texas. In Illinois, it is confined to the southern part of the state, ranging from the Ohio River northward to the Ozarks, on the eastern side of the state along the Wabash valley as far north as Lawrence County, and on the western side along the Mississippi and Illinois river valleys as far north as Jersey County.

VIBURNUM PRUNIFOLIUM Linnaeus

Blackhaw

The Blackhaw, fig. 69, is a shrub or sometimes a small tree 6 to 24 feet high with smooth branches and branchlets, which bear ovate to broadly oval leaves that are obtuse to acute at the apex and narrowed or rounded at the base, 1 to 3 inches long, and very finely serrate on the margins. The surface is glabrous or nearly so, both above and below, as are the petioles also.

The flowers are borne in sessile or very short-stalked cymes 2 to 4 inches broad, which bear several neutral flowers along with the fertile flowers, which open at about the same time that the leaves expand. The fruit, ripe in September, is an oval, bluish-black, bloom-covered, sweet and edible drupe up

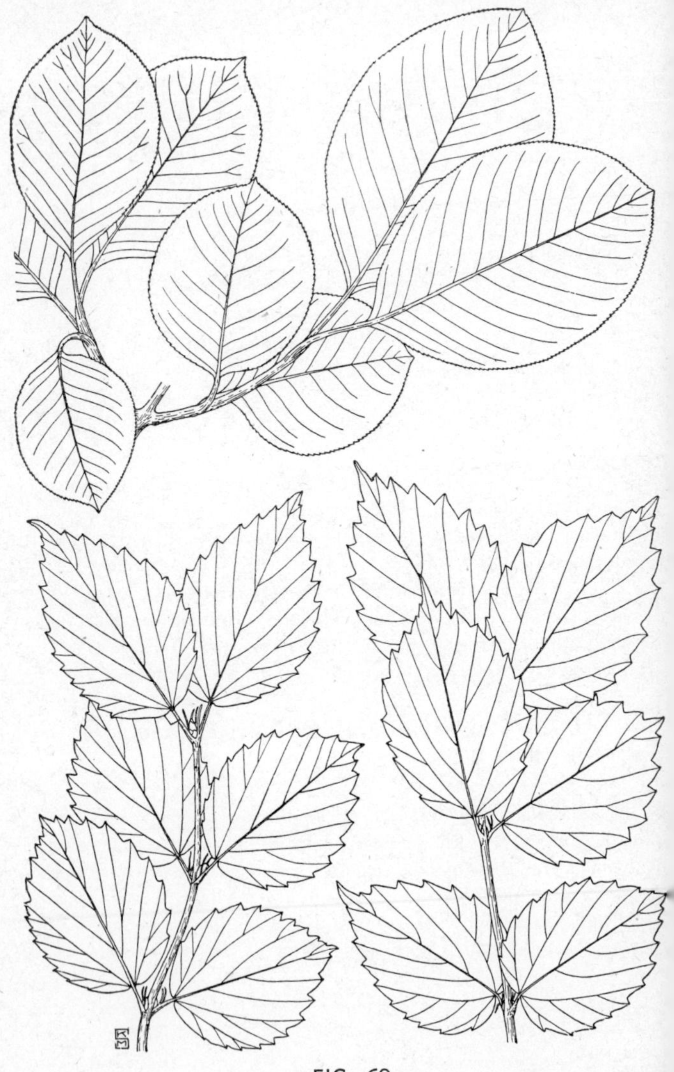

FIG. 69

Viburnum prunifolium

Viburnum dentatum

Viburnum affine

to ½ inch long, which contains an oval stone flat on one side and slightly convex on the other.

Distribution.—The Blackhaw is an inhabitant of dry soil from Connecticut to Michigan and southward to Georgia and Texas. In Illinois, it ranges from Cook, Lake and Jo Daviess counties south at least to Pope, Johnson and Union counties. There are no records, however, for the lowlands and swampy regions south of the Ozarks.

VIBURNUM DENTATUM Linnaeus

Arrowwood

The Arrowwood, fig. 69, is a shrub sometimes 15 feet high with slender, gray branches and glabrous branchlets. The leaves are ovate to nearly orbicular, acute or short-acuminate at the apex, and rounded to somewhat cordate at the base. The margins are closely toothed, and the leaf surface is glabrous both above and below but sometimes pubescent with clusters of simple hairs in the axils of the veins on the underside. The leaves measure 1½ to 3 inches in length and ¾ to 1 inch in width. The leaf veins are pinnately arranged and prominent on the underside of the leaf.

The flowers, which appear in May or June, are borne in long-stalked cymes 2 to 3 inches wide, which contain no sterile flowers. The fruit, which is about ¼ inch in diameter, is globose or slightly ovoid and blue to nearly black, and contains a similarly shaped stone, which is rounded on one side and deeply grooved on the opposite face.

Distribution.—The Arrowwood ranges in moist soils from New Brunswick to Ontario and Minnesota and southward into Georgia. Although Illinois lies to the west of its normal range, specimens referable to it have been taken at Starved Rock, Salem in Marion County, Olney and Parkersburg in Richland County, Carbondale in Jackson County, Rush Township in Jo Daviess County, and in Alexander County.

VIBURNUM AFFINE Bush

Missouri Viburnum

The Missouri Viburnum, fig. 69, is an erect shrub 3 to 5 feet tall with a bushy top made up of smooth or, rarely, minutely pubescent branches and branchlets. The leaves are ovate to broadly ovate, 1½ to 3 inches long by ¾ to 2¼ inches wide, usually long pointed at the apex, narrowed to somewhat cordate at the base, and coarsely and irregularly toothed on the margin with 4 to 9 teeth to a side. The leaf blade is smooth above and beneath, except for the pubescence on the veins and in the axils. The petioles are commonly quite short, usually less than ¼ inch long.

The flowers, which appear from late May on into June, are borne in cymes, 1½ to 2 inches wide, more or less covered with reddish glands. There may be as many as 7 sterile flowers per cyme. The fruit, which matures in September, is black, not bloom covered, and is a little more than ¼ inch long. It contains a similarly shaped stone with a short central groove and 2 faint marginal ones on one surface and on the opposite surface a central ridge and 2 grooves.

Distribution.—The Missouri Viburnum, which prefers dry, sandy, or clay soils in wooded regions, ranges from Ohio to Minnesota and southward into Missouri. In Illinois, it is reported only from northern parts of the state, including Kankakee, Lake, Peoria, Cook and Winnebago counties. A variety, *hypomalacum* Blake, differing in having the petioles and both surfaces of the leaves pubescent all over, occurs in Lake, Cook and McHenry counties. This species has been assigned, as var. *affine* (Bush ex Schneider) House, to *V. Rafinesquianum* Schultes, the species then being, by the reversal, synonymous with var. *hypomalacum*.

VIBURNUM MOLLE Michaux

Soft-Leaved Arrowwood Kentucky Viburnum

The Soft-Leaved Arrowwood, fig. 70, is an erect shrub 4 to 10 feet high with characteristic bark which exfoliates like that of a birch tree, leaving a smooth, reddish-brown under-bark. The branches and branchlets are gray and smooth, although young branches are more or less covered with short glands when they first appear. The leaves, which bear filiform stipules on the petioles, are ovate to nearly circular, mostly 3 to 5 inches long by 2 to 4 inches wide, abruptly acute or acuminate at the apex, cordate at the base, coarsely dentate on the margins, dark green and smooth above, and yellow green beneath. The entire

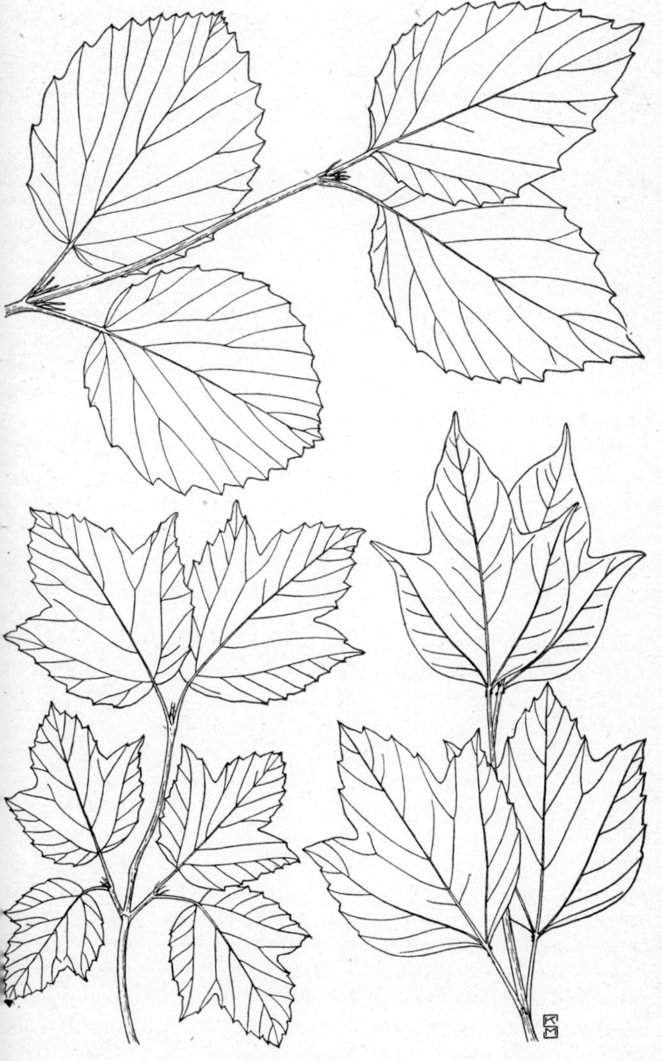

FIG. 70
Viburnum molle
Viburnum acerifolium
Viburnum trilobum

under surface usually is thickly covered with stellate hairs, at any rate along the veins, of which there usually are 6 or 7 pairs. The petioles are ¾ to 1½ inches long and glabrous but covered with reddish glands.

The white flowers, which appear from late in May to early June, are produced in cymes 1½ to 3 inches broad, the rays of which are thickly covered with reddish glands. There are usually 6 or 7 sterile flowers in each cyme. The fruit, which matures in late September and October, is black, broadly oblong, about ½ inch long and less than that wide. It contains a flat stone, one surface of which is marked with 2 marginal grooves.

DISTRIBUTION.—The Soft-Leaved Arrowwood is a shrub that grows on high banks of rivers and streams in Indiana and Kentucky and west to Missouri. In Illinois, it is rare and thus far has been reported with authority only near Marshall in Clark County, and Metropolis in Massac County.

VIBURNUM ACERIFOLIUM Linnaeus

Mapleleaf Viburnum

The Mapleleaf Viburnum, fig. 70, is a relatively low shrub 2 to 6 feet high with short branches and pubescent branchlets, which bear opposite, 3-lobed leaves that are palmately 3-nerved from the base. The leaf blades are generally ovate in shape and 2 to 6 inches long, with about the same range in width. The lobes are acute at the apex, the lateral lobes spreading. The base of the leaf is rounded to subcordate, and the margins are coarsely and irregularly toothed. The upper surface is pubescent to almost smooth, but the lower surface is densely pubescent with both simple and stellate hairs and is covered with sessile glands The round petiole, ¼ to 1 inch long, is pubescent and without glands.

The white or faintly pink-tinted flowers, which bloom from about the middle of May on to the middle of June, are borne in pubescent cymes 1½ to 3 inches wide. There are commonly 3 to 7 sterile flowers in each cyme. The fruit, which matures in autumn, is commonly black, dull, without bloom, globose to slightly oblong, and a little more than ¼ inch in diameter. Its pulpy flesh incloses a lens-shaped stone, 1 face of which is divided equally by 2 deep grooves, the other by a central and 2 marginal grooves.

Distribution. — The Mapleleaf Viburnum, a shrub that grows along the upper part of wooded slopes, ranges from New Brunswick to Wisconsin and south to Georgia and Alabama. In Illinois, it is by no means common. It grows in the northeastern corner of the state, Jo Daviess County in the west, and as far south on the eastern side of the state as Clark County.

VIBURNUM TRILOBUM Marshall

American Cranberrybush

The American Cranberrybush, fig. 70, is an erect shrub 3 to 10 feet high with smoothish, gray-barked branchlets, which bear opposite, 3-lobed leaves with 3 or 5 palmately arranged main veins. The leaves stand on petioles up to about ¾ inch long, which are smooth and bear 2 large glands near the base of the leaf. The blades are broadly ovate in general shape, 2 to 4 inches long, and 2 to about 5 inches wide, and more or less pubescent both above and below. The lobes are acute at the tip; the blade is usually slightly cordate at the base; and the margins are coarsely and irregularly toothed.

The white flowers appear in June in cymes covered more or less with red glands, and all of the outer flowers of the cymes are sterile. The red, translucent fruit matures in September but persists on the shrub. It is globose to oval, about ¼ inch in diameter, and very sour and contains a broadly ovate to nearly circular stone, which is concave on one face and convex on the other but not marked with grooves or ridges on either face.

Distribution.—The American Cranberrybush inhabits rich, low woods from Newfoundland to British Columbia and south to New Jersey and South Dakota. In Illinois, it is a rare shrub occurring only in Cook, Lake and Jo Daviess counties.

SYMPHORICARPOS (Dillenius) Ludwig

Coralberry Snowberry

The coralberries are shrubs with opposite, short-petioled leaves, and they bear white or pink flowers in small terminal or axillary clusters. The sepals are united so that the calyx is 4- or 5-toothed, and the 4 or 5 petals are united into an open, bell-shaped to flattened, regular corolla, to which the 4 or 5 stamens are adnate. The ovary is 4-celled and develops into a globose to ovoid berry, which contains only 2 seeds.

There are about 10 species of coralberries, all of them North American, with individual ranges that extend over most of the North American continent and south into the mountains in Mexico. Two species occur in Illinois.

Key to the Coralberry Species

Branchlets pubescent, purplish; fruit red............ **S. orbiculatus**
Branchlets nearly glabrous, brownish red; fruit white......
.... **S. occidentalis**

SYMPHORICARPOS ORBICULATUS Moench

Buckbrush Coralberry Indian Currant

Buckbrush, fig. 71, is an erect or spreading, often densely branched shrub commonly 2 to 4 feet high with shreddy bark on the main stems and light brown bark and purplish pubescence on the branchlets. The thick, oval leaves are opposite, ¾ to 2 inches long and up to 1¼ inches wide, and entire or wavy along the margins. The blade is obtuse to acute at the apex, rounded or narrowed at the base, glabrous or nearly so above at maturity but more or less densely pubescent with long hairs beneath. The petioles are usually less than ⅛ inch long.

The pinkish flowers, which occur in dense clusters or short spikes in the axils of upper leaves, or terminally, bloom from about the first of July until after mid August. The purplish red fruit, which begins to ripen in September, is a globose to ovoid, rather dry berry, about ¼ inch in diameter, which contains 2 small, bony, flat, oblong seeds.

Distribution.—Buckbrush grows in many kinds of soil and in many situations, from New York to South Dakota and south to Georgia and Texas. In Illinois, where it is perhaps the best known native shrub, it ranges in greater or less abundance throughout the entire state. It is rarer in the extreme north and south of the Ozarks, than in other parts and possibly may be absent from a small region in the northwest corner of the state.

This shrub is much used in cultivation as an ornamental, its slender, red berry-covered branches lending attractive color in fall and winter.

FIG. 71
Symphoricarpos orbiculatus
Symphoricarpos occidentalis

SYMPHORICARPOS OCCIDENTALIS Hooker

Wolfberry

The Wolfberry, fig. 71, is an erect but low shrub 1 to 3 fee high, which branches freely and also spreads freely from th roots to form dense colonies. The young twigs are slender light reddish brown, and puberulent to glabrous. The bark on older stems is gray and shredded. The opposite, ovat leaves are rather thick, entire or more or less definitely an roundly lobed on the margins, 1 to 4 inches long by ¾ to inches wide, acute or rounded or mucronate at the apex, an rounded or narrowed at the base. The surface is dark dul green and sparingly pubescent above and pale bluish green an thinly pubescent, at least on the veins, below. The petiole i distinct, commonly longer than in the preceding species, an pubescent.

The pinkish flowers are sessile in dense axillary and termina spikes, which are in blossom in June and early July. The frui is a dull white berry, which soon becomes blackish and dis colored, and which contains 2 straw-colored, smooth, flattis seeds less than ¼ inch long.

Distribution.—The Wolfberry, a shrub of dry soils i prairie and wooded regions, ranges from Michigan to Britis Columbia and south to Illinois, Kansas and Colorado. In Illi nois, it is a rare shrub limited in occurrence to the extrem north and recorded authoritatively only from Cook, Hancock Du Page, Jo Daviess, McHenry and Carroll counties.

LONICERA Linnaeus

The Honeysuckles

Most of the honeysuckles are shrubs or climbing vines wit opposite, simple leaves and usually irregular flowers borne i interrupted spikes or heads in the axils of leaves. There ar 5 small calyx lobes, and the 5 petals are united into a funne shaped or trumpet-shaped corolla, which is either 5-lobed c more or less 2-lipped. The slender filaments of the 5 stamer are adnate to the corolla. The ovary is 2- to 3-celled an develops into a 2- to 3-celled, fleshy berry that contains fe seeds.

There are well over 150 species of honeysuckles, natives fc

he most part of the north temperate zone but a few tropical. About 25 are native in North America, and the following occur s woody forms in Illinois.

Key to the Honeysuckle Species

Jpper leaves on flowering branches connate; vines.
Leaves glabrous on both sides.................. **L. dioica**, p. 269
Leaves pubescent beneath.................. **L. prolifera**, p. 269
eaves all with petioles; shrubs.............. **L. canadensis**, p. 271

LONICERA DIOICA Linnaeus

Limber Honeysuckle

The Limber Honeysuckle, fig. 72, is a climbing or sometimes omewhat shrublike vine with stems 3 to 10 feet long, hollow ranches, and glabrous branchlets. The opposite leaves are for he most part oblong and 2 to 4 inches long by as much as 2 nches wide. They are either sessile or short petioled, and a ew upper pairs are united around the stem at the base so that t least the uppermost pair forms a disk, which is usually some- hat tapered at each end and more or less constricted at the niddle of each side. The blades of other leaves are obtuse at he apex, variously narrowed to the base, glabrous both above nd beneath, glaucous beneath, and entire margined.

The flowers, which are in bloom during the last part of May, tand on very short peduncles and are arranged in whorls, of hich there may be 1 to 3, each containing about 6 flowers, at he end of branchlets. The flower is light to dark purple, or reenish yellow tinted with purple, and ½ to ¾ inch long. Fruit natures in July and August as salmon-colored berries, each on n elongated pedicel and each containing usually 3 seeds.

Distribution.—The Limber Honeysuckle grows in moist soil long the banks of streams, in woods and in bogs from Maine o Manitoba and south to North Carolina and Missouri. In llinois, it occurs only in relatively sandy woods and on ravine opes in Cook and Lake counties near Lake Michigan.

LONICERA PROLIFERA (Kirchner) Rehder

Grape Honeysuckle

The Grape Honeysuckle, fig. 72, is a climbing vine with stems to 12 feet long bearing hollow branches and glabrous branch-

FIG. 72

Lonicera dioica
Lonicera canadensis

Lonicera prolifera
Diervilla Lonice

ets. The opposite leaves, which are mostly oval, are sessile or onnate or, rarely, nearly circular and on petioles up to ½ inch ong. Usually toward the end of branches 1 to 4 pairs of leaves .re connate or sometimes in whorls of 3, the uppermost pair f which forms a broadly oval disk, the tips of which are obtuse .nd the margins more or less constricted at the middle. The lades of ordinary leaves are rounded or obtuse at the apex, ounded or variously narrowed to the base, entire margined, mooth and dark green above, but very glaucous beneath and :enerally also more or less pubescent beneath.

The flowers occur either terminally or in axils of upper eaves. When axillary they are in clusters of 3 and when erminal they are arranged in 1 to 4 whorls of 3 to 5 flowers ach. Blossoming occurs in late May and June, and the pale ellow flowers are, rarely, swollen at the base. Fruit begins o ripen late in July as a coral-red berry, about ¼ inch in iameter, which contains small, oval, flat seeds.

Distribution.—The Grape Honeysuckle is a vine of woods nd stream banks and ranges from Ohio to Iowa and Missouri nd south to Tennessee. In Illinois, it is the most common of he honeysuckles, ranging across the entire state from east to vest in the north and extending southward to Vermilion County n the east and to Morgan County in the west.

LONICERA CANADENSIS Marshall

Fly Honeysuckle Twinberry

The Fly Honeysuckle, fig. 72, is an erect or sprawling shrub to 4 feet high with stems which contain white pith and bear labrous branchlets. The leaves are ovate-oblong to elliptic, nostly 1½ to 4 inches long, up to 1½ inches wide, acute or lunt at the apex, and rounded or subcordate at the base. The nargin is entire and ciliate, and the surface is bright green nd glabrous above and beneath.

The flowers, which begin to blossom early in May, are borne n pairs on long, slender peduncles that rise from the axils of eaves on branchlets of the current season. The greenish-yellow owers, about ¾ inch long, are distinctly swollen at the base. ruit matures in July as a reddish, ovoid berry, about ¼ inch n diameter, which contains usually 3 or 4 seeds.

Distribution.—The Fly Honeysuckle is an inhabitant of

moist woods from Nova Scotia to Saskatchewan and south t Connecticut and Minnesota. In Illinois, its occurrence is re liably known only for three stations, namely, West Pullma and Wildwood in Cook County, and near the Des Plaine River in Lake County.

An additional species, *L. sempervirens* Linnaeus, is dubiousl reported on the basis of a few specimens taken at stragglin stations through the southern section of the state. The Japa nese Honeysuckle, *L. japonica* Thunberg, has escaped fro cultivation in several places, notably near Anna and Jone boro in Union County, near Pinckneyville in Perry Count in Johnson County, and at Villa Ridge in Pulaski County.

DIERVILLA (Tournefort) Miller

Bush-Honeysuckle

The bush-honeysuckles are shrubs with simple, opposite leav and with yellow flowers borne singly or mostly in small termin or axillary cymes. There are 5 linear calyx lobes, and the peta are united into a narrowly funnel-shaped corolla with 5 lob at the top. The 5 stamens are adnate to the corolla tube. Th ovary is 2-celled and develops into a linear-oblong, 2-valve many-seeded capsule, which opens by splitting along the sept

There are three species in this genus, all of them inhabitan of the eastern United States. Only the following is native Illinois.

DIERVILLA LONICERA Miller

Bush-Honeysuckle

The Bush-Honeysuckle, fig. 72, is a low but erect shrub com monly 16 to 24 inches, or less often 3 feet, high with gra shreddy bark on old stems and green or often red-tinted branch lets, which are smooth or frequently puberulent in lines runni down from the nodes. The opposite leaves are ovate to lance late, mostly 2½ to 6 inches long, and up to 2 inches wide, wi ciliate, rounded teeth on the margin. The blades are narrowe to a long point or acuminate at the tip, rounded or narrowe at the base, smooth above, and smooth beneath or hairy on th midrib and veins.

The flowers are borne terminally and in the axils of leaves

ymelike clusters of as many as 5, but usually 3, flowers. They egin to blossom in late May and continue through the early alf of June. The light yellow corolla turns reddish in age. The uit, which matures in autumn, is a smooth, oblong, 2-celled psule about ¼ inch long, terminated by a beak crowned with e 5 persistent sepals. It contains many small seeds, which are osely pitted on the surface.

DISTRIBUTION.—The Bush-Honeysuckle, a shrub of dry and ften sandy soils shaded by woods, ranges from Newfoundland Saskatchewan and south to North Carolina and Kentucky. Illinois, it is a frequently observed though rather rare rub limited in occurrence to the northeast corner of the ate, where it has been most abundantly recorded in Cook, ake and Du Page counties; also it has been recorded at astle Rock in Ogle County, Starved Rock in La Salle ounty, and Rock Creek in Kankakee County.

MAP OF ILLINOIS

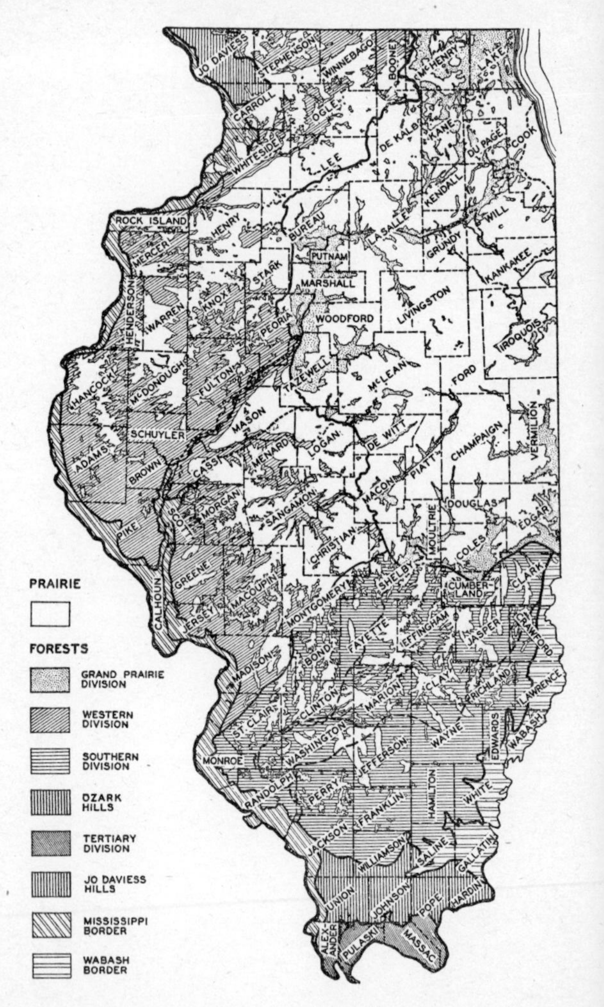

Counties and vegetation areas of Illinois. (Adapted with pe
mission from A. G. Vestal's map of 1930, which was based on C.
Telford's original forests map published by the Illinois Natur
History Survey in 1926.)

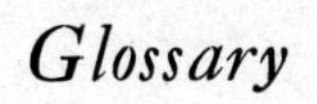

Glossary

GLOSSARY

Achene. A small, dry, hard fruit made up of 1 seed and carpel. Strawberry seeds and buckwheat grains are achenes.

Acuminate. Tapering to a long, sharp point. Usually used with reference to leaf tips but may apply to other plant parts.

Acute. Sharp-pointed. Contrasts with blunt, rounded, and truncate in describing leaf tips and many other plant parts.

Adnate. Grown together. Usually used for flower parts, *e.g.*, when stamens are grown to or united with petals.

Alternate. Any arrangement of leaves or other parts that cannot be described as opposite or whorled.

Ament. A spike of crowded flowers of one sex, among which scales are interspersed. Equivalent for the most part to the term catkin used with willows.

Ampuliform. Like a small, narrow-necked, round bottle. Used especially to describe seed capsules of willows.

Anther. The enlarged, terminal part of a stamen, in which pollen is formed.

Apiculate. Ending in a minute, sharp point.

Appressed. Standing close to or against. Used especially for buds laid close against the twigs.

Aril. A fleshy structure growing out of the scar on a seed and sometimes covering the seed. Used here for the colored, fleshy seed covers of *Euonymus* and *Celastrus.*

Armed. Provided with prickles, spines or sharp thorns, as if for defense.

Ascending. Tending to grow or to curve upward. Used chiefly to describe branches which grow or curve upward so as to be nearly as upright as the stem.

Asymmetrical. Unequal or unlike. Used particularly to describe leaf bases, when one side of the base is larger than the other.

Awl-shaped. Like the point of a shoemaker's awl, which is a short, coarse needle.

Axil. The upper angle between a leaf and the stem on which it is borne.

Axillary. In or arising from the axil of a leaf. Used to indicate the position of buds, thorns and inflorescences.

Berry. A pulpy fruit developed from a single pistil, which may contain one to many seeds but never a stone. Gooseberries and grapes are typical berries.

Bifid. Incompletely divided into two parts.

Biserrate. Provided with teeth which are themselves toothed on the edges. Usually descriptive of leaf margins.

Biserrulate. The same as biserrate, except that the teeth are small.

Bloom. A fine powdery covering of wax on fruit. Readily seen on certain cultivated and wild plums and on Concord grapes.

Bract. A usually small leaf, above which a flower or flower cluster arises.

Bractlet. As used in this text, a very small bract.

Branchlet. A small branch. Used in this text only for growth of the current year.

Bristle. A long, stiff hair. Used in this text for structures less formidable than prickles.

Bundle trace. A small scar inside the leaf-scar, which marks the position of a sap-conducting strand (vascular bundle).

Calyx. The outer, usually green part of a blossom. The term that is applied collectively to all the sepals of a flower.

Capitate. Arranged or formed in heads or in dense or compact clusters. Or, in connection with a pistil, the stigma in the form of a cap at the top of the style.

Capsule. A dry fruit made up of more than one pod, which usually opens at maturity. Violets and poppies produce their seeds in capsules.

Carpel. A simple pistil. In a compound pistil the number of carpels is the same as the number of pistils that have grown together.

Catkin. The crowded flower spike characteristic of willows. See *ament.*

Canescent. Densely covered with close, fine, hair that is grayish.

Caudate. Provided with a tail-like appendage. Used to describe some leaf bases and the sepals of rose blossoms.

Chambered. Divided by cross plates into small rooms. Used to describe the partitioned pith space in certain stems.

Ciliate. Bearing short, usually stiff hairs. Used especially to describe leaf margins.

Ciliolate. The same as ciliate except that the hairs are minute.

Claw. The long, narrow stal into which the bases of petal of some kinds of flower taper.

Collaterally. Placed side b side.

Compound. Composed of number of similar parts. Use to designate leaves wit blades subdivided into smalle leaflets and pistils compose of 2 or more united carpels.

Conic. Resembling a cone i shape.

Connate. Grown togethe Used in this text especially t indicate that the bases c leaves are united around th stem.

Constricted. Drawn togethe or narrowed at some poin Used most often to describ leaves that are narrower i the middle than at the tip an base.

Cordate. Heart-shaped. Use to indicate the general shap of leaves and petals but mor particularly to describe th manner in which leaf base join petioles.

Corolla. The inner, usuall colored part of a blosson The term applied collectivel to all the petals of a flower

Corymb. An inflorescence which the pedicels of low flowers elongate so that all the flowers make a relative flat top.

Crenate. Provided with roun ed rather than sharp-pointe teeth. Used especially to d scribe margins of leaves.

Crenate-serrate. Toothed wi round-pointed teeth. Used describe leaf margins that a not exactly serrate yet a more definitely toothed than is implied in the term crenate.

Crenulate. The same as crenate, except that the rounded teeth are very small.

Cuneate. Wedge-shaped. Used particularly to describe leaf bases when the margins taper to the petiole as a wedge does to its point.

Cuspidate. Prolonged at the tip into a tapering, sharp point. Such points are usually firmer than the tissues from which they arise.

Cyme. An inflorescence in which the central flower opens first and the outer or lower ones later.

Cymose. Having the characteristics of a cyme.

Deciduous. Falling off. Used for trees and shrubs from which the leaves fall in the autumn and also for plant parts, such as sepals and stipules, that fall off soon after they appear. Contrasting words are *evergreen* and *persistent.*

Decumbent. Growing flat along the ground but with stem tips or branches ascending. Used to indicate the growth habit of certain low shrubs.

Decurrent. Running down the stem. Used in this text only for lines of hairs, which begin at leaf bases or leaf-scars and extend various distances downward.

Dehiscent. Splitting open. Used in this text only to describe seed capsules.

Dentate. Toothed. A general descriptive term for leaf margins.

Denticulate. Toothed, but the toothing very fine.

Diadelphous. In two groups. Used for stamens that are separated into two distinct sets.

Dichotomously. Dividing into equal branches. Used in this text to describe the forking of stems and branches and of stalks in inflorescences.

Digitate. Spreading like the fingers. Used in this text only for the arrangement of leaflets in certain compound leaves.

Dilated. Swollen or expanded.

Dioecious. Unisexual. Used in this text to indicate that staminate flowers are borne on one plant and pistillate flowers on another. Contrasting terms are *monoecious* and *perfect.*

Disarticulate. To disjoint. Used in this text for the separating of fruit from the stem on which it is borne.

Disk. A glandlike structure found in certain types of flowers, to which petals and often stamens are attached.

Divaricate. Widely spreading. Indicates that branches extend outward almost at right angles to the stem from which they arise.

Divergent. Spreading or spreading apart. Used to describe the angle of growth of branches and the positions of flower stalks in inflorescences. Less widely spreading than divaricate.

Dorsal. The back of a plant part. For example, the upper side of a leaf.

Drupe. A fleshy fruit with the seed inclosed in a stony covering. Plums, cherries and olives are typical drupes.

Drupelet. The same as a drupe, except that the fruit is very small. Used in this text for the individual parts of the raspberry fruit.

Eccentric. Placed away from the center.

Elliptic. Having the general form of an ellipse. Used most frequently for leaf shape.

Elliptic-oval. Between elliptic and oval in shape. Used to describe leaf shape.

Elliptic-lanceolate. Between elliptic and lanceolate in shape. Used to describe leaf shape.

Entire. Without teeth or lobes. Used especially to indicate that leaf margins lack teeth.

Erose. Appearing as if irregularly eaten out. Used for leaf margins when more accurate terms, such as serrate or crenate, do not apply.

Exserted. Extending beyond, as when stamens are so long that the anthers are held out beyond the corolla tube.

Exfoliate. To peel off in layers. Used in describing the manner in which bark is shed. The term is applied most familiarly to the flaking off of bark from shagbark hickory trunks.

Falcate. Scythe-shaped. Indicates that leaf blades are curved so that their tips appear to turn backward.

Fascicle. A dense flower cluster. Also a group of closely united seed pods.

Fertile. Capable of producing fruit. Used in this text for flowers which bear functioning pistils and for branches on which such flowers are borne.

Filament. The stalk of a stamen.

Fleshy. Consisting of more than the usual amount of tissue. Leaves are fleshy when they are exceptionally thick, and a fruit is fleshy when it has either soft or firm pulp.

Fluted. Provided with longitudinal ridges and hollows. Used for surfaces of stems marked by alternating ridges and hollows; more definite than striate.

Foliaceous. Leaflike. Used in this text for stipules, bracts and sepals that are larger than usual and resemble leaves.

Foliate. Having leaves or leaflets. Used in this text especially for compound leaves, to indicate the number of leaflets that compose the leaf.

Follicle. A dry, podlike fruit formed from a single carpel which opens along one side only. A milkweed pod is a giant follicle.

Free. Not attached, adnate, or united to any other plant part. Used in this text to indicate that filaments of stamens are not united with one another.

Glabrate. Nearly glabrous, that is, with only a few, often scattered hairs.

Glabrous. Devoid of hairs. This is the opposite of pubescent.

Gland. A small plant organ which has the function of secretion. Glands may occur on petioles as small warts, on the tips of teeth as minute enlargements, in the midst of leaf tissue as minute clear spots, and as caps on the tips of hairs on leaves, stems, sepals and fruit.

Glandular. Bearing or furnished with glands or, sometimes, similar to or of the nature of a gland.

Glandular-punctate. Dotted with glands. Used to describe leaf blades containing dark or translucent, glandular dots.

Glandular-ciliate. Bearing cilia that are gland tipped. Used to describe margins of leaves and sepals.

Glaucescent. Becoming glaucous.

Glaucous. Covered with blue, white, or pale green bloom. Used especially to describe under surfaces of leaves. The blue-white covering of a cabbage leaf is a familiar example.

Globose. Having the shape of a globe. Used for many plant parts.

Glutinous. Sticky or mucilaginous. Used especially to describe seeds but frequently also other plant parts.

Hastate. Shaped like an arrowhead, but with the two basal points long and spreading. Used to indicate leaf shape.

Head. An inflorescence in which the flower stalks are very short and the flowers numerous, so that they make a very compact group.

Herbaceous. Like an herb, *i. e.,* with stems that die down to the ground each year.

Hip. A hollow, generally fleshy fruit with seeds on the inner wall. In this text, restricted to rose fruits.

Hispid. Clothed with stiff, bristly hairs. Used especially for the hairy covering of stems.

Hypanthium. A part of some flowers upon which calyx, corolla and stamens are seated. The tube formed by united sepals sometimes is called a hypanthium.

Incised. Deeply cut. Used principally to describe lobing of leaves.

Inferior. Beneath, but used generally to indicate that the ovary is inclosed beneath the base of the sepals.

Inflated. Blown up. Used for any bladdery or baggy condition.

Inflorescence. Any flower cluster.

Internode. The stem between two leaves or leaf-scars.

Involucre. A group of bracts situated below a flower or an inflorescence, or surrounding a fruit.

Involute. Having the edges rolled inward.

Irregular. Dissimilar in size or shape. Used in this text for flowers when petals or sepals differ in either size or shape.

Keeled. Provided with a ridge that resembles the keel of a boat; also, in flowers of the pea family, the lower, boat-shaped part of the flower.

Lanceolate. Shaped like the head of a lance.

Leaf-scar. The scar left on a twig when a leaf falls.

Lenticel. A small, rough opening in bark, which permits passage of air.

Limb. The blade of a petal, or, in a collective sense, the expanded part of a corolla.

Linear. Specifically, like a line. Used for leaves and other plant parts that are very much longer than wide.

Lipped. Provided with lips. Used to describe flowers with petals united through most of their length but divided at the end to form an upper and a lower lip. The snapdragon flower is a familiar example.

Lobed. Incompletely divided.

Used to describe leaves the blades of which are not completely divided into leaflets, to describe the calyx or corolla of flowers the sepals or petals of which are united so that the individual parts are separate at the end of the tube, and to describe fruits developed from compound pistils the individual carpels of which remain only partly united in the mature fruit.

Lunate. Moon-shaped or crescent-shaped. Used in this text for certain seeds.

Mealy. Coated with a floury deposit. A coarser covering than a glaucous bloom.

Membranous. Having the texture of a membrane. Used in this text to describe the wings of some seeds and the coverings of some podlike fruits.

Monodelphous. In one group. Used for stamens that are held in one bundle because their filaments are united through part of their length. See *diadelphous.*

Monoecious. Applied to plants if pistils and stamens are borne in separate flowers but both kinds of flowers are borne on the same plant. Contrasting words are *dioecious, polygamous and perfect.*

Monotypic. Having but one type. Used in this text to indicate that a genus or family consists of only one species.

Mucronate. Ending in a short, stiff, abrupt point. Used in this text to describe tips and teeth of leaves when veins extend through the edge of the blade.

Node. The joint of a stem. Recognizable as the place where leaves or buds are attached.

Oblanceolate. Like the head of a lance, but with the widest part beyond the middle. Used to indicate the shape of leaves and other plant parts.

Oblique. Slanted or having unequal sides. Used especially to describe bases of leaves when one side of the base extends farther down on the petiole than the other.

Oblong. Oblong in general outline but, with plants, carrying also the idea that both ends are broadly rounded.

Obovate. Oval but with the wide part away from the stem. Used especially to describe leaf shape.

Obsolete. Rudimentary. Used particularly in describing flowers, to indicate that some parts are either suppressed or present only in rudimentary form.

Obtuse. Bluntly rounded at the end. Used for tips of leaves and other plant parts.

Odd-pinnate. Consisting of an uneven number of leaflets. Indicates that a compound leaf has leaflets set in pairs along its rachis and has a single leaf at the end of the rachis.

Opposite. The term used when leaves occur in pairs at the nodes. Contrasting words are *alternate* and *whorled.*

Orbicular. Like an orb; essentially spherical. Used frequently to indicate the shape of fruits.

Ovary. The ovule-bearing part of a pistil.

Oval. Broadly elliptical.

Ovate. Egg-shaped, the wide part basal. Used to indicate the outline shape of leaves and many other plant parts.

Ovoid. More or less oval or egg-shaped. Generally not quite so definite as ovate or oval.

Ovule. The body in a pistil which, after pollination, becomes the seed.

Palmate. Lobed or veined like a hand. Used commonly in describing simple leaves. The similar word, *digitate*, is used for compound leaves.

Panicle. An inflorescence with both a main stalk and lateral branches, the flowers on stalks rising from the lateral branches.

Papillose. Bearing papillae, that is, small, wartlike roughnesses.

Pedicel. The stalk upon which an individual flower in an inflorescence sits.

Peduncle. The stalk of an inflorescence or, if there is only one flower, the stalk of the flower.

Peltate. Shield-shaped. Used for round or oval leaves that have the petioles joined to the main vein somewhere within the area of the leaf rather than at an end and also for other plant parts that resemble a shield in shape.

Pendulous. Hanging or drooping. Used in this text to describe the general appearance of branches and branchlets.

Perfect. Having both stamens and pistil in one flower. Contrasting words are *dioecious*, *monoecious* and *polygamous*.

Perianth. The calyx and corolla taken together.

Petal. The individual part of a corolla. In most flowers, one of the colored parts.

Petiole. The stalk of a leaf.

Pilose. Covered with soft, long hairs.

Pinnate. With a main axis from which branches go out on either side. Used in this text to indicate both the veining of leaves and the arrangement of leaflets in compound leaves.

Pistil. The organ in a flower which accepts pollen, contains the ovule, and develops seed.

Pistillate. Pistil-bearing. Used to designate flowers that bear pistils, and plants that bear pistil-bearing flowers.

Polygamous. Used when both unisexual and bisexual flowers are borne on the same plant.

Pome. A fruit resembling an apple.

Prickle. A short, slender, weak spine. In this text, intermediate between bristle and spine.

Puberulent. Covered with very fine hairs.

Pubescent. Covered with hairs. A general term for all hairy coverings; contrasts with glabrous.

Punctate. Marked with small dots.

Raceme. An inflorescence having only a main axis, from which the flower pedicels arise. Flowers at the bottom of the axis blossom earlier than those at the top.

Racemose. Having the characteristics or appearance of a raceme.

Rachis. The axis of an inflorescence or of a compound leaf.

Rank. A row. Used in describing the positions of leaves, one above the other, on the stem.

Ray-flower. Used in this text for the sterile, enlarged, whitish or greenish flowers in

Hydrangea and *Euonymus* inflorescences.

Receptacle. The tip of the flower pedicel, to which are attached all parts of the flower.

Recurved. Curved downward or backward.

Reflexed. Bent downward or backward abruptly. Used in this text especially to indicate the position of the sepals on rose fruits.

Regular. Having all sepals, and all petals, alike.

Reniform. Kidney-shaped. Used in this text to describe leaf shape.

Repand. Undulating. Used for leaf margins that are not sufficiently toothed to be called crenate.

Resinous-dotted. Covered with small dots of resin. Used in this text to describe leaf surfaces covered with small dots of exuded resin.

Reticulate. Forming a network. Used especially to describe leaf veining.

Retrorse. Turned backward. Especially descriptive of long hairs and bristles.

Revolute. Rolled backward or under. Used in this text to indicate that leaf margins are rolled under.

Rhombic. Having sides obliquely parallel. Used especially for fruits when the axis of the fruit is not a straight extension of the pedicel.

Rhomboidal. Having a rhombic shape.

Rotund. Rounded and swollen. Used in characterizing fruit.

Samara. A dry fruit with wings. The maple seed is a familiar samara.

Scabrous. Covered with hairs or rough projections, so that the surface feels rough to the touch. Used in characterizing the surfaces of leaves.

Scale. One of the small, dry flakes that form the outside of a bud; also a small flake found on some stems and leaves.

Semicordate. Used for a leaf base with a somewhat heart-shaped attachment to the petiole.

Semilunate. Almost crescent-shaped. Used to indicate the shape of certain seeds.

Sepal. The individual part of a calyx. In most flowers, one of the green parts.

Septum. A partition. Used in this text for the partition that separates the carpels of a compound pistil.

Sericeous. Covered with very fine, silky, usually shiny hair.

Serrate. Bearing sharp teeth that are directed forward. Used to describe leaf margins.

Serrulate. The same as serrate, but the teeth very small.

Sessile. Without a stalk. Used for leaves that are attached directly to the stem, for leaflets that are attached directly to the rachis, and for very short-stemmed flowers and fruits.

Shoulder. The large lateral branch in the inflorescence and fruit cluster of some species of grapes.

Simple. Not compound. Used to indicate that leaf blades are in one piece and that pistils are not united with one another.

Sinus. The open space between lobes in a leaf blade.

Smooth. Smooth to the touch. Lacking hairs or projections which would give a feeling of roughness. Used in characterizing leaf surfaces; almost equivalent to glabrous.

Spatulate. Shaped like a spoon. Used for leaves that are wide and round at the apex and taper gradually to the petiole.

Spike. An inflorescence with a long central axis upon which numerous flowers are borne without pedicels.

Spine. A sharp-pointed, rigid, thornlike structure. Used in this text only for modified leaves and stipules. Intermediate between prickle and thorn.

Spinulose. Bearing small spines.

Spur. A hollow, elongated extension from a petal or sepal, which contains nectar. Each petal in a Columbine flower has a spur.

Stamen. The pollen-producing organ of a flower.

Staminate. Stamen-bearing. Used to designate flowers that bear stamens, and plants that bear stamen-bearing flowers.

Standard. The broad, top petal of the flower of a plant belonging in the pea family.

Stellate. Star-shaped. Used in this text particularly to designate plant hairs that have broad or slender branches arranged like the points of a star.

Sterile. Not capable of producing seed. Used in this text for flowers that lack pistils and for branches that do not bear flowers.

Stigma. That part of a pistil, usually the apex, that receives pollen.

Stipitate. Stalked.

Stipulate. Bearing stipules.

Stipule. A small or large, leaf-like outgrowth at the base of the petiole.

Striate. Marked with fine parallel lines. Used in this text to characterize the surfaces of stems and certain seeds.

Strigose. Covered with stiff, straight, sharp hairs, which are closely appressed. Most commonly used in describing branchlets.

Style. The part of the pistil connecting the base, where the ovule is situated, with the stigma.

Sub- A prefix meaning almost, nearly, or somewhat. Used in this text with such terms as *cordate*, *coriaceous*, *conical*, *dentate*, and *glaucous*, to mean, a little less definitely, the same as the stem word would mean by itself.

Superior. Indicates that the ovary is set above and free from the base of the calyx.

Superposed. One above another. Used in this text to indicate that two or more buds stand in a row above a leaf-scar.

Suture. The line of union between parts. In this text, the junction of carpels in a compound fruit.

Terete. Approaching cylindrical; at least, circular in cross section. Used to describe twigs; contrasting words are angled and square.

Ternately. Having parts arranged in threes. Used in this text to indicate that a compound leaf is composed of 3 leaflets.

Thorn. A large, sharp-pointed, woody spine. Used in this text only for spines resulting from the growth of a bud. Technically, such thorns are dwarfed branches. See *spine*, *prickle*, *bristle*.

Throat. The upper part of the corolla tube in a flower with united petals.

Tomentose. Heavily covered with cotton-like or wool-like matted hair.

Tomentulose. Finely and closely tomentose.

Tomentum. An entangled cottony or woolly, hairy covering.

Truncate. Abruptly cut off so as to appear squarish. Used often in describing the apices and bases of leaves.

Tube. The portion of a corolla or calyx formed by the union, edge to edge, of petals or sepals.

Tuberculate. Bearing small warts or tubercles.

Umbel. An inflorescence in which the flower pedicels all arise from a common point at the top of the peduncle.

Undulate. Wavy or sinuous. Used in describing leaf margins; differs from crenate in that the waves are long and not very toothlike.

Undulate-serrate. The same as undulate, except that the waves are shorter and somewhat resemble teeth.

Urn-shaped. Having the shape of an urn; that is, broad at the bottom and constricted into a throat near the top. Used in this manual only to indicate the shape of certain fruits and flowers.

Valve. One of the sections into which a dry, dehiscent capsule divides when it opens.

Verticillate. Arranged in whorls. Used to indicate the grouping of leaves in threes or more at the nodes. Contrasting words are *alternate* and *opposite*.

Villous. Covered with long, soft hairs. Used especially to describe the hairy coating of leaf surfaces.

Wedge-shaped. Tapering to a point. Used in this text especially to describe leaf bases that taper regularly and sharply to the petiole.

Whorled. Arranged in a circle or ring. In this text used particularly when three or more leaves occur in a ring at each node; practically the same as verticillate.

Winged. Provided with a wing. Used in this text for thin outgrowths which serve as wings in distributing the seeds on which they grow.

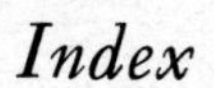
Index

INDEX

Important or principal references are indicated by numerals in bold face type. For scientific names, but not common names, illustrations are indicated by (fig.) *following the page number.*

C

M

W